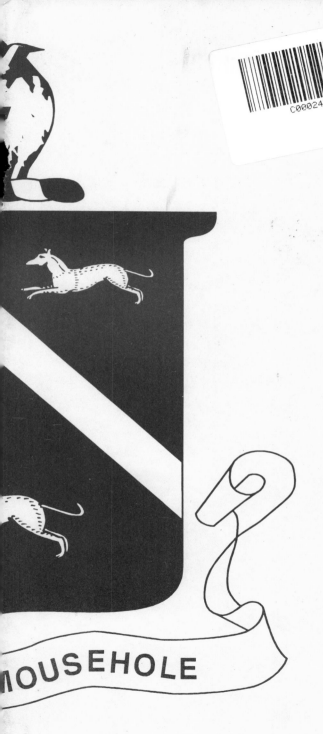

MOUSEHOLE

THE PIRATE AND THE PROPHECY

THE
PIRATE
AND THE
PROPHECY

*...of the Keigwins of Mousehole
and the Spanish Raid on Cornwall*

John Wilkinson

UNITED WRITERS
Cornwall

UNITED WRITERS PUBLICATIONS LTD
Ailsa, Castle Gate, Penzance, Cornwall.

British Library Cataloguing in Publication Data

A catalogue record for this book is
available from the British Library.

.

ISBN 1 85200 059 7

Printed in Great Britain by
United Writers Publications Ltd
Cornwall

to Greta

ACKNOWLEDGEMENTS

If this book should please you, then there are those with whom I would wish to share your gratitude.

There is Doctor Todd Gray, Leverhulme Research Fellow in British Maritime History at Exeter University, who gave me valuable advice and pointed the direction my researches should follow.

Rachel, my wife, who lent the support that gave me the confidence to put my thoughts into words.

Theo Hayward, always constructive in her criticism and suggestions, who enthusiastically interpreted my scribbles.

Rodney Alcock, the curator of the excellent Portland and Weymouth Museum, gave much colour to the events and the town during those historic times.

The staff at the Institute of Cornish Studies were both helpful and incredibly well informed, producing as by sleight of hand, numerous books that provided the precise information I was seeking.

Librarians appear to be a very special breed. Whether at the Guildhall, in the City of London, Greenwich Maritime Museum, Morrab, or your local friendly Public Library, they, and the Cornwall County Record Office, have taken a great interest, going to endless trouble in the search for the whereabouts of the tomes and manuscripts that enabled me to piece together this factual story of Mousehole.

PREFACE

Mousehole. In sheltered bay she lies, some eight miles from Land's End, that treacherous, rocky headland that forms the western tip of England.

A clutter of uncompromising granite cottages approached by steep iron railed steps from narrow echoing streets cluster around the harbour. Lobster pots are stacked along the quay, where walls of massive granite protect inshore fishing boats and punts with their red mizzen sails, bright colours and proud names. A stream empties through a concrete gutter where now gulls wash and preen in the fresh water; where in years long gone, young women would launder their clothes. Hence so it is believed, the name of Moweshayle or Mousehole, for in the Cornish language Mowes is a young woman and Hayle a river, whilst in earlier times the village was known as Porth Enys, The Island Haven.

We saw the house on Sunday morning, ageing and unkempt, whose aristocratic countenance could not be hidden by faded paintwork and neglect. Nor the generous proportions of her rooms be disguised by mean partition and flimsy divisions. A part of the ancient Manor of Keigwin. The historic house of Mousehole, now weary with age.

Rachel and I determined there and then to buy her and to hold her awhile in trust. She must have understood our wish to recover for her some measure of lost dignity, for gradually, as restoration progressed, her confidence grew and little by little she pointed us toward some of the many secrets that a lady of venerable years and breeding is bound to accumulate in a life lived with pace and variety.

With her consent it is my privilege to reveal a measure of

9

those secrets of the life and times of her youth, and those that gathered within her walls.

As one grows older, sadly one's memory becomes dimmed or confused, fantasy entwines with reality filling the detail of fact beyond recall. Thus do the boundaries between history and legend become blurred. If we have thereby willingly or unwittingly wandered from the truth that is better known to others, I apologise. For this is a story, a story of her people, of Mousehole and of Cornwall. A story of fact and of what might have been. Of piracy and politics. Of intrigue and of revenge. Of brave men and traitors.

Where records differ, we have adopted those that have seemed more likely, satisfied in the knowledge that whatever we may say, we cannot embellish the brilliance of the deeds of the remarkable family that lived and loved within her walls. Their exploits will forever remain a part of the fabric of the history of Cornwall.

INTRODUCTION

Whilst the origins of the Celtic peoples are veiled by the mists of time, from central Asia it is believed they came, travelling westwards, warring with and defeating both Greek and Roman. The soldiers, fearless in battle, as a warrior may be whose soul is immortal and transmigrates from one being to another and where, by some extraordinary act of virtue or valour, it will be received into the assembly of the Gods.

Practised in magical arts and rites, the Druids, priesthood of the Celtic tribes, were versed in the mysterious powers of animal and plant; the sacred soul of oak tree and of mistletoe. These wise men instructed their pupils in the movement of the stars and the grandeur of the universe. Applying their knowledge of mathematics and geometry to measure the earth and the planets, and to build circles of stone in which to conduct their rites of magic and mystery.

As a nation's fortunes wax and wane, so did those of the Celtic peoples. Their influence receded before the onslaught of successive alien armies, until seeking sanctuary in the rocky and remote fortresses that now contain the six Celtic countries that we know today. Scotland and Cumbria, Ireland and the Isle of Man are the people of the Goidelic Celts bound by the Gaelic language. The Welsh, the Cornish and the Bretons being the Brythonic Celts linked by their own speech and culture. The legends of King Arthur and Merlin the Magician: that oft repeated Celtic contrast of chivalrous soldier and wise scholar that epitomises the character of the family of Keigwin.

Glimpses may yet be seen in Cornwall of this ancient

race. A breed of people having an unusual insight into the nature and the soul of man. An extension of the senses of other mortals. A certain temperament, fearless yet courteous, sensitive yet bold. A people of principle, faithful to a cause. To be led, but never driven. Blessed with artistic awareness and appreciation expressed in poetry and song. With little outward sign of heritage yet proudly aware of their destiny and importance in the weft and warp of the interwoven tapestry of mankind.

These people are the lingering legacy of their Celtic forebears of whose presence we are constantly reminded by the standing stones and later Christian Celtic crosses which greet us around twist and turn of footpath and highway in the harshly beautiful landscape of Penwith.

Thus in Cornwall still there live remnants of a race, a rare breed of English that are not of England. Of such a people are the family of which I write, the family of the White Dog: Keigwin in the Cornish tongue. Or cigwyn in the Wales from whence they had come in the sixth century as emissaries, it was said, of Arthur the Celtic King and his Wizard, Merlin. Chivalrous warrior and learned sorcerer.

In Keigwin veins ran the blood of heroic ancestors whose courage and culture they personified. A people in whose soul, nourished by pagan beliefs of earlier times, the seeds of Christ's teachings found a fertile home. A people who embraced the simplicity and humility of a new found faith with a religious zeal that inspired them to spread and share this faith as soldier or scholar as they travelled the world of their time.

The House of Keigwin was built in the early part of the sixteenth century, some twenty paces from the harbour contained by the arm of a granite quay built 150 years before. This sheltered anchorage is exposed to the east and fishermen fear the seas coming from that quarter albeit partially protected by the low humped, rocky islet known as St. Clements, upon which then squatted a tiny chapel.

The high moorland to west and north gives shelter from the force of the prevailing westerly and northerly winds. To the south, where granite cliffs fall in ragged steps towards the sea, lies Merlin's Rock.

Here was the first landfall and pure water for merchants trading for Cornish tin, leather and much prized white-skinned slaves. To this harbour since before the days of Christ, Phoenician and Carthaginian galleys were known to venture.

It was not by chance the Cornish merchant Jenkyn Keigwin built his home in this dominant location of a prospering port, with granite walls of locally hewn stone three feet in thickness and oak felled from the now sunken forest of Marazion that surrounded St. Michael's Mount, where the Benedictine Monks from Mont St. Michel furthered their order in the 11th century, to build a daughter house in a setting reminiscent of their Norman Abbey.

The exterior of the Tudor House was handsome in its robust simplicity. The porch, raised upon four, square sturdy granite columns with their horizontal banded collars, was yet to be built. The massive wooden door in moulded granite frame was surmounted by a triangular pediment, now featured in the wall to the right. The windows were stone mullioned with hood mould and leaded panes. The principal rooms of the house were on the first floor, with lofty barrel-vaulted ceilings and huge open fireplaces. The windows commanded views over the south-westerly approaches and from the North East and East one could scan from Penlee Point to The Lizard.

The year is 1587. Behind the house, where now is Wesley Square, the stockyard, where riding horses and pack ponies were stabled in solid, slate-roofed granite buildings. At right angles, in stall and byre, were house cows to supply the Manor with milk, cheese and butter, and a sty of black spotted pigs for ham and bacon. The Keigwin hounds were kennelled at the foot of the Reginnis Hill, upon the site where now stands the Wesleyan Chapel.

In stone-hedged meadows beyond grazed sheep and bullocks, whilst fowls scratched in the dungheap whose wafting aroma failed to compete with that of the nearby pilchard presses. Open-sided net lofts and sheds supported on rough-hewn granite pillars backed on the yard from the quay that they lined. Solid warehouses stored the goods and booty in which the squire traded.

13

Moorland ponies with meal coloured muzzles pulled gurries on steel sleds over the rough stone that paved the narrow streets. Donkeys with withy plaited panniers carried fish or produce from the fields. The hunched and bunched cottages were capped with wet laid slate, or roughly thatched with local straw or reeds from the marshes of Marazion. A maze of cobbled passageways yielded access to a multitude of lofts and presses that squeezed the oil from the bloated pilchard upon which much of the prosperity of the town depended.

There was little sanitation save the sea. The larger rocks that lined the shore were lavatory to many a cottager. The streams that rise in the hills above provided pure water for man and beast and served to drive the great undershot wheels of the two cornmills. Buckets were emptied into harbour or gutter to be sluiced by running springs or mild monotonous rain.

Twice weekly on market days, and days of fair and feast, country came to town. Argumentative tinner and tight-fisted cover, farmer and his labourer, dressed according to degree, to sell their stock and merchandise. To hire or be hired, to buy and to barter with the many traders and itinerant pedlars who pitched their stalls along the wide cliff road that led to the harbour wharf. Fighting, drinking and gossiping, the granite walls reflecting and enhancing the hubbub.

But always, the all pervading smell of the pilchard and the oil, that in rainbow colours filmed and stilled the waters of the harbour.

The Keigwin wealth came from the sea. Fishing, trade and the privateer. The pilchard, bloated and prized by the French and Spanish for its oil, or train, superior than the olive for cooking or soap making. Their ships would return laden with fine wines, or rare fruits and spices, to be taken by pack pony along the high lanes to Exeter. The up-country meat eating English were less interested in the feast days of continental Catholics for whom fish, smoked or salted was an essential part. From late summer to early autumn, when shoals were plentiful and seas calmer, merchants from France and Spain were frequent visitors to the Manor and

14

the merchant squire, patriarch of Mousehole.

Since to travel overland was less costly and less hazardous than by sea, Mousehole was renowned as a harbour from whence pilgrims would embark. For the Holy Land. For journeying to Rome, Loretto, or Assisi. To Spain and Compostella, Guadalupe or Montserrat. To travel across France to Lyons or St. Denis. To pay homage to the relics of the Saints and thus be endowed with a measure of their virtue and the prospect of life eternal.

The Reformation was in full flood. The teachings of Luther in Germany and Calvin in France queried the authority of Rome and papal edicts that stretched the mind to the limits of credulity.

The ritual of the Roman Catholic form of religious cere-mony was particularly applicable to the Latin temperament, but of lesser appeal to the character of the Teutonic and Anglo-Saxon races, tiring of the influence of a papacy prejudicial to their own interests and to the benefit of Rome, tainted by a clergy that oft-times was more interested in political and financial gain than salvation of the soul.

Thus much of England remained Catholic whilst rejecting the authority of the Pope, accepting their Monarch as head of the Protestant Catholic Church of England, whilst others remained Roman Catholic but placed loyalty to their country before that of the papacy. The simple faith of the Puritan was adopted by those of the Church who refused to conform to its liturgy, ceremonies and disciplines believing that the Church of England had not sufficiently distanced itself from Roman Catholicism and needed even further reforms. A few, a very few, retained their faith and their allegiance to the Church of Rome and King Philip of Spain, whom they held to be upholder of the true faith.

The English sea captains were devout Christians. Perhaps the more so by virtue of their calling. But opposed to a papacy that had divided the known world longitudinally between her favoured sons: the wealth of the West, with the bounties of the Americas, to Spain; to Portugal, the exotic East with the precious stones and spices of India and Africa. Under the direction of Pope Sixtus the crown of England belonged to Philip of Spain and England was deemed a

Spanish possession by those loyal to the Vatican. For at Winchester in 1554 the two countries had been made united. Had Philip not married Mary, Queen of England? Whilst Bloody Mary was dead these thirty years, her country was her dowry.

Europe was undergoing a time of religious change. Emerging nations, witnessing that the authority of Rome favoured but the strong, put national interest and pride before the interests of the Pope and his princely powers, and adopted a form of worship to suit their personal or national character. In Spain itself, minds that questioned the authority of the Roman Catholic religion were guilty of heresy and suffered horrendous tortures on the rack at the hands of the Inquisition, or death by burning. Thus was quelled any query of the teachings or disciplines of the Church of Rome.

Pilgrims and merchants were an important source of information to King Philip II of Spain and his plans for the crusade that would embrace the subjugation of England, the elimination of Protestant heresy and the extension of the Spanish empire.

Similarly the Cornish sea captains valued news from Brittany, Spain or Portugal; the whereabouts of Philip's treasure ships, upon which they could prey, as they brought a stream of gold and silver from Mexico and Peru to fortify the wealth and the power of their King in his preparation for war. Valuable spices were also transported from the East by the ships of Portugal which, in the turmoil that followed the death of their Burgundian king in 1580, had been annexed by King Philip of Spain who had secured to himself the crown and added her ships to his fleet. The west country protestant privateers, with Drake as their hero, and with the connivance of their beloved Queen Elizabeth I, regarded the seizure of Spanish treasure as a legitimate sport benefitting themselves, their country and their religion, whilst diminishing the might and power of he who would hold them in thrall.

Jenkyn Keigwin's home was a centre of knowledge, gossip and conjecture exchanged before the great open fires. Fishermen from Brittany speaking the same Celtic tongue, yarning with Richard and Martin, Jenkyn's fishermen sons,

16

with news from those shores. Merchants from Portugal and Spain. Pilgrims with their tales of far off places, changes to religious doctrine, hazards overcome and adventures undertaken. Tongues loosened, stories exaggerated by fine wines and home-brewed ale.

There was a small colony of Spanish in Mousehole. Legacies of shipwreck and trade, some of whom had married into Cornish fishing families, continuing to observe their religion and customs. There were Jewish traders and money-lenders, driven by persecution to this remote part of Cornwall, bound by strong ties of family and religion to others of their race similarly occupied in towns and cities of France and Spain. Place-names and epitaphs to this day record the importance of their presence.

Also, there were many devout English living in Spain under the protection of King Philip. They who placed religious conviction above their Queen. Determined to see the restoration to their motherland of a Roman Catholic Church and Monarchy. These expatriates formed a virtual government in exile, serving in the Spanish army or aboard ship where, with their knowledge of the English coastline and culture, they were valued for their skills as navigators and interpreters as they awaited the inevitable victory.

Thus in the autumn of 1587 Mousehole was a microcosm of the various factions. A centre of spying and intrigue. A fruitful source of information to Lord Burghley, Lord High Treasurer, and the Secretary of State Sir Francis Walsingham, in their struggle to maintain the security of the realm and the well-being of their beloved Queen Elizabeth.

Some too grew rich on intelligence given to Don Bernadino Mendoza, spymaster to King Philip, one time Spanish Ambassador to England evicted by Walsingham in 1584 for plotting against Queen Elizabeth. There were those also in the pay of Le Balafre, the scar-faced Duke of Guise determined to be revenged upon Queen Elizabeth for the execution of his kinswoman, Mary Queen of Scots. Also, there were those, foolish or penniless, who dared to sell intelligence to more than one master; to challenge discovery, torture and foul death.

THE

PIRATE

AND THE

PROPHECY

*...of the Keigwins
of Mousehole
and the Spanish
Raid on Cornwall*

KEIGWIN OF MOUSEHOLE

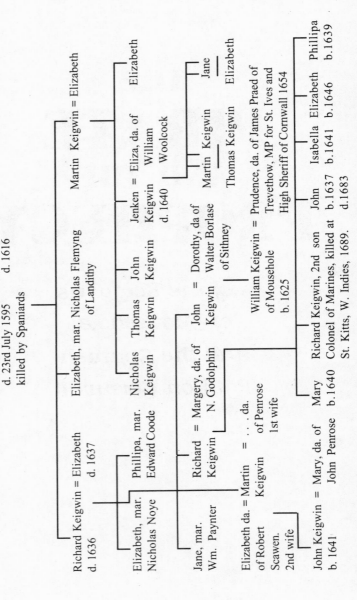

JENKYN KEIGWIN = THOMASINE
d. 23rd July 1595   d. 1616
killed by Spaniards

Richard Keigwin = Elizabeth
d. 1636

Elizabeth, mar. Nicholas Flemyng
of Landithy

Martin Keigwin = Elizabeth

Phillipa, mar.
Edward Coode

Nicholas
Keigwin

Thomas
Keigwin

John
Keigwin

Jenken = Eliza, da. of
Keigwin   William
d. 1640   Woolcock

Elizabeth

Jane, mar.
Wm. Paynter

Richard = Margery, da. of
Keigwin   N. Godolphin

John = Dorothy, da of
Keigwin   Walter Borlase
           of Sithney

Martin Keigwin

Jane

Thomas Keigwin

Elizabeth

Elizabeth da. = Martin = .. da.
of Robert   Keigwin   of Penrose
Scawen.   1st wife
2nd wife

William Keigwin = Prudence, da. of James Praed of
of Mousehole   Trevethow, MP for St. Ives and
b. 1625   High Sheriff of Cornwall 1654

John Keigwin = Mary, da. of
b. 1641   John Penrose

Mary
b.1640

Richard Keigwin, 2nd son
Colonel of Marines, killed at
St. Kitts, W. Indies, 1689.

John
b.1637
d.1683

Isabella
b.1641

Elizabeth
b.1646

Phillipa
b.1639

Chapter One

A Thursday morning in September in the year of Our Lord 1587. Thin, black-hosed shanks drummed the ribs of the aged mule that wound its way through the mass of folk and stock that made the hubbub of the market; neither plea nor punishment could urge his steed above that one slow pace.

Today there were ships in the harbour, a hoy and other merchantmen. Trade was afoot and where there was such prospect, Solomon Fernandes would wish to be attendant. Not for him the rousing risk of adventuring for gold. He had no desire for distress in pursuit of riches, he craved gain by business and would not be frustrated.

This was a day of hope. A fairweather day when merchants of substance might be gathered around the fireside of Jenkyn Keigwin before the storms of autumn came. Beneath black garb his heart beat faster. Men of consequence. Men wide travelled and of interest. Men who might require the services of such as he. A banker. Letters of credit and bills of exchange to be obtained from the money-lender of Marazion.

Who might Squire Keigwin be hosting today? Legs flailed, heels dug, but all to no avail as past the canopied stalls they plodded.

Soon winter would be upon them. A time of dark nights and wild seas when, safe inside the comfort of the Manor, they would engage in conversation, or play backgammon. To the arts of the day he was not inclined, for poetry and plays lacked the substance of the writings of yesteryear. Now of Greece and Rome, that was the stuff, and philosophical discussion, to tease and stretch the mind in argument with one whose wit and breadth of knowledge was equal to his own. That pleased him beyond all measure. Save the gratification of gold well earned.

At last the stableyard. In grudging silence a reluctant Jacob, retainer to the Squire, accepted proffered reins.

"Ah, welcome, good friend Solomon." Keigwin rose from his chair to grasp the money-lender to him, then to address the others present. "He has robbed me this many a year. I know not why it is, but still the rogue remains my banker. John Donne, greet Solomon Fernandes of whom you have heard me tell. Solomon, John too is a trusted friend, a merchant who judged by his apparel prospers well!"

The dark hawk head of the Jew nodded upon his ruff and he clasped with two the proffered hand of Donne, now risen from his fireside chair.

"Once, John traded from Weymouth but now is of Exmouth, venturing in any cargo by which he might earn a crust. My sons, Martin and Richard you know . . . " Solomon nodded greeting, "whilst this fellow . . . " He placed an affectionate arm around the young man's shoulders. "This is Thomas Flemyng . . . " Solomon stared in surprise. "Aye, my grandson has grown. Uncles and nephew — yet are they not as brothers!"

"Little Thomas grown. Aye aye aye, your daughter's boy a man." Solomon shook his head.

By gesture of hand Jenkyn bid Solomon sit near the fire. "Martin, tobacco if you please — Thomas, send Mary for more wine."

"So, you too are a friend of Jenkyn?" Solomon looked closely at Donne, admiring cut of clothes and worth of fabric.

"Perhaps the clothes I wear do tell a story and indeed I confess that I have prospered. But not always was it so, eh Jenkyn?" A cloud rose from John Donne's silver pipe bowl. " 'Tis many years since first we traded, too long since last we met. Yet I shall be ever grateful for your aid, and trust it has not cost you too dear."

Solomon looked on with quizzical eye as Jenkyn waved dismissive hand. "Pray, sir," Solomon interrupted, "I am intrigued and should it please you, I wish to hear your tale."

"So be it my friend, for I would the world to know of a viperous Englishman, Burley by name, and caution as to his traitorous ways."

Solomon nodded an invitation to continue.

"It was the summer of 1580, from Exmouth I had left aboard the *Jennet*. Ill-named, I fear, for our voyage was slow, it being thirteen days before we made St. Sebastian."

"The pearl of Cantalabria," Solomon recollected. "I have an uncle there who likewise trades."

Donne nodded. "The wind favoured us not and the seas were fierce. Safe in harbour I sought to dispose of my cargo to best advantage when Richard Burley arrived in the *Minion of Bridgewater*." He paused. "Know you of a merchant named Thomas Burley, Solomon?"

The banker nodded.

"This Richard is his eldest son. Now Burley had intelligence of my being there and determined that he would cheat me to his advantage. He was factor for some merchants of whom Pedro de Zaubiaur was one. No doubt you have heard of him also?"

Solomon cast his dark eyes heavenwards and shook his head. "And dealt with him, to my sorrow."

"Then you must know he is a man to whom it is best to give a wide berth. 'Tis the interests of himself and the Devil alone he serves. De Zaubiaur was envious of my goods, since I was carrying fish and oil for the feast of St. James. The family of Burley have long borne a grudge against my own. They hail from Melcombe Regis, and are of consequence, whilst I am of Weymouth. Twin boroughs, now united, yet separated not by the river alone, but by rivalry and bitterness in trade. Each endeavours to score off the other, to the detriment of both. As a consequence I am now to Exmouth for my business. But forgive me, gentlemen, for I digress." He sipped his wine. "Do I bore you, Jenkyn?"

"No, indeed not. Continue if it so please you."

Donne drew upon his pipe, watching the smoke rise high to hover beneath the barrelled ceiling.

"De Zaubiaur is the spider that sits in the centre of a web of trade and intrigue that provides intelligence for Mendoza — the spymaster of Spain. It was he who stooped to connive with Burley that together they might gain my cargo for themselves and greatly profit by it." He paused as he recalled the hurt. "Burley denounced me to the Bishop of St. Sebastian

23

as both a heretic and spy. A spy of my Lord Walsingham, so they alleged, in the false guise of a merchant, come to gain intelligence of Irish bishops gathered there and of their trade with Spain."

"Bishops in trade?"

"Aye, Martin. Religious tracts and vestments. Both to ensure and encourage opposition to the Protestant rule." He sipped his wine as Jenkyn continued in his stead.

"There is much that travels from Ireland to St. Jean de Luz that is magicked across the nearby border at Fuenterrabia, there to finish the journey in Spanish stomachs — we know that to our cost, is it not so, Solomon?"

"Indeed, Jenkyn, beef and corn outward, to return with wine."

"Aye, and oft-times to traffic in intelligence writ in cipher; thus, having gained from their unlawful voyage, those merchants can undersell upon the return cargo. Not all obey the laws to trade as fair as we." Jenkyn finished.

"My friend is reticent," said Solomon, "but pray continue, Master Donne, for yours is surely a tale of interest."

"They caused the Bishop to write to the General of Fuenterrabia with orders that I be taken, my goods detained. 'Tis God's truth I profess." He cast his eyes about his listeners. "Upon his orders the Captain of St. Sebastian searched my lodgings for that which might betray me. Yet did he look in vain, nothing could he find; but whilst they were about their handiwork I was carried to the border, a prisoner of the General. Delivered as a trussed hog by armed soldiers, bound hand and foot, slung across the back of a mule as if to the slaughter." He leant forward to look at each in turn. "Which indeed was my belief. Upon the orders of General Allgoheils I was imprisoned for twelve days in a darkened pit within the fortress there. Each and every hour I expected the bolts to be slid, the door to be opened, and to be taken to the chamber for my tongue to be loosened upon the rack. Such was my fear, the loneliness, the thought that none would know my plight." He paused, nodding his thanks as Jenkyn topped up his glass and those of the others present.

"Unbeknownst to me, by my great good fortune, Richard Keigwin was come to port, with hogsheads of oil and salted fish to trade."

Richard smiled acknowledgement.

"Thanks be to God, young Dick — for he was but a youth, yet with the wisdom of one much older — together with other English merchants, petitioned the Bishop upon my behalf; pleading for my freedom and giving good account of me. Indeed they became bound for five thousand ducats that I was not such as Burley had told."

"How your heart must warm at the trust of your fellows."

"Aye, Solomon, for upon learning of this, General Allgoheils ordered my release and the return of my goods. Yes, and demanded to know who was so base as to accuse me."

"So the Spanish general was a just man."

"Aye, he was just, God be praised. For doubtless he was given to despise those that played the game that others were wont to practise."

"What, wrongfully accuse that the cargo might be theirs?" Tom was disbelieving.

"Rightfully, wrongfully, they betray for reward. Doubtless in time, Tom, you will learn there is a certain breed of merchant that would skin their own mothers to sell their hides. There are those of that ilk of whom I know, who trade where Spain borders with France."

"Pray tell us, Master Donne, that we may be prepared."

Donne pondered over his ale and lowered his voice.

"If I tell, it must not be repeated."

When each had nodded, he continued. "At St. Jean de Luz is a merchant with whom I trade — but warily, for he supplies intelligence to my Lord Burghley. He also sells to Mendoza, or whoever will bid him most."

"He must live in peril for his life."

"Lest he be too valuable to each. For he also gathers intelligence from London of those that smuggle into Spain. Then he denounces them to Mendoza, his reward — the goods they carry. Take care I say, should you deal with Edmund Palmer, merchant of St. Jean de Luz, for he will betray you if there be a profit!"

"But what of Burley?"

"Indeed, Martin, what of him? He fled, fearing I would be revenged on him."

b

He paused to ponder and to puff upon his pipe.

"That was an adventure that had a fortunate end," prompted Jenkyn.

"Aye, indeed, for that is but half of my tale. Such was my grievance I determined to act as Burley had falsely accused." He laughed aloud, slapping his knee at the thought. "I gathered much intelligence for my Lord Walsingham for a handsome reward, but deemed it prudent to return when learning Burley had once more been received by the King of Spain. Being restored to favour I was afeared he might have me to his advantage." He faced Solomon. "That, my friend, is the measure of my debt to the family of Jenkyn Keigwin, and my hatred of Pedro de Zaubiaur and his henchman Richard Burley." He sipped his wine. "Jenkyn, have you suffered by way of reprisal? For 'twas you that refused to trade with Don Pedro and with Burley and those for whom he factored."

The Squire grunted in reply and smiled. "As was my duty I related intelligence of your plight to Godolphin and also I proclaimed the embargo placed upon their goods. This I believe has harmed us not, for it enhances our reputation and will show that we have little regard for dishonest dealing. Is that not so, Solomon?"

The Jew nodded in assent.

"Martin and Tom should know that as a consequence of the Keigwin influence both Burley and Zaubiaur have suffered." Donne continued with his story. "Zaubiaur must turn from Cornwall to trade for fish with Brittany alone. But there are Bretons who fish from Mousehole thence to trade with him. Thereby does he gather much intelligence of your dealings, Jenkyn; and all that happens here." He looked towards Thomas and Martin. "You have the courage of young men, but heed me, there are those who would go to lengths undreamt if they could but harm the family of Keigwin. Amongst them are Captain Richard Burley and Don Pedro de Zaubiaur. The maggots of their grudge fatten upon their souls, and whilst fortune smiled on me, she is fickle in her favours.

"Burley now a captain?"

"Aye, lad," replied Donne angrily. Thomas smiled to hear

his uncle so addressed. "A captain in the pay of the King of Spain. Some say for five and twenty crowns a month. Remember this, no man detests his country more than he who plays the traitor."

"He must be held in high regard."

"Indeed he is, Tom, for he embraces the Roman way with a fervour few possess and so endears himself unto the king."

"How should we know this Burley?" asked Martin.

"He is older than your brother, Dick. Perhaps of some four and thirty years. His features are fair and not unpleasing. His beard is of the stiletto style, favoured by those who bear arms."

"And his manner?"

"Courtly. But do not be deceived, for his eye is that of the zealot."

"Is he skilled in the use of weapons?"

"At court he would be well schooled in all those matters."

"A man of whom to be wary."

"Indeed, quick to take offence, as is witnessed by the scars he bears."

"Scars?"

Donne placed a finger upon his left cheekbone. "Here, Tom, here he carries a jagged nick, consequence of some duel I am told."

"Come, enough of this," the Squire rose, "for please God your paths will never cross and my nostrils are a'tingle at the smell of good victuals. Let us eat."

As he chewed with relish upon fat beef turned and basted upon the kitchen spit, John Donne sought information from the banker.

"I have spoken of my purpose but what of you, Solomon Fernandes?"

"Master Donne, I am but a poor banker but one who gives just service for little reward, and is also honest. Is that not so, Squire Keigwin?"

Jenkyn smiled and nodded.

"From where do you come?"

"My forebears are of Israel's kind but for many a year we have lived in Spain as my name foretells." With skill borne of long practice he filleted the fish that Thomasine Keigwin had

27

prepared for him alone. "There remain those of my family who in the guise of a Spanish pedigree trade from San Sebastian and St. Jean de Luz. Together, we service the needs of merchants such as Squire Keigwin."

"Pray why, Master Fernandes, did you leave your birthplace? For, as Jenkyn Keigwin is my friend, your secret is safe with me."

Seeing the reluctance of the Jew to disclose further, Donne continued in wheedling tone.

"Mayhap I too would do business with you, from which you may earn a shekel or two, were I to learn this secret."

With a shrug of reluctant acceptance the Jew conceded.

"If you require my services, then 'tis fair you should know what manner of man I am."

He held his fellow guest with an intense gaze as a new found fervour entered his voice.

"I hold to the ways of my forefathers. Whilst once my tribe was welcome in your land most now have been forced to flee these shores, to wander yet again. I have no wish to preach my faith to those about me, and likewise I respect the belief of others. Yet neither do I wish to share their doctrine, or have it impressed upon me, in the manner of Torquemada the Dominican, who converted my ancestors in the torture chambers of the Inquisition."

Slowly, he shook his lowered head in remembrance of the suffering of his people, and continued in hushed voice.

"Here in Marazion I am deemed of little consequence. My tongue is still, my demeanour modest. By that, and honest trading I maintain my freedom." He raised his head towards his host. "Sheltered by the friendship of Keigwin."

Keigwin coughed his embarrassment. "Only whilst you serve my needs, you scoundrel!" His smile belied his words, as Donne continued.

"And what of you, Thomas, do you follow in the footsteps of your grandfather?"

"No, no, Master Donne! Not for me, for there are my uncles Martin here, and Richard, to inherit both my grandfather's wisdom and his worth!"

"He lacks the patience, John, but that will come in later

28

years." Jenkyn Keigwin smiled at his grandson.

"Maybe, Grandfather, when I am older I will perhaps settle ashore, but now I prefer the wildness and the glorious uncertainty of the sea."

"The sea is it?"

"My nephew," Martin answered defensively, "is as good a seaman as you may know and as fine a fellow with a blade as there lives in Cornwall."

"A good man to have on your side upon a dark and dangerous night?"

"Yes indeed, Master Donne, be you at sea or ashore!"

"And so," continued Jenkyn, "my daughter's husband — being this rascal's father — and myself, have given to him one third share in a privateer, by which we three may profit and offer some defence to Mousehole."

"And what is more, Master Donne," Thomas spoke proudly, "she is one of a screen of pinnaces that stretch across the chops of the Channel from the Scillies to Ushant. Drake calls us his eyes and ears, for we keep watch, lest Spain should take us unawares."

"In case invasion threatens?"

"Aye, 'tis our duty to gain intelligence of ships that enter the narrow seas. To alert Sir Francis as to any threat of danger."

"That all may sleep safe in their beds," concluded Jenkyn.

The following spring: May 1588. It was early evening and the heat of the sun was beginning to fade. Within the harbour the blue crystal of the floodtide lapped against the pattern of the great stones of gold-lichened granite that formed the harbour wall.

Through the smoke-grimed glass of The Mermaid Inn, Teek Cornall watched with curious eye as the merchantman lazily entered harbour, to head into the light air and lose all way. As the mainsails cracked and emptied she tied up against the granite steps. Warps fast about granite bollards. Sheets were slackened, sailors climbed aloft to reef the sails. Her tall masts gaunt against the pale background of the sky, her sturdy hull at contrast with the slim, sleek privateer. For the *Golden Hind* lay anchored on the good ground, betwixt harbour and island, cannon now hid behind closed ports; of delicate outline and a gentle name that belied her true purpose. She was a ship of the Western Squadron, the pinnace upon which he sailed as bosun to Tom Flemyng, the fastest ship in those western waters.

Men eased away as a soiled and shuffling figure edged toward him, sharp-eyed terrier at heel and wriggling sack slung over one shoulder.

"Spare me the price of a jar, Teek," the gruff voice pleaded. "Times are hard."

"Times are always hard, Silas."

"Trade isn't what it was," continued the whingeing voice.

Teek leant forward and put out a hand to be licked. "Is she in pup?" He stroked the battle-scarred muzzle.

The grimed face nodded.

"A jar of huffcap for the pick of the litter?"

"Nay, she's in whelp to Penda!"

"Penda?"

"The best ratter ever bred."

"How come 'Penda'?"

"King of the Celts warn't he? Penda is king of his kind an' the bitch be queen."

"Pick of the litter for a jar of ale."

"One jar an' a shilling."

"Jar and sixpence."

"Done!" He spat in his palm and reached to shake and clinch the deal. "A dog at sea? 'Twill bring bad luck."

"No, 'tis present for young brother, Ben. Keep him out of trouble when I'm away." He handed sixpence to the rat catcher and beckoned for a jar of ale.

Beyond the island the fishing fleet could still be seen. Little boats of Mousehole, that circled in the bay as Richard Keigwin directed. Oars tapped the shimmering water as they surrounded the shoals of bloated pilchards. Hungry nets gathered and tipped the silver hordes into jumping heaps to fill the bottom of their boats, then to be pressed and squeezed for oil, or salted down in hogsheads.

A scene of calm and men in harmony.

Teek's brown eyes softened above chestnut beard. Frank

face darkened by wind and salt spray, a golden earring reflected the flame of burning sea coal that spluttered in the hearth of the open fire. A black iron pot of mutton stew was hooked above to simmer in the heat. Mouth-drooling smells of meat and herbs wafted across the black-beamed room, as Landlord Trewhella ladled a mess of potage onto the platter before him and replenished his ale.

With the back of his hand he wiped the froth from his mouth. It was good to be home awhile, to revictual midst peace and friendship, released from the threat of tempest and of Spain.

Market day was near over, pedlar and farmer, chapman and fisherman drifted in and out of the open door. Teek watched them all as they took their places in oaken seats and settles upon the rush-strewn floor. Here at The Mermaid travellers could partake of food and home-brewed ale; or sometimes wines from France and Spain.

Outside the shadows lengthened. Black-cloaked figures of returning pilgrims clambered ashore from the safe-moored merchant hoy. Was this her cargo? Waiting awhile to sort and gather their meagre possessions, broad-brimmed hats pressed firmly down against the tug of a freshening breeze, then, making their way as a group to the comfort that awaited at the sign of The Mermaid.

Their long staves tapped upon the uneven cobbles. Easing himself upon the wooden seat, Teek pondered. How long must these men of simple piety have scrimped and saved for their journey to devotion? How humble must they be, how devout. To sail in cramped discomfort across storm-ridden seas that they might worship the gold-encased bones of a saint long dead. How much had they paid for the voyage? Enough, he mused, for the master to pay for the return cargo, lashed safe below decks. Ah, but a handsome profit would be reaped through these penitents.

Surely, he pondered, had they not returned before time? Was not the feast of St. James the 15th of June? Usually they would have wished to stay and witness the celebration of that great festival. With a puzzled air he raised his empty jar. Something was amiss.

Thoughts of the pilgrims and the hoy were soon forgot

as Becky Trewhella came, barefoot, across the room. He watched with pleasure as, hips swaying in innocent provocation, she navigated between rough tables, to lean and refill the pots from a jug of home brew.

Quickly, Teek half rose, to reach for the blade beneath his jerkin. For he of the black beard had stretched out a hand to finger and to fondle her rounded form. He sat to grin, as with swirl of skirt and slap of wrist, she repelled the advances that frock and smock of tight waist and low bosom did so little to discourage.

Seated once more, the bosun smiled as he contemplated and marvelled upon temptation and the ways of womankind; and Becky, as she tacked towards the window where he sat, deftly scooping and pocketing the coins as she came. With dimpling smile she caught his beckoning nod, a blush touched her cheeks as she served the young seaman of the barque of Mousehole. For were not the exploits of these sailors already legend amongst the harboursides of the west? Yet what strange company he kept! The stink of the rat-catcher assailed her nostrils as she topped the pot from the earthenware jug. Blue eyes caught brown, the pink in her cheeks deepened. Disconcerted, self-conscious eyes cast swiftly down as ale overflowed. White teeth smiled in his walnut face, eyes that crinkled to ease embarrassment only served to deepen her adoration. For here was her hero. She tucked an errant lock of golden hair beneath her bonnet, quickly turned, and hid her confusion by serving another guest.

Silas leered after the departing Becky. Lips moistened by a tongue that flicked through blackened stumps.

"Remember our bargain," Teek reminded him, as with knowing wink, the heaving, rat-filled sack was slung once more upon his shoulders and Silas sidled off. Teek returned to his thoughts, to the merchantman and her cargo. Why were there no other pilgrims to voyage to Santiago de Compostella? Why were they home before the celebrations?

Through the open doorway the returning pilgrims entered, their felt hats adorned with scallop shells. Were these not pilgrims with a difference? Was not their bearing youthful? Whilst they walked slowly, it was not the stiffened walk of middle or crabbed age newly-released from cramped quarters.

32

These folk had no need of time to adjust their legs to firm land.

As a hound's hackles rise at the onset of danger so on his neck the hair began to tingle. The sixth sense of his Celtic ancestors. Certain in the knowledge that here was danger, here lay threat! With feigned weariness, slowly he rose, to ease his way through the throng, to brush against pilgrims girt with cincture from which hung shell and scrip. Faces concealed by broad brim, they made their way toward a darkened corner.

Did not the girdled gabardine betray the waist of crusading youth? Why not the beam of devout middle age? He paused to watch, to wait awhile, to be certain. His captain was supping at the home of his grandfather. He must needs tell him his thoughts and fears.

Free of the inn, he walked quickly along the quayside to the Manor. Nervously, he knocked on the studded oaken door, stocking cap in hand, leather jerkin smoothed straight, uneasy at the reception he might receive. Heavy bolts were slid, the door jerked ajar, he entered the darkened hallway to tell the servant of his wish to see his captain.

The light of the candlesticks reflected in the pewter that stood upon cupboards of fine oak. Never had he seen such comfort. His feet scuffed uncertainly in the pile of the turkey carpets strewn upon the granite floor. Apprehensive, he consoled himself. Captain Flemyng would understand his unease.

A voice bellowed. "What in God's name brings you here, Cornall?"

He looked up to the landing above.

"The *Golden Hind* is safe?"

Teek stammered an attempted reply, his nervousness increased.

"Tell me, man, tell me of your purpose! I've supped well, my belly's full. I shan't eat you!"

Down the stairs he came, of but twenty or so years. Darkly handsome. Slim of build. Dressed in slashed doublet, plum in colour. Beneath an upswept moustache, a smile eased the discomfort of his bosun.

Martin Keigwin, burlier and of fair complexion, casually

followed his nephew down the wide staircase.

The bosun bent to retrieve his dropped cap, to gather his senses and look his master squarely.

"Captain, sometimes I know when things are not as they seem. I have this sense, a feeling. Something is amiss with that hoy moored within the harbour. Pilgrims, pilgrims she carries, Captain Thomas, Master Martin sir! They be no proper pilgrims!"

Thomas Flemyng enquired for more. Rapt with attention they listened. Teek told them of what he had seen. Of how the pilgrims were younger, not the middle-aged and well-found elderly who usually visited France, Spain and even the Holy Land. They had waited, to disembark at dusk, hats pulled low over hidden faces, to sit quietly in the shadow. Nor did they regale their stories, their exploits, and the miracles they had witnessed or imagined, to any who would attend and some who had no such wish, as was the manner of the customary pilgrim.

When finished, Flemyng ordered him to stay whilst he and Martin counselled with the Squire.

Jenkyn Keigwin was seated at the head of the great table, his family about him. Richard at the foot, next to his mother, Thomasine. The Squire sipped a goblet of sack and pulled upon white rounded beard as he listened whilst his grandson recounted the bosun's tale.

He meditated prior to making comment.

"That merchantman is but a rare visitor. She hails from Newhaven, that which the French call Havre de Grace." He drank slowly of his wine that thus he might ensure attention.

"Newhaven is the finest port in Normandy, at the mouth of the River Seine, dependent for trade on the city of Rouen that lies upstream." He shook his head. "Be watchful, for there the Duke de Guise holds sway and de Zaubiaur has spies, with many an English papist in his employ." He savoured his wine. "There are English merchants of that town who claim affection for our Queen, but practise loyalty only to their pockets. That scar-faced duke will gladly give good reward to any who may lay hurt to Elizabeth of England."

Mary the servant girl hovered behind as she waited at table, to lean over whilst he paused, and replenish his goblet.

"I am advised the *Hope* is owned by her captain, Nicholls — he of the black beard who claims he has returned from Corunna with those pilgrims. Also is he laden with wine and salt beef. He offered me a hogshead or two but I cared neither for his manner, nor his price. Our spies give intelligence that ships of Spain were storm battered on leaving Cadiz and are forced to refit at Corunna and will shortly sail against us. 'Tis rare coincidence that he should come from thence at this particular time. Be wary, Thomas, do be wary. Be careful, verify what your bosun feels. Conjure in your mind what Drake would advise. You have little time to do so, for she will shortly sail upon this evening's tide and be gone I know not where. To Ireland do I suspect, for further mischief. Is the *Golden Hind* victualled and ready?"

"Yes, Grandfather. She too awaits the tide."

"Then be on your way with all caution and God speed."

Tom rose to kiss his grandmother upon her apple cheek and squeeze her hand, to leave the company with a cheerful wave. Down the stairs he ran to the hall below, taking rapier and belt from a wooden peg to buckle about his waist.

"Come, Teek, on your way. We'll verify or otherwise the credentials of your 'pilgrims'!"

Hand upon elbow he steered his bosun through the sturdy doors into the dark evening air. Together, the two Cornishmen went their way along lane and quayside; separately they entered The Mermaid.

Using rank and elbow Flemyng steered his way through the ribaldry as thirsty throats drank deep of the ale landlord Trewhella brewed. Upon a chair abaft the pilgrims, back safe against the wall he sat. Teek came to seat himself near to his captain's hand, where Becky brought both wine and ale.

Over the rim of his goblet, Flemyng warily surveyed the inn and those gathered about him. The pilgrims he saw were supping the mutton ladled in steaming heaps upon their wooden platters. The black beard was seated by the fire. For certainty that was Nicholls, master of the *Hope*.

A drop of an eyelid drew Teek's notice to his captain's action, as he watched him tease with pointed toe a pilgrim's staff into the narrow gangway. The returning voyagers, engrossed in their fresh meat, spoke little to each other; with noisome relish they dunked hunks of new-baked bread into rich, still-simmering stew.

The bosun caught his captain's wink. The signal. With a drunken belch he lurched to his feet, full jar of ale clenched within rope-roughened fist, to stumble and trip against the staff and sprawl, cursing, upon the pilgrims' table. His forearm straightened to slide the hot platter into waiting lap. With stupid clumsiness, he rose to gaze with the blank eyes of the drunkard. To grumble and blame, whilst slowly to decant his jug of ale down the neck of yet another stranger.

With a cry of pain and wrath, the pilgrim leapt to his feet, clutching his steaming groin.

"Pox-ridden oaf!" he yelled. "I'll feed your liver to the dogs."

Hand flashed beneath his cape. His beer-drenched comrade was quick to rise and clap restraining hand upon him.

Mouthing words that none could comprehend, Teek staggered to the street.

The tall man in pilgrim's cloth grovelled beneath the bench to retrieve his fallen hat and replace the naked blade. Bare-headed, his fair hair fell close near his shoulders in cut of a gentleman venturer, eyes blazed in contemptuous rage to follow the figure of the drunkard.

With dampened cloth, Becky came to aid the stranger and apologise, for she was shamed. Never before had she borne witness to a drunken Teek, and he bosun of the privateer. The stranger raised his head to utter thanks as Tom held high a spluttering candle. He saw a handsome man, save for the duelling scar that marred his cheek. No humble pilgrim this, but a man of rank mouthing a soldier's oath.

Burley. It must be he.

A coin was tossed upon the table for Becky as she hovered, Tom made for the doorway to cross to the harbour's edge. Idly he seemed to survey the scene below. Footsteps passed behind him. He waited. Black-beard was returning aboard his ship as she made ready to sail on the retreating tide. From the shadows of a narrow alley emerged the sturdy figure of Teek, swift recovered from his drunken fall.

The Squire must be told. Godolphin must be advised as

to the presence of men come to spy, servants of Spain who bode evil for the Queen. Captain Richard Burley was in Mousehole.

Inside The Mermaid, the fair-haired stranger sought answers, "Come!" Becky turned. "Pray tell me, my maid — a bosun you said, off the privateer?"

Becky nodded, obedient to his authority.

"Then who was the other? A gentleman, who held the candle?"

"Captain Flemyng."

"Of the privateer?"

"Yes, sir."

"Drunk before his captain? Curious, don't you suppose?"

Dumb was her response, that was itself the answer. The pilgrim asked no more and turned to his fellows.

In the Manor House it was agreed. If mischief was afoot, Martin's obligation must be to his nephew. Their duty to determine if the *Hope* was on a mission, a mission prejudicial to the interests of the Queen.

They made for the hard alongside the quay where the dinghy awaited, high beyond the reach of tide. The bosun fell in behind, at a distance, a poniard in his palm.

In the darkening evening they shoved the dinghy to the water's edge. Tom and Martin stepped aboard. For Teek the privilege of the final wet-footed heave before she floated clear. Clambering aboard, he grasped an oar in knowing hands. Knees bent, legs splayed, he sculled toward where the anchored pinnace lay.

In The Mermaid black brims touched in earnest converse. Could that be the action of a drunken sailor? Or was there more sinister intent? Might it be they were discovered?

Burley and his companions settled their account and made their way, to scatter in the safety of the dark. Praise God, they had coin and change of garments. Only for the moment would they appear as pilgrims. They had come to act another scene. A part of more importance in the play that shortly would unfold for all to witness.

On the *Golden Hind* stern lanterns glowed softly in the dimming light. Faces grinned a greeting from above as helping hands pulled them over the gunwale.

"Softly now, softly," warned the captain, as the dripping dinghy was hauled aboard.

In the still of the dark, the sound of shouted orders as the merchantman was warped to the harbour entrance. "Douse the lanterns, Bosun," Thomas ordered in hushed tones. "Martin, do the rounds and tell the crew I want them at their stations. Silence is the order of the day. I'll have the ears of any man I hear. When done meet me in my cabin."

Across the water, halliards screeched as hemp made through wooden block and sails outlined against the sky, to fill and billow in the light airs as the *Hope of Newhaven* slowly made her lonely way, to seaward, windward of the privateer.

Tom hissed instructions to the helmsman. "Pentreath, keep watch and see what course she takes, for we shall shortly follow."

Martin followed Thomas below to the cramped quarters of his cabin, that Flemyng might recount all he knew. Martin listened with attention.

"These are no pilgrims that have returned," Tom paused, "but English followers of Rome, sent to create havoc and confusion, to arouse other traitors who await the coming of the Armada."

"So thought your grandfather, he has sent Richard on horseback to alert Godolphin who will surely nip their devilment in the bud."

"Our concern must be the *Hope*. We know not what she has aboard or whither she is bound. 'Tis Grandfather's belief it may be Ireland, there to foment further strife. Teek tells me she took on water enough for a voyage."

Forewarned and forearmed. In that knowledge they made their plans. The strength and direction of wind and tides were calculated in their minds, and a course of action was decided. The helmsman, bosun and master gunner were summoned and instructions given. "Master Keigwin will give orders before the mast and keep watch with Bosun Cornall, whilst I remain aft at my station. There is enough sea-room between us. We must keep careful sight lest she be let slip."

The turning windlass slowly lifted her anchor. Raised sails captured the evening northerly. The *Golden Hind* passed the island and headed south with the tide, in the track of her prey. Off the Bucks beyond Lamorna's cove, Keigwin whistled his orders. Forward, Teek heard and understood. Sails reset for change of course, southwest, in position abaft, the *Hope* to windward. Between her and the coastline's granite heights, the pinnace stalked her prey.

Thomas Nicholls lay in the comfort of his captain's cot. The helmsman following the plotted course. In the moonlight, the dim distant bulk of Land's End would soon approach to gently slip astern. Thence stars to guide them south of Wolf Rock. The captain of the *Hope* would take a late watch. Meanwhile, with noisy relish, he sipped the brandy from the treasured silver goblet. A gift from his master, Pedro de Zaubiaur.

Soon the moon would light the night as day. To wait until dawn would lose surprise. Advantage lost meant wounded men. Martin came to the whistle's beckoning call.

"Take over, whilst I do the rounds, for we are about to pounce."

"Aye, Captain, sir." Martin grinned at his nephew in the dim light. Quiet words of recognition to yardsman and seaman as he made forward to the bosun.

"We maintain to windward of the hoy. On my orders reef in all save fighting sails. We want no heel to spoil our gunners' aim. Under short sails we still have the legs of her. The gunners' tubs?"

"Ready, sir."

"Good, you have your men prepared and armed to follow Master Martin lest we board?"

"All ready, Captain."

"Wait my command. Good man, Teek. Catch such sleep as you may for soon there will be much to do." He strode across the deck to the gunwhale. Six cannon in all.

"Master Gunner?" He peered through the darkness.

"Aye, Captain."

"Is all prepared?"

"Aye, it is."

He reached to feel the budge barrels were at hand, shot lockers duly laden. "Know you your orders, Master Gunner?"

"Aye, sir."

"Await my command." Then, that all might hear, " 'Tis you gunners shall determine if we have fair pickings or none at all!"

"Fear not, Captain, for you shall have your share of booty," called a voice unknown for all to laugh away the tension.

"Master Gunner, all men are to catch such sleep as they may. But be alert for my command."

"Aye, Captain."

The last leg of his voyage before he returned to Newhaven. The fierce spirit bit the back of his throat. Northwards to Ireland and Kinsale and pray there was no fog. To await the coded message, hand over the tracts of Rome with their depths of hidden meaning and ciphered orders, brought down river in secret from Rouen, fresh from the press of Father Parsons. Wise not to know too much lest his tongue be loosened on the rack. But this much was certain. The chieftains of Ireland were hungry for the Armada. With the secret army of English they would rise, united, to overthrow the Protestant yoke. Then might he enjoy the fruits of freedom the church of Rome would grant her faithful followers.

In pensive mood he rose to refill the empty cup. He would give up the sea and France. With his reward he would seek a berth ashore in a papist England. Perhaps to take a wife. A young one. Partridge-plump to keep him warm at nights. A fair one. A comely wench who would breed him sons and work for him. An inn perhaps. A traveller's inn. That maid at the sign of The Mermaid, one such as she. But why not herself? He smiled in sensual bliss as sweet sleep overcame the vision of his life to be.

Chapter Two

Tom kept watch with a deck crew of six whilst Martin and the remaining four and twenty were sent below to catch such sleep as they might. No reason was asked and none was given, sailors knew their captain and perceived adventure was afoot. Where there was adventure, there was coin. They would follow such as he to the gates of hell.

Cramped between decks snug-wrapped, eyes fixed upon timbers close above him, Teek Cornall dwelt on thoughts of a bare-foot girl, slim of waist and full at breast: bright eyes above tip-tilted nose, and full, ripe lips that smiled shy welcome. He had known Becky since she was a child, but now she was grown a woman. The sway of her hips and the challenging lift of her chin proclaimed she had the needs and desires of a woman. A wild rose of Cornwall now in full bloom, an invitation to the wandering bee. He would play the bee, and enjoy his rose in the full flush of her beauty. And soon! Lest others sought to gain her for their own. His eyes in slumber, a smile of contentment about his lips.

Out to sea, waves were building. In the freshening wind the *Golden Hind* heeled, her white wake streaming radiant bright in the waning moonlight. The distant topsails of the hoy could be dimly discerned. The *Hope* must alter course a fraction, for whilst the *Golden Hind* could sail close to the wind, the hoy was heavy laden. Seaward she was bound to steer, further distanced from the shelter of the land.

Martin was wakened in an instant by a knock upon his cabin door.

"Uncle, dawn will shortly be upon us."

From his pocket Flemyng drew and thumbed a well-worn

booklet. Side by side, in the dim light of the lantern, they knelt upon the cabin floor.

"Lord, be merciful to us sinners, and save us for thy mercy's sake. Thou art the great God, that hast made and rulest all things. O deliver us for Thy Name's sake. Thou art the great God to be feared above all: O save us, that we may praise Thee."

Flemyng returned the volume to within his doublet and rose. Martin donned his breast plate and with rapier in hand went up on deck.

Elsewhere Nicholls stirred himself at the change in pitch and roll. Dawn would soon be breaking and he would take watch at first light. He sluiced himself in ice cold water, freshly taken from the Mousehole stream.

"All's well?" he demanded as he reached the deck.

"Aye, Captain," came the reply.

Casting a knowing eye about, he took in the faint line of land astern, then upwards to the set of sail. Indeed, it seemed all was well.

Slowly the *Hope* rose and rolled to crest another wave. Landward, upon her aft quarter, what was that in the distant gloom? He held himself steady to shield his widened eyes, willing them adjust to the northern darkness. For a moment he thought he had glimpsed a topsail. He climbed the shrouds for a better view. It was! The rig of a ship in fighting sail, fast bearing down upon them!

"Mate! What in God's name is she about?" The question was short-lived.

Above the singing wind Flemyng heard his Master Gunner call: "Cannon primed, loaded and ready to fire, Captain."

The distance between the vessels drew ever shorter.

Flemyng bided on a parallel course. The bowsprit of the *Golden Hind* now forward of the hoy. He gave the order to fire a warning shot ahead of the merchantman. Flame flashed from cannon's mouth and ball sped in low arc forward of the *Hope*'s bows to skim across the wave tops in repeating rebound, spray sent streaming in the dawning.

The two ships closed. Now Nicholls could tell who was his aggressor. The six gunned pinnace that lay off Mousehole!

"In God's name!" The black bull bellowed. "Arm yourselves! Cornish pirates!"

Swiftly he looked about him; all that for which he had schemed and planned could now be lost. the intrigue, the danger undergone . . ! Where to? North of him the privateer, no sanctuary there. Ahead, way ahead too far, the islands of Scilly. Should he sheer southwards into the open sea? Yet with none to bear witness, he could be taken, cast overboard, weighted down, a cannonball for company. About, yes about, the only way. And pray to God the gunners' aim was bad. He would head into the wind, as if to obey and hove to, but carry her traverse round and go about. Pray those on land might see his plight and so deter the pirates. His men were craven and had no fight in them. Only guile could win. He shouted orders to his helmsman, the hoy turned her bows north and into the wind.

Flemyng watched the wind and the set of sails, ready to shout encouragement and orders to his crew as the gunners again laid cannon to await their captain's command.

"Wait for it, wait for it." His orders relayed to the gun deck. "She's heaving to," he said to himself. Then, shouting aloud, "Boarding party be prepared to board. My God! Sheer off, Helmsman sheer off, else we be rammed!"

The pinnace too swung north and lost all way, as above her transom the bowsprit of the merchantman continued to come round, to go about on opposite tack, now with all sail swiftly crammed.

"The blackguard has fooled me and damned near sunken us!" Flemyng fumed, angry he had not foreseen the Nicholls' ploy.

"Once maybe, but never twice I'll vow." The pinnace wallowed between the waves. Flemyng whistled his commands and watched Teek's orders were obeyed, as yardsmen raised mizzen and main topsail. At last the *Hind* answered her helmsman's plea and her reluctant head came round.

Once more the chase was on, but now the hoy was fore-warned and had a running start on her pursuer. Steadily the light laden pinnace began to overhaul the *Hope* as the hoy ran with a westerly wind for the harbour she had but lately left. Teek heard his captain's commanding whistle, once more sails were lowered, the heeling deck flattened, as in fighting trim the pinnace carried onward, now a level platform from which the cannon might the better aim and fire. Martin joined his nephew in brief discourse and with wry smile carried the spoken orders forward to the bosun.

The larboard side of the pinnace came closer to the starboard of the hoy, the *Golden Hind* eased ahead in the lightening of the day. Ports open, the bared teeth of her ordnance could clearly be seen by those aboard the merchantman as over, over she eased, to force the hoy's bows landward, to nudge her to the north, forcing the merchantman to alter course a necessary smidgen.

From forward on the *Hope* came a scream of terror and of warning. Nicholls gaped ahead. In her path the angry grey snout of the Runnell Stone reared upwards from the trough, to submerge again beneath a great wash of white and foaming water. At once he knew of Flemyng's game, to ease him onto the rock that lurked below, hungry for another victim. To sink him without outward show of guilt, a victim of poor seamanship. In desperation he swung the helm for his ship to narrowly skirt the ravening rock, the graveyard of many a rotting hulk. Above the hiss and foam of sea came the sound of merciless mirth from the Cornish privateer.

On the gundeck of the *Golden Hind* the command was passed: "In your own time take away her mainsail. Damage her hull at your peril. If we are to take her, I want the prize but little harmed."

A roar of smoke and flame belched from a single cannon. A cheer as the mainsail of the hoy was seen to rip and tear and no more hold the wind. Flemyng watched. The cumbrous merchantman floundered at the mercy of the sea. Terror struck, her crew screamed for pity, falling upon their knees in prayer lest more shot should come their way. The *Golden*

Hind swung to larboard as with immaculate seamanship Pentreath steered her alongside the hapless hoy to lose all speed as with loosened sheets she faced into the wind, to wallow side by side with her prey. Grappling irons arced upward to find safe purchase as beam to beam the two ships clasped. With a cry that Satan would have feared, Martin lead his men to leap and scramble onto the deck above, swords and axes held aloft in further threat to the craven crew.

"Cowards, cowards, fight or we die," the Black-beard roared in response, in desperate endeavour to muster his cowering men. "Now, you Cornish devil!" He sighted Martin and drew a primed pistol from his belt.

Perched high in the rigging of the *Golden Hind* Teek fired first, snagging the sleeve of Nicholls, whose ball sped wide and failed to find its mark.

In blinding fury he flung the discharged weapon at his foe, with fearful bellow the black bull charged, intent to gore, rapier in right hand, dagger now in left. Martin, alerted by Teek's alarm, timed his sway to turn as the steel by a hairsbreadth raked his side. Nicholls' rush carried him crashing against the coaming to buckle over, breathless. A grip upon his collar, prick of steel against his ribs and rapier and dagger dropped to the deck at Keigwin's hissed command.

With his hands roughly lashed, Nicholls was bundled across his deck over the gunwhale and to the pinnace rafted close below; encouraged by prod and jibe from Cornishmen delighting in his discomfort. The game over, Martin's men searched their prize from stem to stern.

Frogmarched by the bosun, Nicholls faced a stone-faced Flemyng in his cabin. The prisoner's eyes blazed their hatred and fury. Lips pursed, defiant above a jutting beard, his head jerked forward as with all the venom he might muster, he spat full in the face of his captor.

The saliva trickled down his cheek, Flemyng laughed a mirthless laugh and wiped away the spittle. Slowly, his hand went to his belt from where he drew a dagger from its sheath and placed it upon the sea chest that stood between them.

"By God, I'll have you racked!" roared Black-beard as he lunged to wrench at his bonds, only to be half throttled from behind by the brawny arm of Cornall, who grinned with pleasure at his chore.

"Steady, Bosun!" as Nicholls' voice was choked into a gurgle. "Else you'll strangle him for sure."

"That gladly, Captain." Cornall eased his hold reluctantly.

Emphasising his words, Flemyng stropped the blade of the dagger across his palm. "Now answer me: what know you of Spanish ships? What numbers of galley and of galleon? Where do they muster?"

"Heretic dolt, go see for yourself. You will learn naught from me."

Again the muscled arm hooked around his throat, there was a muffled yelp as a naked poniard pricked deep the blackbeard's ribs. "Take that for Becky," the Bosun muttered.

"Steady as ye go, Cornall. Answer me, Nicholls, or by the fires of hell, to the stern-post I'll tie and tow you!"

But Nicholls' fury still outweighed his fear. "I'll tell you nothing," he hissed through clenched teeth. "Harm me at your peril. I have powerful friends. God's vengeance be upon you!"

"Return him to his cabin and see him guarded well, Bosun. I am in no mood to treat with scum. Let us make our way homeward."

Threats were to be of no avail and would not unlock his captive's tongue. He dared to go no further. Should Nicholls be proven innocent, the Keigwin influence would not suffice. Then, he would face the hangman's noose.

Orders were given to cobble the hoy's main sail as best could be to help her homeward run. A prize crew was set aboard, Martin in command. The pinnace followed her captive on their return journey.

The sailormen aboard the *Hope* could reveal little of the cloaked travellers. The pilgrims were both aloof and arrogant, barely acknowledging the existence of the crew, yet they were devout, and constantly at prayer. However, there were rumours. Rumours of ships of all degree summoned to gather, Spaniard and Portugee. A fleet as man never before had witnessed. High-castled galleon, low-waisted galley, armed urca, proud gallease, called from the seas of the world, to gather in the Bay of Lisbon and set sail against England; late in May. But they were beset by a terrible storm that scattered them, and now they were met at Corunna, there to be cast once more into their squadrons, to refit and victual, to prepare to sail against England. The *Hope*'s crew had been afraid, lest they too be pressed to serve, yet had Nicholls not said that whilst they sailed with him there was naught to fear? When questioned about their captain, it appeared that Nicholls was a fine seaman who rewarded well, whilst keeping company and counsel close to himself.

As Martin continued his assiduous search, the holds of the *Hope* gave up their treasure. Lashed stoutly together were hogsheads of fine wines from Spain that would find a home in Keigwin's warehouse to await the pleasure of the gentlemen of the west.

In Nicholls' stern cabin, by the light of the swinging lantern, Martin pulled free the handsome sea chest wedged tight between the hull's wooden ribs. Bound with thick straps of pierced and ornamented steel and closed with locked bolts, the lid was firmly fastened. Martin looked about. From a hook set in the ceiling timbers hung a thick leather belt with scabbard and rapier. He drew the weapon to admire the craftsmanship and ornate engraving on the fine Ferrara blade and the rich adornment of the hilt. He hefted the sword in his hand to feel its balance, enacting parry and thrust. This would be a fine memento for nephew Tom, to mark the night's adventure. While he would hold as keepsake the pistol that, but for Cornall, would surely have had him dead. He returned his attention to the trunk lid and slid in the blade of his dagger, but the stout locks would not yield.

The door crashed open. Nicholls stumbled across the threshold to fall against the far wooden wall, as roll of ship and shove from Teek sent him sprawling within. "Beg pardon, Master Martin . . . "

"Leave my chest be, you thieving dog."

Nicholls lunged but Martin grabbed the captain by his beard, hoisting him to his feet in fury, and for the first time noted fear in Nicholls' eyes. His free hand reached below his prisoner's jerkin and ripped apart the linen shirt he wore. He had supposed right. From a leather thong around the bull neck hung a heavy key, nearly lost amongst the forest of

47

black hair. Still he held Nicholls firmly by the beard, tearing at the thong which parted, to drop the key upon the floor. Martin loosed his hold and bent to retrieve it, Nicholls leant back to gain leverage from the cabin wall, lashing out with all his strength and landing a fierce kick beneath his victor's ribs. Felled to the floor, Martin rose slowly, clutching both key and stomach, falling across the chest to vomit his agony. In wrestling throw, Teek flung his maddened prisoner to the floor to hold him there with poniard pricking at his throat. Droplets of blood spilt upon the pine boards to darken in a widening pool of scarlet. Martin rose and with a glare of hate at the floored and bleeding Nicholls, he turned the key in each of the locks and lifted the groaning lid.

Beneath a pile of Catholic vestments he groped, to hold aloft in triumph a canvas bag drawn at its mouth by a knotted cord. Holding it above the unmade cot where Nicholls had lately slept he cut the drawstring with the Spanish steel, a shower of gold and silver fell upon the bedclothes.

"You heretic devil," mouthed Nicholls as Keigwin scooped the coins back into the sack.

"Hold him well, Bosun, there is yet more to discover." Again he leant over the chest, delving into the depth. "What have we here Nicholls?" he smilingly enquired of his glowering captive. "Ah, so be it, 'Seek and ye shall find'." He lifted out bundle after bundle of printed tracts and placed them on the floor. "A scurrilous blasphemy upon our Sovereign? If so, Nicholls, I will see you at your hanging."

"I know naught of it," was the sullen reply. "I am but paid to transport goods. There is naught of mine within that chest. I know nothing of its content."

"Tell that to Master Topcliffe when he greets you upon the scaffold."

With care all was safe returned as found, except the coin and samples of the pamphlets. The bolts then shot and locked. Martin tossed the key in his hand before safely placing it within his doublet.

"Guard him well, Bosun," ordered Martin Keigwin as, painfully, he carried the canvas sack to his nephew aboard the *Golden Hind*.

*   *   *   *

48

Velvet hat upon his head, calf-bound volume open upon his lap, Jenkyn Keigwin sat in his favoured chair, surrounded by the books he loved. Books of learning in neat rows upon their wooden shelves, hand-written ledgers wherein was carefully recorded income and expenditure of business and of household. His white beard, neatly barbered, sunk into his ruff, eyes closed in gentle doze, belly rumbled, lips quivered, for he had eaten too well of the brawn and hams which adorned the hooks of Thomasine's pantry. Cold capon from the chickens that scratched and crowed upon the farmyard dung-heaps. Fresh baked bread, mouthwatering scents that even now wafted from the bakehouse ovens beneath the window. Cheese made from the milk of the red cattle that grazed the rich meadows at Reginnis. All washed down with home-brewed March ale. Thomasine, home-maker, housekeeper, mother of his children, had overseen it all.

He awoke with a start. He looked through the window across the bay where he had peered ten thousand times before. God's truth! there they were, hoy and pinnace, prisoner and escort, sailing into view. What malice had been uncovered that they should thus return? He called Richard to walk down to the harbour to see them safe ashore.

Martin rightly guessed that his father and brother would be watching his seamanship with critical eye. The wind was luffing, awkward, over the hills, a glance at the sky and the direction of the scudding clouds, where the wind bore the languid pennant, and the movement of the flotsam upon the water. He saw it all. The ship was strange to him and he was at the helm, the wind and tide against her bows unfamiliar. He had yet to find the feel of her and must needs be watchful how he handle her.

He shouted orders, men jumped the gap to fend off and catch thrown warps and bend them around the granite bollards. The sails, reefed in haste, were now neatly furled by yardsmen. Martin went below to cast his eye where the men would quarter, and to check the victuals. On pain of death the French crewmen were commanded to do naught that would harm or hinder ship or cargo as they carried wine-filled hogsheads to the Keigwin warehouse. A guard of trusted men to keep vigilance over Nicholls' cabin. The

c

watch was set.

Outside the harbour the *Golden Hind* dropped anchor in her accustomed place; both sentry and gaoler to the captive hoy.

Only now was Martin aware of weariness. Burdened by the sack of coin he clambered to the wall, greeted by an approving nod from his father, and quizzical stares and questions from those now gathered on the quay. Rolled within his doublet were samples of the tracts. A scholar such as his father would find interest in their content and interpret their worth to the enemies of his Queen.

The three men watched the dinghy swing out to be lowered away as Thomas was sculled to ground upon the shingle shore. Silently they made their way past slip and wharf up the steep short hill that led to the Manor. Little could be said to answer the questions of excited town and fisher folk, whose curiosity could no longer be contained, who had been alerted by the distant roar of cannon as it rumbled across the sea.

Rumour fed on conjecture to fatten into false fact. Folk rushed to greet the merchantman, to gloat where ball had rent her hull, or savour the plight of wounded seamen. And left disappointed, denied those pleasures.

Within the beamed hall Thomasine greeted son and grandson with fond embrace of undisguised relief. The menfolk retired upstairs to be waited upon with wine and toast while dinner was prepared. At ease they could recount the story of their adventure. Martin untied the drawstring knot, to tip a heap of shimmering gold upon the richly-patterned carpet. By Keigwin's law the prize was theirs to keep. None of Mousehole dared say them 'nay' and thus incur his wrath. Only the crew would share, to them one third, their right, paid as their rank deserved.

Jenkyn Keigwin addressed his eldest son. "Whilst the bosun oversees the unloading, will you ensure the casks are stacked in proper order. When done, it would be prudent to send a cask to The Mermaid, tell Trewhella to charge one third, no more, that all may share in our good fortune."

"Aye, you old fox, Father, and buy goodwill."

"True, if we look after Mousehole, my sons, then surely

will Mousehole look after us — if that is the price of loyalty, then so be it. I prefer to believe that our family extends beyond these walls. And to that family we have a duty." Keigwin was irked and adopted a pompous tone. "Our rank commands respect, and that must be earned. Thus does it behove us to deserve that deference." His sentence finished, he nodded at Richard in gesture of mild reproof.

"Come, Richard," Thomas rose, "let Martin rest, but I must keep faith with my men. They must know that the prize will be shared tomorrow, and that tonight there will be merriment at the inn, for which Trewhella can give them credit."

Teek Cornall led the donkey and cart upon which the wine was laden, he had offered to undertake the task. Well-scrubbed and shaved, dressed in best attire with all due ceremony, he led the reluctant animal to the courtyard of the inn. Trewhella appeared, drying his hands upon soiled cloth, to gratefully accept his share of booty. More comely than even he could recall, Becky too came forward and blushingly echoed her father's thanks. With nonchalant, dismissive air Teek accepted their gratitude, whilst seeming to convey the gesture was his doing and by his actions alone The Mermaid shared their fortune. News quickly spread. Seaman and fisherman and folk of all sorts descended upon the inn, to celebrate the capture of the traitor.

Teek watched as Becky passed through the inn's back door to the cobbled yard behind. Masked and unseen amidst the merriment, Teek followed. He watched as she leaned over the stable door to pet the soft muzzle of pack pony and nag that whickered their greeting to her. She spoke their names and patted their necks lovingly, talking softly. Stamping gently, they returned to nuzzle their racks of forage. Warm horsey smells mingled with the sweet rich scent of hay newly-mown and loosely-pitched into the loft above. Peace, serenity, a sharp contrast to the sound of ribaldry from within the inn.

Silently, Teek stole up behind her, watching, amused, as she stroked the velvet muzzles. Unseen he slipped his arm about her waist. She stiffened, stifling a yelp of surprise, then turned and relaxed at the sight of him. Holding her hands in his, in hesitating tones he told her of his love.

"Becky, my rose, when I am ashore it would please me should you consent to link thine arm in mine and walk with me."

The darkness hid her blushes as she raised her hands, still clasped by his, and put her lips to his rough knuckles: "If, if my father does approve, I would do so — willingly," softly, she stammered her reply.

The voice of Martin Keigwin rose above the din, his men were ordered back on board, thus Teek was saved from the temptations of the hay loft. Reluctantly he released the hands of his sweetheart and bade her a lingering farewell.

Easing through the packed inn, Trewhella accompanied him to the doorway, repeating his thanks, as Teek ushered him by the elbow to the street.

"Landlord," said the seaman, covered in confusion, "I am Bosun aboard the *Golden Hind*. Captain Flemyng is my master. The family of Squire Keigwin look favourably upon me. If it so please you, I would wish to walk out with Mistress Rebecca."

For a brief moment Vaughan Trewhella was taken aback. His little Becky now approaching womanhood. Aye, it was to be expected some lusty lad would soon wish to escort her. He reflected awhile; no need to be too hasty. Yet, here was a man worthy of her who had brought him wine withal, from which had come a tidy trade. What he had done once, he might do again if given due encouragement. He scratched his head beneath his cap.

"You are both honest and sober, so far as I know." He paused in deliberation. "You have yourself a good berth and a future too, I'll be bound." He paused again, not to seem too swift in his approval. "Aye, it will please me for you to walk with her — should she so agree, always providing her duties are complete, and in the light of day, not abroad o' Mousehole mind!"

Teek nodded his assent to each condition, and shook the landlord warmly by the hand. Then, turning, he ran with joyful heart once more to join his ship.

Chapter Three

It seemed so much longer than the four and twenty hours since first they had fired the warning cannon. Gone low water, the sun was lightening the eastern sky; away from land there would be strength in the north-westerly wind now blowing.

At high water the *Hope* had been warped about within the harbour to face the open sea. The unladen hoy could steer a straight course around the Lizard's head without cause to tack. Martin gave the orders, and at a signal from the *Golden Hind*, sails were slowly raised to give her steerage way. The windlass of the pinnace groaned, raising the iron-shod anchor; the wooden stock now peering above the water, she gathered way as line astern the two ships sailed, east-south-east, against the tide.

Slack water passed, they gathered speed as the flood now urged them on their way. South-east of Mullion they sped, off Kynance Cove where white waves washed and lathered the face of Lion Rock, out from the head, sails trimmed to take them on a course north-east; the Mannack Point, where lie the dreaded rocks, past the guardian forts of Falmouth to the loom of St. Anthony's. The day was late when they rounded Rame Head, and passed St. Nicholas Island to join the hustle of shipping in the sanctuary of Plymouth Sound, there into the Hamoaze. Anxiously they paid proper deference to the *Revenge* and other of the Queen's ships lying at anchor, taking in flags and striking topsails as they passed. In safe haven, away from the busy, bustling channels, they dropped anchor.

So many eyes upon them. Thus they troubled to ensure

that sails were neatly reefed and furled, cordage wound and stowed in the fashion of the fleet.

In his cabin, Thomas dressed, grooming himself with utmost care, for now was the time of reckoning. Now was the time he must report to his Admiral. He rehearsed his address and comments. The pleasurable anticipation of the Admiral's congratulations yielded to trepidation as in the day's cold light he realised the enormity of his deeds.

For too long had he forsaken his post, that screen of pinnaces that were to be Drake's first warning of foreign threat. Could even now the dreaded Armada be sailing through the gap left in England's defences? 'Tell the truth and shame the devil', oft he had been told. So challenged, he must recall to tell how he had left Mousehole only when he had learnt that the fleet of Spain remained fitting out in Corunna and were yet ready for sail.

But what if challenged on his attack upon an innocent merchantman? He would say that the pilgrims' strange behaviour had been the cause for concern, had convinced him of the justification for his seizure of the ship. Was not Mousehole a port from which to sail or search vessels lest they be carrying letters prejudicial to the authority of the Queen? When the mystery of the discoveries was unravelled his actions would be justified, for he was positive that Thomas Nicholls was in the pay of those loyal to 'Le Balafre' — the feared all powerful Duke of Guise, he of the scar: persecutor of all Protestants, and arch enemy of Queen Elizabeth.

Sir Francis Drake had supped aboard and now was retired to his cabin, surrounded by charts spread upon floor and table top. Goose quill in hand he recorded notes and orders upon sheets of parchment.

Flemyng's presence was announced as he ducked beneath the wooden lintel. He doffed his cap in deference. Drake raised his bearded face from the ruff in which it was sunk and rose to his feet. He was of medium height, his strong frame dressed in embroidered doublet, stuffed breeches, and fine hose that displayed the sturdiness of his limbs. He stretched his hand in greeting, the brown penetrating eyes queried the presence of his captain as he bade Flemyng be seated.

Flemyng recounted his tale midst grunts of encouragement from his listener.

"You have done what you believed to be your duty. Yet also have you taken a handsome reward. You have been both judge and jury and inflicted your own punishment. Whilst those in Cornwall may feel far placed from Normandy and the English enclave at Le Havre, the arm of justice is long as indeed is that of the Duke of Guise. Tell those at Mousehole that are aware, they must be sworn to secrecy or face complicity."

He paused awhile for full effect. "Nicholls will protest that he is innocent of any crime," he continued. "A man not without influence, with powerful friends upon whom he can call. The lords of the Admiralty have orders to give the greatest protection to those captains engaged in honest trade and to punish in the gravest fashion those who dare to molest them. They are anxious to ensure the country remains united before a common enemy and will protect Roman Catholic and Protestant alike. In the face of the Armada our sovereign is anxious not to antagonise any of her own community or to give them offence." Again he paused to give weight to his words. "Piracy, for such your deed may yet prove to be," he shook his head, "is a grave offence that their Lordships are determined to punish with severity." Flemyng paled before the words Sir Francis spoke. "Our Queen may glance away whilst we pillage in the Americas. To do so in our own waters, alive with merchant ships of other countries, and with whom we trade? That, my friend, is a different matter."

Drake stared frankly at his captain as he spoke aloud his thoughts. "The hoy I will retain in my service whilst Nicholls returns to Newhaven. He will doubtless report your deeds to their Lordships. He will claim he is innocent, knowing naught of the goods he carried. He has no alternative but so to do, for, should he fail to protest, as he must, being a victim to so grave an act of piracy, then so would he admit by default to his own guilt, if treason should be discovered. Wait aboard the hoy until you are relieved by my captains. Then return with all speed to your post and stay there, in safety, until I summon you. Keep sharp watch for the Spaniards and advise me of their coming. Now, go, and may God protect you." With a stern nod Flemyng was dismissed.

He rose to his feet to stammer his leave. His Admiral had confirmed his worst fears. His action could be interpreted as piracy by their Lordships. The peril in which he had placed himself was now to dawn. He returned to the *Hope* to acquaint Martin of Drake's warning.

Soon after his arrival, a gig came alongside. The stern-faced figure aboard introduced himself: Sir Nicholas Clifford. To the dismay of Flemyng, he courteously greeted the captive Nicholls. With profound concern he made enquiry as to his well-being and his needs, and bid him to breakfast with him and Sir Francis upon the morrow, whereafter arrangements would be made for safe return to Newhaven.

Puzzled by these overtures, Tom returned to the *Golden Hind*. In foul temper he invited Martin to take command whilst he retired to his cabin, to ponder upon that which might await him.

With utmost care Sir Nicholas had followed his Admiral's orders. "Before Nicholls you must display our displeasure with Flemyng, thus the better to gain his confidence." Drake had instructed. "With guard dropped we may thus determine whether or no the man be merely fool, rogue or — the traitor I suspect. Mayhap we shall glean intelligence of Parma's forces, of insurrection in Ireland, or when the Armada is to depart."

At the helm of the *Golden Hind*, helmsman and mate took turn about, as they sailed a long tack close into the headwind by star and by instinct to resume the watch that they had too long forsaken.

In the bows where the salt spray tingled his face, Teek was concerned as to his captain's humour and surmised that Drake had not received him well. But even his captain's mood could not depress his spirits. Thoughts of Becky were forever in his mind. The innocence of her beauty and bright wit. Her love of nature and of the animals for which she cared. Those hard working hands and nimble fingers, violet eyes and soft lips. He looked down at the rough knuckles that now gripped the gunwhale before him, the hands that she had kissed. For a woman such as she he would give his all. Flemyng's ill-humour would shortly pass and with captain such as he, there would be adventure and prizes a-plenty! Gold enough to wed! He need not wait too long before Becky would be his, and then they could enjoy the full fresh fruits of love.

In Mousehole, the excitement of the day before had passed. The pilgrims had departed by foot and by horseback to Paul, thence to Madron and beyond, along the Pilgrims' Way built by the Romans. Burley was aware that his outburst might cause Flemyng to alert the militia.

Becky was alone in the yard of The Mermaid Inn. To nag and hireling she could confide her maidenly secrets. Her innermost thoughts were theirs. They would not betray her. One by one she fondled the soft ears and meal-coloured muzzles, dreaming of a strong arm around her waist, dreaming of Teek. At night, in truckle bed, she tossed and turned. Window flung wide to myriad stars and a full, round moon. A moon whose reflected rays cast a pathway of silver across the calm sea. She imagined a lane of love that would lead her to him. She had lain dreaming he held her in his arms. Pillow clutched tightly to her, she imagined their limbs pressed close, his thighs against hers, his restless fingers clenching her buttocks, pulling their two bodies tight, in ecstasy, to entwine as one.

Strange thoughts had entered her head and strange desires now roused her body, thoughts that she had never before encountered. Thoughts and feelings that she must and could not confide to human ear. Was it wicked to think as thus she did? Were all maidens placed in such turmoil? Oh! If only she knew, if only she had mother or sister in whom she might confide. Such pain of conscience, such frustrated rapture!

*   *   *   *

Jenkyn Keigwin had spent many an hour gazing out to sea, wrapt in contemplation. His distracted manner worried Thomasine as she sat quietly in company with him, engaged with needle and silk in an intricate pattern of embroidery. She watched his lips mouth words she could not hear and lids close over eyes she could not see. Thomasine knew her man: knew that he was engaged in solemn converse with his God, with the Maker in whom he believed and trusted with faith unquestioning.

Jenkyn wrestled with his thoughts. Had he advised young Thomas wisely? Or had his words placed son and grandson in mortal jeopardy? He feared for their disgraceful death, the death of a common felon, hanged from the gallows for an act of piracy. Had the counsel they had sought of him been tainted by a merchant's greed? Was Thomas Nicholls truly a traitor? A man in the pay of the enemies of England who even now plotted against his Queen? Silently he continued his prayers for their safety and their deliverance. Sorely he needed God's help, that with His aid he might unravel the mystery which, instinct told, was concealed within the text of the tracts that still confounded his enquiry.

Of the great fleet there was no sign. The seamen aboard the barque relieved the boredom of the long June days by trailing baited lines for blue shark as she patrolled her beat between Ushant and the Islands.

Flemyng's natural humour had returned in the long languid days of summer. Water and stores would soon be running low. He would return to Mousehole for provisions — and intelligence.

There were no pilgrims at The Mermaid. No merchants. None but the lone traveller, with time on her hands Becky had fussed and fed the post horses and ponies. She had completed her chores, there was little to do save attend the wants of the pale-faced young gentleman who had ridden in upon

58

a tired sweat-stained horse. Dismounting stiffly, he had handed her the reins and asked the whereabouts of the mayor, clutching a leather satchel as he did so, leaving her to remove his trappings and stable the exhausted creature.

At mid-morning, Mary answered the hammer on the great front door of the Keigwin Manor House to admit the Mayor and two bailiffs that kept him company.

"We have a desire to see your master, to bring him news of dire import," the mayor announced.

Mary bobbed and retired to seek the Squire.

The three looked about with curious stare, as the serving maid reappeared to lead them up the great carved staircase into the handsome room above, where they were received by the impressive figure of the Squire. Curiosity turned to awe amidst the grandeur of the room. Rich oriental rugs covered the wide oak boards, silver and pewter plates and candlesticks were displayed upon open cupboard and sideboard. Stools were scattered about and chests lined walls from which rich embroidered tapestries hung, draped beneath ornamental plaster frieze.

"Good day, Mayor Hicks. Gentlemen," Jenkyn Keigwin nodded his greeting to each in turn. "Mary, fetch wine for our guests." A dismissive hand. Servant maid departed. "And to what purpose do I owe the pleasure of your company?"

"Squire Keigwin," said Hicks. "We have news of grave concern." He handed the Squire a parchment scroll. "This letter of assistance has arrived this day by post from Plymouth."

Keigwin unfolded the manuscript and read the letter.

Thomasine had heard the heavy knock.

"Mary, whom do we have arrived?"

"Why, Mistress, 'tis Mayor Hicks, he says he has news of dire import for the master."

Thomasine looked up from her work, needle poised, was this news of the Armada? Or the danger they had feared for Martin and for Thomas? "Serve wine of the finest, Mary.

Serve from the flagon of silver and the goblets that are of glass. Better still, fill the pair of flagons."

Mary curtsied and left to do as she was bid. With troubled mind Thomasine resumed sewing, her fingers moved rhythmically. Her mind was alert to sense the tone of the male conversation upstairs.

With studied care Mary carried the pewter tray to where her master stood and at his command placed it upon the table. The ceremony of serving his guests was completed in ritual intended to render them ill at ease, daunted in the presence of their Squire. With studied deliberation Keigwin sipped the wine, smacking his lips, pausing to hold the glass to the sunlight's glare to admire the filter of the rays, to twist and turn the rummer then to roll the burgundy about his tongue, savouring its rich flavour. He paused for further effect; then, in quiet tones, with the subtlety of a merchant's mind, he recounted the story of the false pilgrims, of the Spanish sword, of the sedition which he would shortly prove was contained within certain religious tracts. But of the gold and wine, he said nothing.

He told all in terms of such conviction that none dare say him nay. His word was evidence enough. Thus did they know the master of the hoy to be a paid servant of the dreaded Duke of Guise. Friend of Spain, enemy of England!

"It is well known," he continued, "that in Newhaven, to the shame of England, there are English captains and English merchants who value trade with Spain and papists above loyalty to their Queen. Men who would sell their mothers' soul to the devil for one ducat. There are spies in the pay of the Duke of Guise, sworn enemy of our beloved and Protestant Queen. Men such as De Zaubiaur who, as God is my witness, would see her racked and tortured then burnt at the stake for what they claim is heresy. Such a man is Nicholls, Master of the *Hope*." A pause that they might savour both words and wine. "Aye, therefore neither will she — or we — bend our knee to Spain."

The mood of the forceful lecture changed, he placed his arm upon the shoulder of the Mayor, and looking at all three in turn continued in terms of growing confidentiality. They gathered closer to him, as he spoke in whispered words.

"There are gentlemen hereabouts, known to me, but more I cannot say since I am a Justice, and privy to this advice. There are these men I say who protest their loyalty yet only await the coming of the Armada and the landing of Parma's soldiers. Then will they be seen in coat of a different hue!" His arm lowered, he nodded knowingly. "But, in truth, these hungry men, these greedy men who seek only to dominate us, will be routed out neck and crop before they can succeed in their evil task. Keep close watch, I pray you, and hold every man as suspect, saving the four of us!"

His audience looked on in rapt attention as he continued now in louder and commanding tones. " 'Tis a poor day for we Cornish when gentlemen in London wish to arrest a loyal son of England in rightful pursuit of our enemies. A man of Cornwall, a seaman, who even now is doing his duty off the Islands, guarding you and me from the papists, that we and our children may sleep soundly at night." He poured more wine. As he did so, he looked at each man squarely and held each gaze in turn. "Do I speak the truth?"

"Aye, Squire," they replied as one.

"Then I say the galleons of Spain will soon be off our shores. Drake will need all the ships and fighting men he can muster. Are we to let good men rot in dark dungeons?" he queried, with chin thrust towards them. "Wait 'til danger is past, the Spaniards defeated, and then arrest him when next he enters harbour. Till then I say, by Jupiter," the scholar's oath as he rose to his theme, "we of the west shall take no note of what up-country coxcombs may command. Are we agreed?" Looking to each in turn, daring them to contradict him.

" 'Tis God's truth you state, Squire," responded Mayor Hicks looking to each of his companions as they nodded their assent.

"Another glass of sac, gentlemen. Sirs, you act wisely." The Squire stated in profound tones. "But this must be our secret."

Once more they nodded in agreement.

61

"Do tell me, Master Hicks, gentlemen, find you this wine to suit your taste?"

" 'Tis of the finest, Squire Keigwin, I have never savoured the like on't."

"It will be my pleasure, gentlemen, to ensure that this is not the last you relish and, knowing of your appreciation of life's good things, I shall send to each of you a goodly ration."

The three men made their departure in terms of the utmost joviality, at odds with their sombre arrival, conscious of the confidences the Squire had entrusted to them. Proud in the secret pact they shared with this man of consequence, overwhelmed by the strength of his authority, his character, and his wine. The Squire had told them nothing they did not already know, or could not have ascertained for themselves, but the manner and surroundings in which it was presented had served the purpose and bought Thomas Flemyng much needed time. No mention dared Jenkyn make of the Spanish gold or the whereabouts of the wine that was concealed within his cellars and of which they had partaken. By acceptance of the promised gift he could claim they too were party in the felony, if felony there be.

A tall figure sauntered along the Totnes quayside with casual air. Soon it would be high water, the flood to stem the outgoing waters of the Dart where the merchantmen were moored. A sailor seeking a berth, sack of sailcloth slung over his shoulder, stocking cap now replaced the broad brim of the pilgrim. Beard now unkempt, his clothes were of the homespun kind. To the enquiring eye the scar upon his cheekbone might add some further interest to his handsome features. What was the sight of one sailor amongst so many? He stopped where a Breton boat was lading with wool, and stepped aboard.

Burley had completed the first act of his charge. He had seen the Jesuits upon their way, to where, in safety, they might lie low. He who would represent the Pope in England, hid where none would find, awaiting the day he might leap forth to proclaim that England was one with Spain; that the army of King Philip was now landed to claim his just inheritance, that both countries were of a common faith. England and Spain. Spain and England. One.

He had also garnered intelligence. The Western Squadron lay at Plymouth. Two squadrons more were east of Dover, forbidding Parma to cross from Flanders to England. In all were mustered one hundred and eighty ships. Now he must hasten to Lisbon, by courtesy of Pedro de Zaubiaur and a ship of his fleet, to share his knowledge with his masters.

The lazy days of early summer passed slowly as rumours of the threat of all-out war spread throughout the land. English pilgrims flocked to English shrines, Canterbury and Walsingham, fearful to venture abroad, since invasion was now imminent. Few merchants of Spain now travelled to Mousehole, only to Brittany dare Squire Keigwin ship his hogsheads of salted pilchard and oil for the feast days of Europe.

A game of backgammon lay on the table between Soloman Fernandes and Jenkyn Keigwin, though neither had his mind on the state of play.

Fernandes broke his silence. "This warrant gives me worry, Keigwin. If, at this late hour, our Queen should sue for peace before the might of Spain, then would she be persuaded to make an example of such as Thomas?"

Jenkyn nodded his agreement. " 'Tis possible, Solomon. Albeit the chances are but slim."

"Still, it is possible, for she has a devious mind. Let us amuse ourselves in another form, my friend. I would see the tracts of which you have told me."

Jenkyn rose and from a nearby cupboard took the sheaf of papers. "Mayhap together we shall unravel them, for within is a clue that will vindicate our actions, or else my instinct is a liar."

Solomon selected a tract, read it closely, and when done held it to the window's light. "The Psalms of David? And the *Hope* and her captain were of Newhaven?" The Squire nodded as Fernandes continued: "Then methinks this is a pamphlet from the press of Father Parsons."

"That Jesuit priest?"

"No less, for he is at Rouen, close by to Newhaven."

"Aye, and servant of the Duke of Guise. He dares not return to England, but plots his pestilence from afar with symbols of a common cause."

"Thus to give comfort and support to those papists who wold overthrow the Queen."

"Come then, Solomon, let us take up the challenge."

"Challenge?"

"Let us discover if these are as harmless as they seem. Such as Nicholls would hardly be called upon to deliver an innocent text!"

From his shelves he took a leathern book and grunted as he flicked the pages, his mood now lightened. "Now, had it been but Histaeus."

"Histaeus?"

"Aye, a Greek of Persia. Now he had a simple way . . ."

"Where does this lead to Keigwin?"

"He sent a message by way of a slave, who was half-blinded."

"What is this nonsense."

"Aye," he read on, "he shaved his servant's head and writ the message upon his crown."

"What then?"

"When the hair had grown, sent him to his friend, Aristogaras, for a cure for the blindness. Then this Aristogaras did shave the slave and so discovered the hidden words."

"Mmm, I doubt from what you tell that such is hidden beneath the beard of Nicholls!"

"No, but is something hid within these pamphlets?"

Each resumed careful reading of the papers upon their laps.

"Pray tell me, Solomon, where would you best hide a tree?"

"A riddle? Ah, within a forest."

"Exactly so, therefore, maybe the shorter Psalms are but blinds and 'tis the longer wherein the message is hid."

"What is this, Jenkyn? 'Diligam te Domine' — Psalm 18 and of many verses." Solomon peered at the text. "The tract is well printed, as are they all, yet there are two smudges that I had not noted before. See," he pointed, "verse 28 . . . 'Light my candle' is blotched and again, verse 49 . . .

'setteth me up above'."

" 'Light my candle, setteth me up above!' That is it, Solomon, we shall follow the instructions." Jenkyn spoke very quietly.

Carefully Keigwin held the paper above the flickering flame of the candle so as not to burn it. Between the lines of printed prose brown letters gradually appeared.

"Milk and juice of a lemon, an old trick of spies. Now, let me see." He passed the passage to Fernandes. "In secret cipher. This will test our minds. If we can unravel this, it may save my grandson from the gallows."

Together they pored over the pamphlet.

"There are a great many codes, some of great complication." Solomon was gloomy.

"Yes, but not hidden so within the text, and in invisible writing. To break it may be easy, for those for whom it is intended will have neither complicated key, nor mind to match. Thus it may be simple." Jenkyn Keigwin closed his eyes, slowly to recite the psalm aloud.

"A moment. You forget!" Fernandes held the pamphlet in his hands. "Your memory fails you."

"Not so, not this far into the verse."

"It does my friend, it does!" Solomon laughed at his comrade thus caught out.

" 'The earth trembled and quaked . . . ' "

"No, no, my Protestant friend! For here it says: 'He sent out his arrows and scattered them . . . ' "

Once more Keigwin went to the book-lined shelves to return with his prayer book, carefully to turn the pages. "My memory had not failed me, for you have read verse fourteen. Let me read aloud and you correct me against that which Parsons has printed. 'The Lord shall reward me . . . ' "

"No, for here is writ 'With the clean thou shalt be clean.' "

"Here are verses seven and fourteen transposed as are verses twenty and twenty-six."

"Twenty-six you say, Jenkyn?"

Each sunk his chin in silent thought.

"The same as letters in the alphabet. Eureka, Jenkyn, Eureka!"

"You have found it?"

"Transpose the second seven letters of the alphabet with the first seven," he counted on his fingers, " 'h' becomes 'a' and 'i' becomes 'b'," he paused. "Then that leaves twelve letters, from 'o' to 'z', twelve letters. Divide those into two, six letters in each — and transpose them! 'u' then becomes 'o' and there you have it. That is the clue." He drew the code upon the paper.

All sense of time was forgot as on they worked. Many tracts were blank whilst others, when close examined, held a hidden text of incitement to rise against the English. When the soldiers of Parma came from Flanders, fierce rebellion would erupt. There was news of the Bull from the Bishop of Rome for the deposition of England. Dr Allen was now made a Cardinal and his secret legate was hid in England, to appear when the time was ripe in order to invest King Philip with his English kingdom.

Was he one of the number that the *Hope* had landed? The coincidence was too great.

"Our work is complete, Solomon." Keigwin rose to clasp his old friend by the hand. "With your help is Thomas free. Tomorrow, Godolphin will be told." His eyes filled with tears.

"Yes," Solomon spoke drily, "doubtless the gold and silver may safely remain within these walls."

"You shall have your share, as you may deserve, rogue that you are!"

Solomon Fernandes grinned and rubbed his hands in glee.

They were troubled times for Jenkyn and Thomasine, with Martin and Tom away. Where, they could only surmise. Patrolling. On watch for the Spaniard in those wild waters betwixt the Isles of Scilly and Ushant. Ushant, where centuries before St Paul had made his home.

The fishermen were few that worked the waters of the bay, the young and hale now impressed into the English fleet of Lord Howard of Effingham. Cornwall, remote extremity of England with her young men taken, remained reliant upon the wildness of her seas and her granite walls, on Drake and Hawkyns and their Western Squadron. Protection against the bloody hand of war.

High upon the steep of St. Michael's Mount, Silas Tregenza paused, wiped the sweat from his brow, and looked downwards and about across the empty sea. He slipped the bundle of faggots and needled furze from his bent back and paused, seating himself upon a friendly rock. His duty was to tend the brazier upon the chapel. One of the first of the beacons that criss-crossed the south of England, it was to be lighted upon the sighting of the Armada. An alarm, so he was told, as would reach London in twenty minutes! Alerting the country, and calling her men to arms. "Too old to be impressed as may be," he muttered to himself, "but not too old to earn eight pence a day!" He cackled as he slid the leather straps once more across his shoulders and carried on his upward path.

Chapter Four

Throughout the boring sultry July days the *Golden Hind* continued her patrol of the sparkling seas. Seas that were empty, save for the schools of dolphin that romped about the privateer in the glide and tumble of their play, though they did little to relieve the monotony. However, the days of light airs and clear skies had lasted too long, mares tails patterned the heavens, westerly winds now freshened. The skies had darkened and the blue sea become one of sullen grey. Tom studied the horizon for sign of the enemy, but there was no sight of sail, only the ever-darkening sky.

The winds freshened to squalls as he put the barque about, for in the sky he read foreboding and he ran for the shelter of the Islands, as gales whipped the water to a frenzy of white foam.

The repast was over. To the delight of Jenkyn and Thomasine, their daughter Elizabeth, with husband Nicholas and their granddaughters, had supped at the Manor. The menfolk had now retired to Jenkyn's study, to ponder the secrets of the tracts that with God's good grace, would save Tom Flemyng from the hangman's noose. The subject of Tom's destiny was one only men might share.

From the withdrawing room came the sound of girlish giggles, peels of merriment as mother and daughters were gathered around the spinet, candlelit in the fading evening sun, to sing to their grandmother the madrigals of William Byrd. A smile of proud contentment softened Thomasine's mouth as she bent over her tapestry. Now she might be both happy and relieved for had not her wise husband proven the justice of Tom's deed, thus his innocence? God was merciful.

In the sunlit shelter of the great harbour at Lisbon, they lay at anchor. In the wide River Tagus too. The beauty, the majesty of the scene as the fleet prepared. La Felicissima, the Fortunate, nay the Invincible, Armada!

In the gloom of the Cathedral of the Patriarch had been held the ceremony of the blessing of the banner. The great flag that was to be flown from the masthead of the flagship. The *San Martin de Portugal*. Sanctified by Pope Sixtus. Emblazoned with the figure of Christ crucified, the blessed Virgin and Mary Magdelene upon each side, it would stream out, as a constant reminder of their cause. Now had seaman and soldier been confessed and blessed by friar and by priest, a medallion issued for each to bear about his neck; Christ upon one side, the Holy Virgin the other.

Once more they were mustered at Corunna, where Burley was commanded to serve with the Andalusian Squadron. Ten ships from Cadiz, intent to revenge the ravages of Drake upon their harbour. Ten ships and a patache, of the one hundred and thirty about to sail. He rolled the words across his tongue. The *Nuestra Senora de Rosario*, the flagship from whose high sterncastle he was now watching. Her commander, Don Pedro de Valdes, of a breeding and bearing that commanded respect. A mighty merchantman, forty-six guns, larger than the largest ship of England.

And his soldiers. Three hundred at his command, well armed, well trained, fretting for the fray. Three hundred of twenty thousand aboard the fleet. And Parma, with his seasoned soldiers in Flanders awaiting. What was their number? Thirty thousand! What match was the puny force of England against these overwhelming odds?

He looked down upon the bustle of little boats lading the great galleons with altar and ducat. Prayer and recompense, thumbscrew and the rack — the penitant and the heretic, each must be rewarded in accord to their deserts.

Friday 22nd July 1588. For too long had they languished where English seamen called the Groyne. For some five weeks had the fleet regrouped neath the shelter of the forts of Corunna. Beset by tempest and adverse wind, they had made but little progress since leaving Lisbon. Now, repaired and revictualled, they were ready to voyage on. Of those other English that were aboard, it was Stucley gave him greatest comfort. Did he not profess to know every cape and cove of England, and of Ireland also? Not to mention the mood of the weather and the way of the tides. Thanks be to God, that William Stucley was to navigate the *Rosario*.

The 26th July. The Great Fleet lay becalmed in the Chops of the Channel. Between Ushant and the Isles of Scilly, the soft breezes of the previous days now waned. A lull, the calm before the storm. Too quickly, ominously northwards veered the wind. That evening and for two days that followed, gales and mountainous seas once again battered and scattered the ships, many untried and unsuited to such weather, used as they were to the tideless calm of the mediterranean waters. These were forced to seek shelter, and a few to run for the sanctuary of the coast of France, never to rejoin their command. Stucley piloted the *Rosario* that the squadron of Andalusia might safely follow, to anchor within the lee of the Isles of Scilly. There might they ride out the fury of the storm.

Burley gave praise to his God for the skill of the Englishman who had led them through the savage seas.

Early evening on the 28th July. The wind was now beginning to ease whilst horizontal squalls of rain still mercilessly beat upon them. The incoming tide lifted the *Golden Hind* as she lay at anchor, nestled in the safe haven amongst the Isles of Scilly, where Tom and Martin had so often ventured.

Safe-sheltered beneath the dark and blustering sky, Tom dozed, cozy in his cot. A hammering on his door brought him swiftly awake as the watch called him topsides. Aloft from the cross trees sharp-eyed look-out had called an alarm. Tom climbed the rope-laddered shrouds to look aft, where half-hidden by the mizzen, the seaman pointed. South-east, in a window in the squalls of rain, ships, Spanish ships sheltering off St. Agnes and the Isle of Gugh. As the barque rose upon the flood, clearly could he now see the high castles, stark outlines against the low horizon. Nine could he count. His eyes searched the rocky headlands lest there be more to be discovered. Satisfied at last he summoned his uncle, to point where the enemy lay. This was the day, this was the sight for which they had been waiting. The relentless rain closed down his view. All hands now alerted, the spritsail ready to be raised as the groaning windlass lifted the anchors. Larboard-side forward and freely she came. To starboard of her bows the anchor fouled; a cry of anguish as sails began to fill, and she swung upon her kedge, dangerously close to rocks. Thank God for Teek, who saw in a split second the danger that could befall and slashed to cut the cable with an axe. The *Golden Hind* leapt free. Tom breathed relief. Now to think, to concentrate. The safety of his ship, his men and England now depended upon him. Too little water to cross Crow Bar and hide behind St. Mary's bulk, too much wind to be helpful. The slightest sail, and they would be seen. Reefed in to pass Bartholomew Ledges. Southward of St. Mary's, safe into the deeper water of the sound. North of Spanish Ledges. To the south-west he peered where now was clearly to be seen an array of sails, emblazoned. The red cross of the Knights of Malta. A squadron of fighting ships of Spain, topsails and mizzen raised. Eastwards ran the privateer for the freedom of the open sea, and to Mousehole: to leave far behind the squadron of Don Pedro de Valdes, in which Richard Burley served.

Tom took the wheel, Master of his ship, whilst Martin and all but deck crew gathered such rest as they may. They sped that night neath a smugglers' sky. One moment naked in bright moonlight, time to take a bearing, then pitch dark, to be lost once more from sight of enemy. Before the face of the full moon, fringed by the silver of her rays, black clouds were raced and chased by pursuing wind from the north. That same wind eerily whistled through the rigging of the homeward-bound pinnace, pushing across the water, to punch her way through waves. A tail of white wake streamed astern.

*   *   *   *

71

The family had yielded to Thomasine's entreaties and slept at the Manor, thus to relieve the loneliness of their grand-parents. The horses had been stabled, their servants asleep in the loft above.

Early the following morning of the 29th day of July, Jenkyn eased himself from the soft down of the great carved bed. A restless night, sleep had eluded him as his mind was filled with the dangers that beset his sons at sea. A danger that in her trusting innocence was little shared by Thomasine. He would not enlighten her, or confide his fears.

Tenderly he looked upon the plump and crumpled form, as she fidgeted and reached a hand behind for reassuring presence no longer now beside her. Through the mantle of sleep came his soft words of love. Once more her face relaxed in slumber's peace, as tenderly he tucked the bedspread over. A hint of smile softened her mouth as she dreamed of happy days, of simple games played with the grandchildren she adored. Slowly he dressed, to pray and then to study the tome once more, before he broke his fast.

Across the bay the sun began to peer above Goonhilly Downs. Low slanting rays shining through the storm clouds. Their sullen grey transformed into a picture of awesome grandeur, a blazing panoply of vivid colour, orange and yellow and red. The rolling, sulking sea stained bloody crimson to reflect the skies in her tarnished mirror.

Jenkyn gazed at the magnificent vanity of Nature. Was this display deliberately conjured that mere mortals be reminded of their puny powers? That she alone had authority to command, and to destroy? Only at her behest could winds rise or tempest form, to spoil and shatter the frail creations of presumptuous man. He pondered as he gazed. Could this sunrise be an omen? Was it to favour his beloved country or the forces of Spain? He shook his head in wonderment, once more reminded of God's almighty power.

At her visitor's bedroom door, Becky tapped again, waiting with filled pitcher for his command to enter. A call from within, she lifted the latch, bobbed curtsey and poured the warmed water into the ewer atop the cupboard beneath the open window. She paused as, looking southward, she saw the homecoming pinnace, the rig of which she knew so well.

Nightcap awry, the young man wiped the sleep from his widening eyes and gazed at her female form. A peach, ripe for the plucking, her breasts ill-confined by the tight bodice of her dress. Did she thus hold herself that she might tempt him? This was an invitation that must not be refused. He savoured her form outlined against the morning light. He lay back in the bed, hands behind head, lost in admiration at the picture she created. What a pleasurable prospect with which to commence the day.

"What do you see?" he queried.

"Sir, 'tis only a barque that is about to come into harbour." She turned to look at him.

He kicked the bedclothes away and swung his thin shanks to the floor. His passion rose. He must not rush, lest he might lose her. Yet, he had little time in which to woo. He would claim the benefits of his rank. That surely was what she sought. A coin or two would settle the account! Barely clad in rumpled nightshirt he came from behind, to rub his thighs against her roundness, and clasp her firm breasts within bejewelled fingers.

Aghast and afraid, she stood still, silent, rigid. Experienced hands pursued their pleasure. In dismay she felt her nipples rise to his fondling. Dismay to anguish, anguish to anger, anger to action at advantage taken of his degree. Quick as a ferret she turned within his clutch to crash the empty pitcher. To shatter against his cheek.

Sobbing, she ran from the room. Sobbing in shame, shame with herself, ashamed she had been aroused, and, but for Teek, most sorely tempted.

In low water, the harbour dried out, the pinnace circled, head into wind and dropped anchor on the good ground between wall and island. The sails furled, a boat was lowered as Teek sculled his youthful captain through the lumpy water. He leapt out to pull the skiff above the high water mark.

Midst shouts of greeting from ground floor of the Manor, Thomas bounded up the staircase where he knew his grandfather would surely be. The older man rose to welcome his grandson with a close embrace, calling for Nicholas Flemyng that his son was now arrived.

Earnestly the three men talked as Tom was warned of the letter of assistance for his arrest. The worst of their fears had come to roost, yet there was hope in the message discovered within the Psalms. They would ensure Godolphin knew, that Tom might be reprieved. Dark, restless eyes searched the face of father and grandfather, to seek their reassuring guidance. With brief and grave farewell each clasped him to their chest in gesture that words could ill convey. Tom hurried to rejoin his ship.

Upon the shingle, Teek idly watched the turnstones as with stuttering steps they followed the retreating wavelets. A movement to his right, a flying figure. Becky, his Becky, raced along the wharf's uneven edge. Uncaring for any who might see, she jumped the granite stones down to the pebbles, there to fling herself into the comfort of his arms. Tightly he held her, fondled her soft golden hair and kissed her forehead, her upturned lips, kissing away the salt tears from her violet eyes. Protective in his love he clasped her to his breast. She wished that it had been his hands that fumbled, he would not have been denied. She sighed in blessed relief, consoled by his strength.

The emotion of the moment eased, he held her hands to tell of the Armada's coming. Even now he was awaiting his captain's orders. Becky nodded, filled with a blend of pride and fear as she told him what all Mousehole knew. A hue and cry was abroad, seeking the detention of his captain. The *Golden Hind* was being sought for piracy. Teek, with a casual air he little felt, cut short her fears, seeking to distract her by a change in subject.

"My robin, will you go visit my mother?" He unfastened a purse at his waist. "I have not seen her for many a month. Tell her as Teek says to buy a new bonnet for the merriment that will greet our return. For now I suppose we shall depart to fight." He handed her the silver coins. "Know you my brother Ben?"

She nodded her reply.

"He is a Jackanapes," he said affectionately. "There is a

74

puppy awaits him with Silas the rat-catcher. Pick of the litter. See he chooses well!"

There was a call from his captain as Thomas jumped the wharf to the granite below. Teek gave the little boat a shove, bows first, into the shallow water to hold the transom.

"Tell him to name it Skillywiddon," he called over his shoulder. "Pray for me and wait for me."

"For ever, Teek," she said that none save she could hear.

The advice of the older men had been forthright: Tom must sail with all haste to Plymouth and warn the High Admiral, Lord Howard of Effingham, of the approaching Armada. Then he must report for duty to his kinsman, John Hawkyns, to go and defend his country and defeat the foe. There was no alternative. In duty might he find salvation. That and the translation of the tracts.

In the waning storm the *Nuestra Senora de Rosario* set her sails to creep from the lee of St. Agnes Isle to lead forth the Squadron of Andalusia which, together with other storm-swept stragglers, would remuster off the Lizard thus to accord with the orders of their King.

Jenkyn and Nicholas Flemyng gathered family and servants to them. Solemnly they related the intelligence Thomas had newly brought. Together they knelt in prayer, seeking deliverance for their menfolk and victory for their country.

"I too must play my part," said Jenkyn. "Mary, fetch me Jacob." He went to his desk to write in neat and flowing hand, sealing the parchment with hot wax. Ill at ease Jacob ambled in and fingered his forehead to his master.

"Jacob, hasten to my Lord Godolphin with this letter. Take it to his place and give it to none but he, with the compliments of Jenkyn Keigwin. Tell him what Master Thomas has witnessed, ships of Spain sheltering off the Islands, and that even now he takes the *Golden Hind* to Plymouth to apprise the admirals of the news. Go with speed, man, but go with care. God help you on your way. We shall alert all town and village. Take the fastest and the

75

fittest nag. Here is a shilling. Return as soon you may."

Jacob stuffed the letter inside his woollen vest. Touched his forehead and departed without a word.

With the tide in her favour and the wind veered south-west, the *Golden Hind* ran free. From her bows Tom looked towards the rough waters off Lizard Point. Directly aft he could still see in the hills above Penzance the stump of the tower. The church of St. Maderne at whose font he was baptised. Behind, the Manor of Landithy where he was born. Ahead, an unknown welcome at Plymouth, the prospect of a trial for piracy. If guilty, to be hanged in chains and left upon high headland that all might see, a warning to others. Left to hang until the gulls plucked his eyeballs from their sockets, and stole his flesh, till all that remained were rough rags clinging to whitened bones.

On his larboard side he watched the hazardous rocks of Men Hyr, that he must so closely skirt. To starboard, out to sea a multitude of topsails. The Spanish fleet was mustering.

Danger was ahead. Danger, the temptress, beckoning her flirtatious finger, luring him to war, the ultimate adventure of youth, soon to be shorn of innocence by the waiting hand of horror. The blood of his fighting forebears raced through his veins. A breed born to battle, whose only fear was to be afraid.

Rounding the rocks, clear of the Spanish fleet, Martin joined him. In release of relief, together they hummed a boyhood tune, a soldier's hymn. A hymn of prayer to their God, to protect their homes and loved ones until they returned from the war they must fight for freedom's sake.

By the mainmast, Teek listened. His deep chest filled with salt sea air, eyes flashed as he sent forth his tuneful voice into a paean of praise, soon transformed into a fervour of song as the Cornishmen about him joined the chorus of the martial prayer their forefathers had once sung. A chorus that, could they but hear, would have struck a note of foreboding into the hardiest hearts of the sons of Spain.

*   *   *   *

76

Regrouped, the enemy coast a blur in the intermittent rain, the signalling flag was raised. The Duke of Medina Sidonia called a council of war on board his flagship. The battle plan decided upon, orders were given. The admirals and captains returned to their commands. From the foremast of the *San Martin de Portugal* the Royal Standard of King Philip II of Spain was broken out, followed by the Battle Insignia flowing forward from the mizzen. In every squadron each galleon and ship flew the flags of their provinces, saints' flags, personal standards of the officers and gentlemen adventurers on board. A breathtaking galaxy of brightly coloured taffeta and damask streaming bravely in the summer breeze. Burley watched, breast aching with tearful pride, as from the maintop drifted the huge banner of Christ Crucified. Soon they would engage the little ships of England. How they would grapple at close quarters, to decant their soldiers in overwhelming numbers upon the English decks. The might and right of Spain would never be denied!

Seaman and soldier, admiral and adventurer celebrated Mass in sight of the country of their enemy. With pounding heart Burley rejoiced at the certain prospect of victorious homecoming. England belonged to the King of Spain. His army would obtain his just inheritance!

In the battle formation of a huge crescent, horns to the rear, seven miles from tip to tip, the might and majesty of Spain sailed in awesome splendour. Favoured by wind and tide, they sailed toward Plymouth and the narrow seas. There to escort the Duke of Parma, his twenty thousand seasoned soldiers, and the cavalry that awaited them in Flanders. Escort to a vast flotilla of flat-bottomed boats, waiting to ferry them across to the shores of Kent, thence to march upon London. Throughout the land, the secret army of English Catholics would rise up to greet their brothers in arms, now come to liberate them from the Protestant yoke! Scotland would march upon England! Ireland would rebel against the Protestant lords to join the overthrow of the heretic Queen.

Lord Howard and Sir Francis Drake had dined well on board

the *Ark Royal*. Their fleet was now revictualled. Why, but why, was the Queen so frugal? Her parsimony might cost them dear. The wind and tide that favoured the fleet of Spain kept England's ships harbour-bound as it blew and ran against them. There was little more to be achieved in these warm, soft July days. Theirs to wait. To await news from spies or screen of pinnaces. The rain storms had ceased.

It was the wont of Lord Howard and his captains to amuse themselves with the Plymouth game of bowls. They played a game of leisurely skill that vented their frustrated energy. Forward from this high vantage of Plymouth Hoe was a commanding seawards view, and behind, the Hamoase in whose shelter lay the English fleet.

There was no time to lose as from harbourside and up the steep hill Tom ran. His lungs ached with effort. But he must make his report to the one man he knew he could trust.

Panting he ran to where they were gathered in their game, the sea-captains of the Western Fleet. The tall, elegant grey-bearded figure with the commanding presence, he knew was the Lord Admiral, Howard of Effingham.

His hat doffed in obeisance, they gathered around Tom as he told of that which he had seen and witnessed: the Armada. Great ships of Spain, their towering castles and lofty masts, sails emblazoned with the blood-red cross, now assembling off the Lizard.

Orders were issued. All ships to be made ready. Their crews attendant at their posts. Soon to be aided by an ebbing tide to be towed by long boat and hauled by warp out to the safety of the sea, to anchor off Rame Head.

With restraining fingers upon Drake's elbow, and backward wave of elegant hand Lord Howard bid his commanders resume their game. Quietly he questioned Flemyng as to the strength, position and formation of those ships that he had seen. Head to one side, he listened attentively, on occasion prompting with a pertinent question. The examination concluded, the grey eyes of Saxon nobleman held the Celtic privateer. With steadfast gaze and probing comment he queried the family of Flemyng, his background and his loyal ties, and the reasons for his piracy.

Unflinching, Flemyng answered point by point the voice

of conviction lending weight to words. He told of how his suspicions of Nicholls had been aroused. That Jenkyn Keigwin, his merchant grandfather, had intelligence of Nicholls and the English merchants of Newhaven, spies in the pay of the Duke of Guise. How information was garnered from English seamen and Spanish merchants in England's ports, that they suspected the tracts to contain messages in secret cipher to be delivered to Ireland, that they might light the spark of rebellion when the soldiers of Parma landed upon England's shores. That there was a secret army of traitorous English that would rise up to overthrow Elizabeth, whereon Philip of Spain would seize the throne of England. Was not Mousehole a port where ships might be searched for letters prejudicial to the Queen's authority? Was this not what he had achieved, as was his duty?

The High Admiral glanced quizzically at Drake, who nodded his head in ready affirmation. For Flemyng had confirmed much that he had already gleaned.

"Know you of any more of the tricks of Spain?"

"Only, my lord, that there is an Englishman named Richard Burley, a captain in the pay of King Philip. My grandfather has heard tell of him, as indeed have I. By devious means he comes to England for clandestine meetings with others of his kind, and to solicit on their advice the assistance of English navigators familiar with our shores and harbours, tempting them to join with him for considerable reward. There are such men who are believed to be aboard and sailing with the Armada. Their souls sold to the Bishop of Rome."

" 'Twill do." Effingham's gaze was stern. "Hasten now and with your crew lend assistance, for our ships must be warped out to sea. Take your orders from those in command. You, Master Flemyng, will serve with John Hawkyns. Keep close station on him, for we need a fast pinnace with a captain whose seamanship I trust to link the two of us. Your own tongue is your best lawyer and I will join with Sir Francis to speak in your defence, for 'tis well known the Privy Council seek your detention. But for now there are other matters more urgent to be resolved. Go! Serve your Queen. She will not betray you!"

79

He clasped his hand. Tom bowed to the Admiral and with tear-filled eyes gave grateful glance towards the blurred face of Sir Francis.

"Come, let us continue," he heard Drake call to his fellows, "there is plenty of time to finish the game and beat the Spaniards too!"

The game of bowls went on. The players contemptuous of their enemy, knowing that at least one of nature's forces would soon be turning to their aid. The tide. When on the ebb, the tide would enable the English to sally forth whilst delaying the fleet of Spain.

Thomas and Martin took their men to join with the other captains and seamen. Sweating and straining with warp and with long boat they hauled and heaved through the warm early evening. To be bottled within the harbour? Never! Corked within, at the mercy of the might and men of Spain! The thought lent fresh vigour to tired sinews, as they tugged the English fleet into the deeper water of the sea where, with the help of the retreating tide, they rode at anchor in the lee of Rame Head, that which points its crooked finger into the narrow seas.

The invincible Armada was at evening devotions. Lanterns were lighted and before their altars, ships' companies were assembled. Burley sank upon his knees with joyful heart whilst the blessing of God was sought for men and for ship as the priests led them in prayer. Friars recited with religious invective the many crimes of their enemy, the Queen of England, inflaming the passions of the faithful. Noblemen and adventurers, bejewelled and bedecked in plumed finery, stood shoulder to shoulder with simple sailormen. Hand thrust within doublet, Burley fingered in comforting reassurance the medallion that hung next to his heart.

At the house of Keigwin, and from the Manor of Llandithy, watching eyes saw the spurt of white flame, as Silas Tregenza, atop the chapel on St. Michael's Mount, put torch to brush wood. In her bedroom that overlooked the bay, Becky sank to her knees and prayed to God for her lover's safe return. From hilltop to hilltop the beacons flickered into blaze, the war-flame spread as the guardians of the braziers alerted their countrymen, and called the English to arms.

In stately magnificence the great and invincible Armada continued its imposing way: the formidable galleasses of extravagant and exotic name, the fore and aft castles of the ornate galleons, decks of cannon peering and probing through open ports. Noble pennants streamed forward in the westerly wind that urged them on 'neath lowering skies and through the grey, bickering chop of the English Channel. Never before had an ocean borne witness to such an arrogant array as the crescent of the fighting ships of Spain.

On the night of Saturday 30th July, hidden beneath the cloak of darkness under storm-swept skies, out from the haven off Rame Head crept the *Ark Royal*, as Admiral Lord Howard led his squadron to cross the face of the Armada and take up position to rear of Spanish southern horn.

Following in their wake, came the great ships of the Western Squadron, to turn close inshore. As a cygnet follows the parent swan, the *Golden Hind* followed the glow of the stern lantern ahead, to play the tides and tack into the wind, that they too might fall behind the foe and steal the weather-gauge. Theirs now to be favoured by the wind. The all-prevailing westerly, that would waft them on, upon the heels of Spain.

Prospect of a fight drove the gritted tiredness from his eyes as Tom led his men at morning prayer.

Each fleet was at devotions. Each to beseech that the one and only God would grant to them a righteous victory.

Dawn streaked the sullen clouds with fingers of light. The *Golden Hind* took her station off John Hawkyns in the *Victory*. A swift messenger to serve as link with his command.

"Blessed relief," the squadron now all in position Martin was free to speak. "Now to us the advantage, Tom."

"Maybe so, but with all those ships about us, we must take care as not to be caught napping — Teek!"

"Aye, Captain?"

"Ensure close watch is kept. Beware of galleys!"

"Sir?"

"Those lumbering urcas cannot go about into this wind — no more the high-castled galleons, but in a calming sea the galley can and would have legs of us on shortish run."

Teek touched his brow and went forward to shout the captain's orders to the look-out.

"Martin, go forward if you please and keep close watch lest there be orders signalled."

"What do you expect?"

"Soon we must engage — for do you see, Sidonia must decide. Either his fighting ships must take in sail to slow and give protection to his laggards, or else make haste to join with Parma. Ahead, he knows, lies the fleet of Seymour but then the Spaniards will have the weather-gauge of him as we do now on them. One way or other he must choose."

"Not so, he may decide on nothing and let events dictate."

"True, but I go now to see all is prepared upon the gun deck."

"Aye, Captain."

Martin gave a grin and touched two fingers to his forehead in mock salute and forward went as he was bid.

Chapter Five

Sunday 31st July 1588. To be alone awhile, to think his own thoughts away from the crowded clamour of the decks, to ponder and to muse, as a man does when away from the land of his birth.

Short, sickening seas broke upon the ornate stern as he gazed down from the aft gallery. His men were armed and mustered. Each dark-eyed countenance at contrast to his own fair visage. Yet all were of one accord, ready and awaiting the prospect of the fray and the glory that would follow. Musketeer and pikeman, now clad in breast plates, and helmed in burnished steel, their captains waiting on his command. They clustered in ship's waist, grappling irons ready, to be flung to arc and claim, to close and overwhelm by weight of numbers and thrust of steel.

He squinted into the murk where, across the ridges of furrowed sea, the billowing sails of England were vaguely etched. Through the squalls, beneath the lowering sky, lay the dull headlands of his country, far from the blue Atlantic and sun-drenched shores of Andalusia. That place of bright colours, festivals and dancing, home of the squadron upon which he served. Ships of proud and saintly name. *Nuestra Senora de Rosario*, *San Juan de Gargarin*, *El Espiritu Santo*. By contrast. *Ark Royal*, *Revenge*, *Victory*. All was contrast.

He spat and tugged his hilt free to slam the hungry blade home into its scabbard. Bejewelled fingers toyed with the guard.

"Soon, soon my friend. Your thirst will be quenched upon the blood of heresy."

About him the Armada wallowed.

* * * *

At the council of war, Hawkyns had received his orders and issued his own commands. Now must Tom keep close watch. To anticipate the flow of battle, ever alert for signals — orders that he must relay to others in the squadron, lest they go unseen in the heat of war.

To Jonas Bradbury had fallen the privilege to fire the opening shot. Would it had been himself, thought Thomas. His eyes eagerly sought the pinnace. The *Disdain*, how apt her name, as she leapt from the pack of England's ships, pennants bravely flying, sails billowing, to run towards the fleet of Spain, the wind drowning the English cheers.

The tall fair figure started.

"Ah! Captain Burley, alone I see." Above the hiss of waves and crack of rigging, he had not heard the Commander coming. He turned to salute de Valdes, smiling in welcome.

"Yes, alone, Don Pedro. But to command is a lonesome task, is it not so?"

"Indeed, my friend, sadly one I know too well. But soon it will be action. Battle will dispel our anxious moments, 'tis the waiting is the worst."

"For too many years I have waited upon this moment. A time that, but for my faith, I thought might never happen. My country," he swept his arm toward a blurred headland, "soon by the grace of God to be free once more." His eyes blazed in accord with the words. "To worship in the true faith. I thank my Maker that He has granted me a part amongst his cast of players. Ah yes! For by His grace, a great victory will soon be ours."

"I pray God, Richard Burley, that your prayers are fully answered."

"You do not doubt it?"

"The Spaniard pulled on his beard, eyes searching the distance for the English ships. "No, but I have long learned not to take God for granted. When we are overly confident, sometimes He has a way of confounding us and thus does He humble our pride."

84

Each held his own thoughts, close coupled, as side by side they leant upon the rail to await the onset of battle.

"The English have advantage of the weather-gauge," mused de Valdes. "Our intelligence declares a further fleet of England and of Hollander lies awaiting us off Flanders. I trust that Parma . . . "

"Look, see, Don Pedro, yonder towards the flagship!" Burley pointed to where the diminutive *Disdain* was closing upon the towering bulk of the Capitana General, the *San Martin de Portugal.*

"Every man to his post, Captain Burley. Our waiting is now at an end!"

Unleashed and alone, under press of sail, towards the mighty ships of Spain, to go about 'neath the ornate aft castle. A flash, a sullen roar, the long-barrelled culverin had fired the opening challenge to accord with the courtesies of war. A gesture of scorn her name declared, as the *Disdain* raced to return to the safety of her squadron.

Now were the ships of England to close upon their enemy. South from the *Golden Hind* they saw their Lord Admiral lead by example and engage a great galleon. Pentreath stood at the helm, his captain at his side, signalling his commands to Teek; for as the cygnet does obey, so must the privateer follow in the wake of the *Victory*, ready to alter set of sail as speed or direction might require. Now they would join the battle, as in line astern toward the northern horn of the Armada sailed the *Revenge*, as Drake led his ships in attack upon the Biscayan Squadron.

From a perch in the shrouds Martin kept close watch for signals: a dip of topsail, a lone cannon's roar, all to be interpreted in the confusion of battle.

Flame stabbed the dull of the day to ripple along the gun-decks as with broadside upon broadside the English fighting ships ranged upon their enemy. Nostrils tingled to the pungent smell of burnt powder, as cannon smoke lingered above the wavetops, deepening the gloom of the day.

"Cheer, Tom — cheer!" Martin shouted and pointed, as shot from the *Revenge* tore away mainsail and shrouds of the Biscayan flagship.

Burley recalled de Valdes' words. Upon whose side was God to be? He had never before doubted. But now the cold hand of fear lay icy fingers upon his nape. He shuddered.

The English ships were fleet and nimble. Their shot outdistanced that of Spain. Tempt as the Spaniards may, there was no close quarter action. Theirs not to close and grapple, but to fight loose and at large. Unfettered by strict command, the English sea dogs could snap and snarl and harry at the heels of the herded ships of Spain.

He must cast off the doubt de Valdes had first sewn.

"Why do we break off the battle, Tom?"

"Powder and shot. Powder and shot, Richard. There is all too little to spare. Besides, it is our Admiral's tactics to usher the Spaniards along the coast that they may not land. Seymour and Wynter wait ahead with the Hollander. The invincible Armada is as a nut, ready for the cracking between the fleets!"

"Don Pedro, see, the English are withdrawing!"

" 'Tis but brief respite. They have done sufficient for one day, Captain Burley," de Valdes grunted a laugh. "Now they retire to re-arm: that we cannot do." He screwed his eyes to peer where once had been the Northern horn. "We have been fortunate to escape such damage as Recalde and the Biscayans. Our duty is now to him. I fear he has suffered pitifully, at the hands of Drake I suspect. Without our aid he will not survive the morrow."

At his command the Andalusian Squadron slowly turned to work their way up wind and tack close hauled to aid their battered brothers.

Squalls of rain drove spindrift from the rising waves as Burley willed his eyes to delve into the dull confusion, as the two squadrons mingled and merged in the crowded water. With threat of battle ended for a while, others of England came upon deck to join with Burley, to seek opinion as to whom fortune had most favoured. And thence to prayers.

A sudden cry from the pilot, Stucley, who had clenched him on the arm.

"Swing the wheel for the sake of Christ! Swing the wheel!" Slowly the *Rosario* answered to the call of the rudder and set of sail as there loomed a great Biscayan across her bows. Aghast Burley watched, as so very slowly the flagship began to come about, her pointing bowsprit to traverse beneath the Biscayan aft-castle. But all too late. With rip of sprit sail, further round she bore as crossyards locked, to snap from each others embrace, to tumble with sail and rigging in loose jumble upon the deck.

With way lost, she wallowed in the heaving sea and gave no answer to her helm. Burley ran forward to gather men who with axe and knife might clear the mess. A warning cry from aloft, he looked upward from his task.

"God save us," he flung himself to the deck as the towering presence of the *Santa Catalina*, a ship of their own squadron, hove through the misting rain, to strike and bear away bowsprit and foresail halliards of the flagship.

Hapless, the *Rosario* rolled in the mounting seas. Alone, bereft of help, as the galleons of Andalusia and Biscay made way to shroud themselves in the safety of the fleet, and leave their capitana to fend alone.

Early afternoon. The mutter of cannon ceased. Tom glanced at the sails above: through the rigging the wild wind whistled, accompaniment to the hiss of sea as it bore along her beam. This was the tune he knew and loved, singing a song of freedom.

Ahead, the stern of the *Revenge*. Hawkyns would be pleased at the ploy of his ships.

"There, Bosun, there," Flemyng shouted over the starboard beam for Teek to turn.

A flicker of far-off flame. Fitful. To falter and flare again, lightening the distant sky. Tom gazed in awe as a roar of thunder echoed across the waves. Teek came to his captain's side. "In the name of God, what of that sir?"

"I know not, Bosun."

"The Devil's work! Or of God; surely it is a ship of Spain engulfed by fire. An omen?"

"We shall surely learn."

Fearful of the return of the English fleet, seaman and soldier hacked and sliced at the litter of sail and cordage that lay entangled upon the foredeck, cutting adrift spar and sail that trailed alongside hindering her safe return. At last the task was complete. Sails raised, the *Rosario* ran before the still-rising wind.

To their larboard side a flash and then a great roar. They watched in awe and wonder at the blaze, their own plight for a moment was forgot. "That is surely de Oquendo and his squadron of Guipuzcoa."

"God be merciful, 'tis Don Miguel." Don Valdes, squinting through hand-shielded eyes, was aghast. "Surely the *San Salvador*, that bears the paymaster. The *San Salvador*. Laden with Imperial gold, enough to purchase England."

"Purchase?" queried Burley.

"In her chests is payment enough for those who would rise up and overthrow the heretic Queen. See those who go to her aid? Our Admiral knows of her importance too well."

"That out-ranks our own, de Valdes?"

"Yes Burley. I fear that if Sidonia has to choose only one to save, it would be the *San Salvador*."

"That choice will not be needed. We are making on our squadron. Our fears will be over, safe between the horns."

"Ah, speak not so soon, Burley. For yet do I fear this strengthening wind."

" 'Tis the driving of the wind, sir, that hastens us to our comrades."

"Or to our death!"

"Do you doubt your God, Don Pedro?" There was more than a hint of contempt in Burley's voice.

De Valdes turned to smile and shake his head in mild reproof. "Not my God, Captain Burley. Merely the strength of those few and weakened halliards upon which depends our foremast."

No sooner had those words been uttered than there came a

crack — as a musket shot, and a great splintering as the foremast snapped close by the deck, to fall into the main-mast in a confusion of canvas and cord.

"What now, Don Pedro? In God's name, what now?"

"On your knees and pray that God may hear, whilst we fire our cannon. Pray that Sidonia hears our distress signal!"

Once more the tangle was cut and sent overboard as the *Rosario* was left to drift astern the fleet. Yet still no sign of succour, no galleasse that with sail and oar might prevail against such winds, to throw a line and tow the hulk to safety.

"If help is not soon at hand, we are lost, my friend."

"But we have the King's money aboard."

De Valdes shrugged and shaded his eyes once more to search for some sign from the departing fleet.

"All that can be spared, give aid to the *San Salvador*. 'Tis as I feared, the Duke of Medina has decided he must press onwards and so deny us aid."

Burley tugged upon his sleeve. "Should Drake take us, Don Pedro, you will be treated with the dignity your rank bestows. But I, I, Don Pedro, as a traitor!"

Don Pedro turned to face him with enquiry in his look. A pleading note now entered Burley's voice.

"I will be given as a gift to Topcliffe, the torturer of the Tower, to treat me as he may, my naked body stretched upon the rack," his frame shuddered, "then must I reveal all. Others now in England will suffer a similar fate." His voice rose. "Then hanged and drawn, Don Valdes, hanged and drawn, my head upon a pike paraded — God save me!" Again he shook his commander by the arm, his voice rising in further pitch of anguish. "I know too much, Don Pedro, so many more will die. Jesuit and true believer, as consequence of my revelations!"

Most had now deserted the *Rosario*, save for an attendant pinnace that alone remained at station.

"You make a fair point. Go, take Friar Gongora with you; hasten now. He will be at devotions, praying for deliverance. Muster such English as you quickly can, and with them board the pinnace. Entreat assistance from our Lord Admiral. Prevail upon him. God speed you, Burley, and may your pleas be not in vain. Save us."

Ushered into the ornate cabin, Burley saluted with but slight
semblance of flourish and proffered a courtly bow.

Flanked by his captains, Medina Sidonia was seated before
a chart-strewn table. Worried eyes stared from a tired and
noble face, raised eyebrows made their question.

"We are off the *Nuestra Senora de Rosario* which is in dire
need. Her bowsprit broke and foremast lost. Now she falls
prey to the English fleet as she falls back from without the
protection of your Grace." He paused for his words to take
effect. "I am come to speak for Don Pedro de Valdes as
honour forbids him to leave his command. I pray, your
Grace, send ships to his aid so they may cast a line aboard
and tow him hither."

"There is little to be done, Captain Burley, for the enemy
gathers in strength and I must heed the advice of our King.
We must make haste toward Parma."

"May it please your Grace, but apart from Don Pedro
there is many a gallant aboard, as well as much gold and
silver."

"So I am aware, Burley, yet all that may be spared have
gone to the aid of the *San Salvador*. She too is grievously
stricken, by fire and, as well as her men, carries the gold
without which our mission is in jeopardy. I fear de Valdes
must be risked and must mend his own ship."

The Duke of Medina Sidonia looked up at his officers who
with nod and mutter gave to him their support that he might
continue. "Soon it is dusk. Should we take in sail the *Rosario*
may make toward us, but," he gave weight to his words,
" 'twill not be perceived by the foremost of our fleet.
Onward will they press as I have commanded, to leave us
far behind. Our weakling force then might well fall foul of
Drake." He paused and pursed his lips. "Leave us now, for
we will salvage such as we may and plan our tomorrow." A
nod of dismissal.

Dejected, Burley bowed his departure. The doubt de Valdes
had sowed now rooting in his brain.

*   *   *   *

It was morning, Monday 1st August. Onward pressed the English fleet, always in motion, tacking and playing about the heels of the enemy. A Morris dance upon the sea. Pouring in their fire, then sheering off out of range, only to return and fire another broadside; once more to sheer away without retort from Spain.

The Armada shepherded upon its way, leaving the *San Salvador* to fall astern, a smoking, ravaged hulk. Relieved of much of the gold and silver that she carried and most of her men, but of both there was that which they had not time to take.

Dawn was breaking. Dutifully they followed the *Victory* as she closed upon the payship. And there too was the *Golden Lion* that Thomas Howard commanded. But what of the *Revenge* — and Drake? There was little time to wonder.

"Have you ever seen a ship so stricken?"

"Never, Martin. Was it by the hand of God, for surely none of England was in cannon shot?"

"Aye and 'twould take many a broadside to wreak such havoc."

The brothers watched from before the mainmast, with blend of awe and wonder, as the hulk drifted before them upon the surging seas.

They circled beneath where once was the ornate stern-castle. Now her gilded galleries were broken, splintered masts lay upon the deck, spars held by their cordage to trail astern. Reeking smoke drifted, to hover above the wave crests. From within the wooden walls came the wailing of the wounded, their screams to drown the shrieking of the wind and hush the voices of those who watched in wondering pity.

Across the reeking decks they picked their way. The old slaver Hawkyns locked his arm in that of his youthful kinsman. Alert to assess the degree of damage. Out of earshot of other English, with free arm he pointed, that they might see he was intent upon the destruction, but his whispered voice betrayed that pose.

"Now hark to me, Tom. In the cloak of darkness Drake went a-plundering, and has taken a great treasure-laden galleon. That of De Valdes, he alone will command a handsome sum as ransom! Sauce for the goose is sauce for the gander!" He winked from his close set eyes and said in louder voice, "Now, young Thomas, take me below that we may see her harm. For upon you depends whether she will stay afloat."

They fumbled their way between decks. And again he held his kinsman close.

" 'Tis as I supposed. She has been relieved of much, but a great wealth still remains untouched."

He put the wet cloth once more to his face to foil the evil odour, and led their way upon deck through a clutter of fallen canvas. A shroud for mangled bodies that lay scarce hid, to rejoin the other captains.

"Now, Flemyng will take the hulk to Weymouth, to ground in the lee of the headland. Thomas, you will return as fast ye may with ball and powder from her and with all God's speed replenish the cannon of our ships, for there is a great dearth aboard us. Gentlemen, we have taken time enough, return to your commands whilst I give young Tom further direction."

He turned his back in dismissal and walked the privateer toward the broken helm, whilst still the moans of the fallen made record of their sobbing presence. Once more his voice dropped in conspiring tones, "Swiftly Tom, are all your men of Mousehole?"

"Or thereabouts."

"They may be trusted?"

"As much as any who is not a saint."

"But they come of pirate stock?"

"Don't we all, yet we serve our Queen?"

Hawkyns grunted.

"They are as you and me, sir, they serve for gold — and love of country. I pray you, say on."

"Be discreet. Confide only in those you must. For so your life will depend." Hawkyns spoke in earnest tones. "On board I suspect there remains much gold and silver, as well as shot and powder. Put all that which may be quickly taken aboard your ship. Well hidden. then return with haste that ye may provision the fleet and none may be the wiser." He tapped Thomas upon his chest. "The folk of Weymouth are but brigands. Leave a small part for they will surely steal, then they may be blamed for the taking of the whole. Thus we remain unsuspected." He gazed aloft where torn sails were limply draped. "When all this is done, we will have the reckoning in the house of your grandfather and celebrate with his finest fare. Betray me not, and may the Lord watch over you and give you safe return." He looked about him. "Beware the tidal race off Portland."

"I know it well and will take good care. We will do your bidding, sir, never fear!"

Hawkyns looked about, then clasped his kinsman to his chest. "Attend on me as soon you may." A gesture of farewell, he turned to clamber down the charred sides to where his skiff awaited.

Tom shouted a signal, the *Golden Hind* closed, with Richard in command, as Martin and Teek scrambled on deck to join him. Together they took stock of the prize, excitement of their venture dampened by the sick, sweet smell of mortifying flesh; a rotten odour, that smelt but once is never lost from a soldier's senses.

"Order the living to tend the dying as best they may, for I can take this no longer," Tom gasped the freshening air as from below deck they climbed. "Teek, ensure the pumps are manned. All must be on deck, let no one go below. I will put lines aboard to take her into Weymouth, if the Lord is willing, for we navigate through horrendous waters. Martin, call out the men you need and set them about their tasks. I return to relieve Richard."

Sails were lowered over her damaged sides that the weight of sea might press home to give a canvas bandage to wounds that lay gaping below the water-line. Thus to deter the further ingress of the water that sluiced and slopped and rose within the bilges. The tangled mass of rigging was hacked and cut to turn adrift. Warps made fast, the tiny English terrier took in tow the Spanish mastiff.

The bodies of the fallen were laid in rows upon the heaving deck. Pockmarked by powder burns, torn apart, lined in grotesque array. Nimble fingers delved into pocket and purse for trinket or for jewel, a providential gift of war. The dead had no need of ducats.

As custom demanded, the spoils were heaped at the main-mast foot for a fair division later.

They weighted the bloating bodies with shot or chain, to be tossed overboard with brief prayer into those chopping waters. Earthly bodies of proud men took their final rest upon a foreign ocean's bed.

Now the wind was easing, the sky clearing; bright moon-light the lamp by which they worked, repairing torn canvas, rigging jury sails as aid to steerage and to catch such wind as might assist them on their way.

Tuesday morning the 2nd August. Burley sniffed the untainted air and watched the sun rising, thanking God for his good fortune.

The *San Martin* had resumed her rightful place and once more was in the van. About her the Armada now re-formed and ready. For the wind veered north-east and would aid Seymour and his mix of English and of Hollander, should they seek to launch attack upon the Spanish front.

De Valdes . . . had God punished him for doubting His wisdom? Why else had He smiled upon his servant, Burley, and aided his escape? He shook his head in wonderment, and closing his eyes he offered a silent prayer in gratitude for his safety.

Prayers done, his eyes now fastened upon the north where, in the distance, loomed the great headland of Portland Bill, off which ran the dreaded tidal race that rent the sea in two. Did Holman still command the battery atop? He had connived to prosper well. Beyond, his birthplace, Melcombe Regis, the town where his father still lived. How he would wish to return as a victor! Acclaimed by those who once had scorned. Melcombe Regis, for seventeen years one with Weymouth. An Act of Union between those feuding boroughs, where those of his kin had served as bailiff and then first alderman of that place. Here could he have been a man of some consequence, but he had cast the dice and chosen to follow the fortunes of his faith and thus was now with Spain. His loyalty rewarded with twenty-five crowns a month, no mean amount. A servant of King Philip.

Might he have risen to some high rank? Perhaps Mayor of Weymouth? Ah, may be so. But did not that downy bird Pitt hold office? 'Twas said he had lined his nest at the expense of others and now was a man of wealth. So be it, he vowed. But Richard Burley would one day return and make amends.

With the wind now shifted, back they sailed from whence they had but newly come. Ahead, no sign of Seymour could be seen. Behind, the English fleet. Still could he discern the *San Salvador*, taken in tow by a barque to taunt and mock the might of Spain. The English fleet had altered course, alert to the advantage Spain now held. Close-hauled were they to head north-west. If Sidonia was not soon aware, the English would outflank once more to steal the weather-gauge.

Orders were shouted, whistles sounded. Thank God for the rear-guard that now engaged the enemy. The thunder of their broadsides echoed across the water. To and fro the battle raged. His helmet firm upon his head, breast and back plate tight-fastened, he gripped the halliards for support and hefted his rapier in right hand. The blood chased through his veins in the excitement of imminent battle, as he willed the English to close that they might grapple, to be locked in sensuous embrace.

Danger. Danger and hint of fear, the glorious arousal of the senses of a soldier. What were those orders? He looked aloft. The fore topsail backed. An invitation to the English flagship. Surely Howard would accept. Refusal was the coward's way. Thank God, the gauntlet taken, as the *Ark Royal* led the squadron in line astern, about to close.

He must prepare to lead his men! What Devil's trickery! Flame flashed along the flank of the English flagship as she fired her larboard cannon, near point-blank, into the Spanish hull. Then leading her squadron on and about, to fire her starboard cannon with scarce response from Spain. Shot that thudded into the sides of the *San Martin* did little harm, but other sang their song overhead to rip through sails and rigging. Tears of frustrated fury coursed his cheeks.

He knelt upon the deck, to cross himself and gaze where once from the mainmast had flown the blessed banner of Christ crucified, now rent and torn asunder by the English shot. Was this another omen? He recalled De Valdes' words. The fury was now fled from him, and only fear remained.

Wednesday 3rd August. Two leagues out from the Head, slowly the *Golden Hind* towed her prize upon a starboard tack.

"Steady as you go, Pentreath," Tom advised his helmsman. "We have crossed the worst. Keep well out, lest we touch upon the Shambles. Many a well-favoured ship has breathed with relief when the Race is crossed, only to foul upon the shoal."

Slowly the stately cortege sailed. The ravaged hulk, water-logged, ten times the size of the barque of Mousehole that led her by the nose into the relief of the calm waters within the Weymouth roads. At the signal, into the wind they headed, and hove to.

Tom ordered a flag to be raised, to call a council upon the *Golden Hind*.

"Have you made a good search, Martin? We can scarce forbear to learn what is discovered."

"Curb your impatience whilst I gain the deck!" The salt-tanned face split into the broadest grin, as he straddled the gunwhale to clamber aboard.

"There," he grasped with one his nephew's hand and clutched his shoulder with other, his eyes creased in smiles. "Richard!" He clasped his brother to him. "Ah! anxious fellow!" And gave a wink. "Come nephew, to your cabin, and bring me ale. I am parched. The water aboard is fouled, the stench of the dead still lingers and I would wash it from me."

"Surely, Martin, surely." Tom gave orders for ale and wine, and no disturbance.

The three were seated, each with own jug. Martin looked about the cramped quarters. "Can any man hear our discourse?"

"None save us, but it is well to be cautious!" said Tom.

In soft, now serious voice Martin looked at each in turn. "Whilst Teek, good man that he is, has kept all others occupied at their duties; manning pumps and such sails we now have, watching the helm and tending to the wounded, I have made a most diligent search and discovered much."

"Yes, but aught of value?"

Martin drank a deep and grateful draught. "There is shot in plenty, and fine corned powder too! Some two hundred quintals by my reckoning. Sufficient in itself, so I assess, to last our fleet for two days fighting."

"Aye, that alone is prize enough. But what of treasure?" asked Richard.

"Treasure?" He gave a teasing wink to his brother, gazing into the froth as if to contemplate the answer to the eager question, then supping his ale, before replying with a deep-throated chuckle. "Never fear, there is silver in plenty, enough to satisfy all our needs. Those gentlemen who sailed for glory saved their skins, but not their ship, nor indeed their silver! There is both coin and plate and jewellery too, that we must salvage."

"But what of those aboard?"

"There are some who are Spanish, but of the common sort, for those of consequence were taken off, save for one."

"Is he worth a ransom?"

"I know not his worth."

"Is he of good family?"

"Again, Richard, I know not, but if arrogance is a measure of his breeding, then he is of a Royal line."

"Arrogance?"

"Aye! He boasts of those English who serve in King Philip's cause."

"Aught of whom are Cornish?"

"None of whom we know, yet one, that Richard Burley of whom John Donne first told, sails with the Armada."

"Ummh. And so far as I recall 'tis from here he hails."

"Yes, but of prisoners. Will they betray our actions when landed safe ashore?"

"There is nothing to fear from those poor wretches, they are in the main so sick or so bemused that their sole concern is how best they can survive."

"That is a relief."

Tom slapped his knee and rose to stretch as best he might within the confines of the cabin. "Gentlemen, the time has

97

come when we must plan our action, the tide is now making and we should head for Weymouth."

"Nephew."

Tom looked at Martin.

"There is one thing more to tell."

"Tell us Martin, but please be swift."

"I near forgot. Stowed tight, rammed close within the forepeak I discovered a great, iron-bound chest, one of the Nuremberg kind favoured by the Spanish for the hoarding of their coin."

"Did you open it?"

"No, for it is stoutly locked and one would need resort to gunpowder, and that would draw attention where none is needed. No. There it remains, but few would know its presence, it is too closely hid."

"Then we must remove it here," said Tom.

"It is too weighty for me alone to shift, hence I believe the prospect of coin within."

"Whatever the risk we must take it, for should it eventually be discovered and Hawkyns not receive his share, I may as well become a ploughboy, for the sea will hold no future for me."

"Never fear. If all else fails we will blow it open. I have another plan. As I am told a Juan de Huerta was the paymaster. If I learn which were his quarters, by chance I may discover if the key be hid."

"Yes brother," Richard spoke with the authority of the eldest, "then we can more easily relieve the chest of its treasure, if treasure there be; and yet leave a smattering of coin for others to discover, as Hawkyns bid us do, since we will return the key to where it may readily be found. Thus we will be absolved of any consequence. All must be recorded and counted with great care and proper inventory made. Start your search, Martin, begin seeking! Our future is in your hands. Doubtless there is much to attend on board?"

"Aye! To ensure the *San Salvador* remain afloat! If she is to be beached, then it must be where we cannot be approached o'er land and have our actions spied upon."

"I must oversee the lading of the powder and shot, for that

must remain our principal aim: to replenish the fleet as quickly as we may!" said Tom.

"I have given that some thought. In no time you can conceal the bounty beneath the powder in marked barrels, then stow them below within the *Golden Hind*." Martin was proud of the plan.

Richard nodded. "Just so. Whilst you are attending to your duties I will venture ashore to make provision for the wounded and the prisoners and arrange fresh victuals. Fly such flags and banners as we may, Tom, for this is a time to savour."

"To savour perhaps, but do not lower your guard Richard. Be wary, for I fear you may be treating with a nest of vipers! Recall what Donne did say."

"I shall take good care! And buy you such time as I may."

"Then take Pentreath with you."

"If that will ease your worry, Tom, so be it. But see those that gather upon the hillside, come to greet us? We must play the part and give them a show to long remember."

And so it was agreed.

Chapter Six

Slowly groaning capstans raised the anchors. Lines had been fastened, sails raised. A panoply of flags streamed from the mastheads and with teeth of her cannon bared through open ports, the *Golden Hind* proudly towed her battered prey toward the shelter of the Nothe, determined to put on a brave show for those that watched.

"Easy, Pentreath. Easy now. We have no room for error. The eyes of England are upon us!"

Luffing sails were taken in, as foresail and tide eased them on to a safe anchorage; in the lee of the watch lay the steepsided promontory that guards the approach to the haven of Weymouth town.

Anchors splashed into blue water, prisoners sweated at the pumps, manned to contain the further ingress of the sea. Aloft, sailors clung to the yard-arms reefing the ragged sails. At last Teek could take stock of his surroundings. He cocked his head to listen, above the lapping of wavelets the rumble of a cannonade as the fleets pursued their onward passage.

Clustered upon the hill were people. Never had he known so many. Crowds of people, on foot and on horse, by cart and by carriage; their appetite whetted by the battle that had gone before off Portland Bill. They relished the plight and taking of the *San Salvador*, sated their hunger upon the fruits of victory. From the harbour entrance, a flotilla of small boats made their approach.

Between the ravaged decks Martin could define the semblance of what once had been the cabin. That of Don Juan de

100

Huerta, Paymaster to the invincible Armada. He rummaged and searched amongst the shattered timber seeking that precious piece of metal, the key to the Nuremberg treasure chest.

The awaiting skiff bumped gently against the barque. But first Richard must make the final touches to his neglected toilet and don fresh doublet and hose. Fine feathers make fine birds. The greater the consequence he could command, the greater the authority he would carry. Had he not been his father's witness? Well he knew that game and there was a handsome prize for which to play!

"Do you see, Tom. I'll be damned as a heathen! Look, an armada of punts is come to greet us."

"Or to steal! Recall what John Hawkyns said of Weymouth. Pirates he said."

An arm was placed about his shoulders. Uncle looked close into nephews eyes and grinned. "And what of you, Tom, eh? You know nought of pirating I suppose?"

"Well, so be it, but you are no better Uncle." They laughed together.

"None-the-less, take care Tom. Tell 'em we have the plague aboard! That'll put the fear of God in them, I must leave. Come, Pentreath, you are to act the wet-nurse and see that I am not harmed."

The burly figure winked his one eye at his oarsman, opened his shirt to tweak the nipple of his hirsute breast. "I shall nourish you well, master, never fear." He ordered the boat upon its way before Richard could make a reprimand.

Atop the harbour wall a curious crowd was gathered to cheer and applaud as the skiff made fast. A motley gathering, interested in news of battle. In pride of place a cluster of dignitaries and in their midst a stout figure whose dress and bearing proclaimed him to be a man of note. He stepped forward, hand outstretched in greeting.

"I, sir, am Richard Pitt, Mayor of Weymouth. We welcome you to our town."

"And I, sir, am Richard Keigwin of Mousehole and thank

you for your courtesy."

"That is a name I well recall. Are you of the family of Jenkyn Keigwin?"

"My father, sir."

"Then come, sir, come with me. Gentlemen, join us!" He thrust an arm through that of Richard with patronising air and eased him through the throng.

"Pray accompany me to my home, 'tis close by, and tell me of what service we can be."

He led Richard to where stood a house of Portland stone, lighter in colour, softer than the harsh granite of Mousehole. Yet hood, mould and mullioned windows were of similar style and pattern.

The door was opened at their approach, host ushered guest within where the dark stone-flagged floor was strewn with rich patterned carpets. A servant relieved him of his cloak. A goblet of March ale was thrust into his fist as the small assembly gathered round, waiting.

"Master Keigwin. From Portland Bill have we watched the distant battle rage. The fleets have now ventured eastward on the wind and all we now hear is the distant roar of cannon. Exaggeration fathers exaggeration that fattens till no semblance of the truth remains, we are hungry for the truth, Master Keigwin; I pray you feed us on the facts. Is danger past? Is the battle won? Or will the Armada link with Parma and land upon our shores? How was this ship of Spain taken?"

"Such a broadside, Mayor Pitt," laughed Richard. "Give thanks that God has seen fit to place the elements upon the side of England. The wind and weather have been greatly to our aid." He paused to sip his ale. "Our ships are better founded and our gunners better drilled. Whilst we may be outweighed both in ships and men, we are the greater in heart and will. Pray God that He continues to hold us in his favour. For with His help we have all the advantage we should ever need."

Pitt nodded his amen to those words. "What may we do to assist?"

"We need victuals, we need water. But more so we have prisoners, some of whom have suffered severely and we must bring them ashore."

"What benefit do we derive should we do so?" It was a new voice. Slowly, Richard turned a disbelieving gaze into the pale eyes of the tall man who now addressed him. He looked with enquiring eye from above the rim of the pewter jar to gauge the avarice upon each face as with deliberation he slowly supped his ale.

"Aye, I support what Burley says," muttered another.

Richard, his anger plain to see, waited that it might subside before continuing.

"Aboard the hulk is that which we need for victory — gentlemen — surely victory is your greatest reward?" He paused, as if in doubt, then to continue. "Burley, your name, sir, is Burley?"

"Indeed, sir and what on't?"

"I trust sir," deliberately Richard toyed with the hilt of his poniard that they might see. "I trust sir 'tis an English victory, you seek?" The latter words with emphasis. "For on perfect authority am I told that there is one of that same name, Burley, and of this town, who, a traitor to his country, now sails on the side of Spain." A silence. "Would that traitor, a Captain Richard Burley, be kin of thine?"

"How dare you sir!"

"Very easily, and I am always at your service." Richard gave a mocking bow.

"I will stay no longer to be insulted thus within the bounds of the town that I have served so long!" He turned abruptly to fling open the door and slam it in his wake.

"I am sorry Master Keigwin but you have wounded him before his peers. For indeed there are kin that he would wish to disown. The wounded bull is the one to be most feared."

"There it is, Mayor Pitt." Richard sadly shook his head. "The truth has no respect for feelings and often hurts the more. My apologies gentlemen. Yes, there is that aboard of which we are in dire need to ensure the tide of war runs in our favour."

"What is that?"

"Powder and shot, sir, powder and shot. More valuable than gold itself. I am asked that you direct that all assistance be given to ensure that from this carrack and any other that we may take, all powder and shot is sent swiftly to our fleet. And, sir, that you order that all ships attend and carry such they may."

The lazy figure of the one-eyed man leant against the wall, and stopped stropping his dagger upon the rubbing stone, to watch the tall man leave the house. There seemed anger in his steps. He shook his head in puzzlement and rubbed his thumb across the blade's edge. Satisfied, he slid it into the top of canvas leggings, where his hand might readily reach. He looked about. No other in sight. What would Master Richard wish? At a distance that was discreet he followed the hastening figure.

Martin rose from bended knees to punch the air in glee, to toss and with other hand, catch the ornate key. Surely this was the one, the only one to marry with those mighty locks. There was no one about. Teek was entrusted that should be so, all were at their duties, stripping that which might benefit the *Golden Hind:* cordage and cannon. Others were too ill to care. With but little light to guide him, Martin fumbled his way forward into the pointed bows. Each lock he felt with fingertips and fed the key. Each yielded to the twist of iron. Carefully he raised the lid and gingerly delved beneath. Coin tinkled to his touch. He looked about, held his breath and listened lest there be strangers hidden in the dark, but all he heard was the lapping of the water slewing in the bilges. None was there in that dark corner to witness the smile that briefly lit his face.

The cosy mummer's mask was dropped, gone was the benign, concerned disguise that hid the inner man and would lure the unwary into a false move. Richard watched the transformation with quiet amusement as Mayor Pitt gave his orders with an authority and precision that denied discussion. "This man would almost match my father." He thought unto himself. "I must be chary lest I make false move."

"Come, Richard, now all are gone about their duties, it would please me if you join me in a pipe and another jar of ale."

"I should be returning, but since all I sought is now in place . . ."

"So be it." Pitt reached to ring a silver bell that summoned the serving maid. "Fetch our finest ale for our guest and I wish your mistress to present herself." He turned to Richard. "Sadly I am a widower, but I am blessed with a daughter, my only child and boon companion. You may speak freely before her, for we have nothing that is secret which might separate she from me."

Light footsteps trod the corridor without. A gentle tap upon the door. The Mayor turned the handle to admit a maiden as comely as he was portly.

"My daughter, Jane." The pride was evident in his voice. "Our visitor, Richard Keigwin of Mousehole. Master of the barque that towed that hulk of Spain which now lies off the Nothe."

Richard chuckled and raised a hand. "Not so, sir, not quite so! Mistress Jane, your servant." Jane gave hint of curtsey in response to bow.

" 'Tis my nephew is the Master. I being merely both fisherman and merchant for my father. Yet am I required to serve with our fleet in times of danger."

"And the name of your nephew is?" A cautious note had entered Pitt's voice. Richard laughed aloud and raised his ale in salute to his host: "You have guessed aright, by Jupiter, in truth you have sir!"

Now the Mayor and daughter briefly locked glances, as Pitt raised his brows and shrugged his shoulders in puzzlement and Jane gave sweet smile as her response.

"Yes indeed, sir, the barque is the *Golden Hind* and her Master is Tom Flemyng."

"But there is a warrant for piracy!"

"Yet now he is reprieved; why else would he be entrusted with the urca?" Briefly Richard told of what had transpired.

"Now all is changed and he become a hero?"

Richard smiled and nodded his agreement. "Yet still he is a privateer! As are so many of our fleet. Thus does the King

105

of Spain make contribution to the wages of the seamen that fight against him!"

Pitt held his jar of ale in both plump hands and looked with enquiry at his daughter. "Jane, both a merchant and a privateer?"

She raised her chin and wrinkled her delicate nose as if to scent the air, and turned to Richard. "Sir, methinks my father has sniffed the smell of trade!"

The Mayor looked into his ale, then raised his head to look thoughtfully at Richard.

"Your ship and your prize lie anchored, safe within our waters. The waters of Weymouth. Thus are dues payable to my town."

Richard opened his mouth but the Mayor raised a forefinger to quell the interjection.

"However, we are at war, thus must we render all assistance that we may. I know where my duty lies, but there are those of Melcombe Regis would take issue on this point, Burley being perhaps but one. There is that aboard the Spaniard which we have long sought, and been denied by the frugality of our Government. Cannon for our defence. Thus I would ask that you leave aboard the carrack that which will benefit this town."

"The ship is torn asunder and might well sink. She needs ten men to man her pumps. We have but little time and so few men to spare. Thus we can carry only a small part of that which our Lord Howard needs so greatly, the ball and powder of which I spoke."

"What of gold and silver?"

Richard gave an earnest response. "As I have remarked, near all was taken by the Spaniards. We have had no time to make a proper search."

"No time sir? Nonsense sir! A privateer with no time for plunder?"

There was serious air beneath the outward chaff. Now was the turn for Richard to shrug his shoulders.

"Wish that we had, but most was removed before our fleet could arrive. But now we must return to our duties, or bear the brunt of John Hawkyns' tongue — or worse!"

"Then hark to me," Pitt tapped jewelled finger on

Richard's chest. "You and yours merit a reward for that which you have done, as indeed does Weymouth, for we have made our contribution too! To tow that ship through such hazards is a feat deserving of recompense. Let no stranger come aboard privateer or prize save he come with my authority. Allow no man, no man I say, except those you trust, to venture below decks. Come dawn tomorrow, we shall have that which I have commanded, fishing boat and fly boat to load with powder and shot. Keep them busy so there is no time for mischief, then escort them to the fleet that the cannon may be fed. Look not for gold or silver. When you have departed, men of my choosing will man the pumps. Men of my choosing will seek for any treasure which may have been overlooked." He paused that his words might be well heeded, supping his ale before continuing, "Depend upon me to make proper account of all that is found, and to set aside each man's share as practice does dictate. Then to take her cannon for our town. We shall await your safe return, when I would wish once more to delight in your company and learn of your adventures, ah, and meet with this Tom Flemyng."

"That, sir, is a generous gesture. Now if you please I must hasten."

"One further moment of your time. Burley is of Melcombe Regis and I, I am of Weymouth. Whilst we are now one, 'tis a false marriage. There is still deep distrust and enmity between us. I am afeared of his mood. You have not yet done with him. I know the man too well, keep careful watch. Guard against him lest he steal that which he may."

"Thank you, sir, for your warning and your courtesy."

"A fraction longer." Jane placed her hand upon her father's arm that she might speak for both. "I pray you, sir, do not think too ill of Weymouth or her folk. Many of our men are gone to sea or stay on land to fight. Our ships too are sent to join the fleet." She counted upon her slender fingers. "The *Katharine*, the *Heathen*, the *Golden Ryall*, and the *Bark Sutton* too is gone!" Her eyes filled with tears. "All left from here to serve their country. All are not, sir, of the same ilk as Richard Burley!"

With embarrassment he looked into the brimming eyes.

107

"Mistress Jane. No matter how well tended is the garden, amongst even the most favoured blooms a weed will on occasion grow. If Weymouth be that garden, then surely have I been privileged to observe the most beauteous of her blossoms. That will be the Weymouth I recall."

With bow and doff of cap he departed into the street. Pentreath to follow, close behind.

The skiff cast off, to row out of the harbour toward where the barque had rafted alongside the great hulk that towered above her.

"Master Richard, free to speak, sir?"

Richard nodded.

"There was a gentleman left the house, sir."

"Yes, I know."

"Seemed he was peeved, sir, and in ill-humour."

Richard smiled for it was patent Pentreath wished to draw from him the reason why. Thence to tell and romance upon the tale in the darkness of between decks. He had the story-teller's gift, being renowned for the tales he could relate.

"I believe he was somewhat distressed."

"I took the liberty of following him shortways."

Richard leant toward him the better for to listen. "Did you now, and saw you ought of interest?"

"He boarded a punt that sculled him across the river to the far side. That is to Melcombe Regis, others awaited him there. But not gentlemen, sir, a ruffianly crew." He grinned. "More my sort, sir. Rapscallions all!"

"Would there were more ruffians of your ilk, Pentreath. They could crew for me any day. Was that all you discovered?"

"That was all, sir." The helmsman leant back within the skiff. Content to please his master and banter with the rowers.

"Lower away, 'tis the last." Teek called to the barque beneath. Anxious hands steered the barrel safely to rest upon the deck.

"Praise God. We can hold no more," Tom murmured to himself.

Sailors struggled to manhandle the cask within the lower deck as their Master directed so that the barque might be trim and best balanced in the water. He must take care to note and mark that which held the coin secure beneath the cover of gunpowder, that which Martin and Teek had long sweated to conceal. One mistake when unloading and a yeoman of the powder would earn a surprising rich reward!

As wearily they supped, Richard told his tale. "So there it is; he of the beautiful daughter will ensure that we even take our share of that which we deliberately leave behind."

"Do we tell John Hawkyns?"

"Aye, Tom, for there is honour amongst thieves. Moreover I fear his wrath should he discover and we will benefit by his gratitude. Besides, all will be seen to be divided in the proper manner and thus none dares to suggest we have had first pickings. Now, what of the key, Martin?"

"I will return it to near where it was found, that when they search it may readily be discovered.

"Yet still must we remain on guard. Soon you will wish to cast off." Richard looked at his nephew.

"Aye, the wind is freshening, the tide on the ebb and the prize will ground. I favour deeper anchorage half a cable off."

"Tom, give me the men and I will take watch. You two have laboured hard. Pentreath has done little and is handy in a fight. Teek will take his turn on the *Golden Hind*, thus will you take two watches on the hulk, whilst we share three."

"So be it. But go well armed, Richard."

"Aye, and if you hear a musket shot then come to my aid. But I have a plan."

Low water, gently as a broody goose upon her nest, the *San Salvador* settled upon the mud bank, but all about her, water.

" 'Tis we that have stole the golden egg," Richard grunted at his joke.

Alone, upon the shattered stern castle where once had been the mizzen-mast, his eyes pierced the dark for danger. Soon that black band of clouds would snuff the lantern of the moon. He watched as the moon-burnished, riffling wavelets of the bay disappeared in the darkness. Sound was now the only sense upon which he could depend. That, and the instinct of the Celt. He willed his ears to listen, to capture any noise that differed from the gentle, rhythmic breaking of the distant surf.

"Master Richard," a whispered voice, " 'tis I, Pentreath, come to take my turn."

"Hush, Pentreath, tell your men keep low, lest they be seen. Hark!"

"I hear nothing."

"There 'tis again."

"What?"

"Ssh!" Silence awhile.

"I hear now."

"What do you hear, Pentreath?"

"That which I have oft-times used. Muffled oars."

"How many?" A long pause.

"Cannot tell, three boats?"

"How many men?"

"Six, eight to each?"

"Will they land under the stern-castle?"

"Aye, to climb upon the rudder, thence through her gaping wounds."

"As I too had hoped."

From below came the sound of bumping, wood against wood, oars being shipped, a whispered voice calling for quiet.

"All men ready, Pentreath?" asked Richard.

"Aye, Master Richard," the hushed reply.

"A moment, and the moon will show again." Richard raised his head above where once had been the stern gunwhale, to peer down into the dark water. Then he made his way along the line of men, stooping as he issued the hushed command.

"Aim well. Have you them in sight?"

"Aye," came the quiet response.

Two fingers into his mouth, a screeching whistle tore the air. Each from on high dropped the burden of his cannon ball, to crash and shatter the planking of the boats beneath.

110

Oath and screams, short lived as came splashes from below and laughter from above.

The intruders threshed the water to make their way to where the third boat lay and hauled aboard, to safety.

Thursday 4th August. The sun rose brightly, without hint of the foul weather of earlier days. As Pitt had promised, fishing and fly boats in steady stream came out the harbour. Too small to fight, but with their part to play. Gathered about, to nestle close to what once was the proud *San Salvador*, to lade with powder and with shot and, when replete, stand off.

Teek cajoled and pleaded, sweated and strained. Another barrel lowered, to be swallowed by the boat below.

"As little pigs, they suckle at the old sow," he grunted to himself.

From across calm waters came the grumble of distant cannon.

"We must on our way, Martin, lest English cannon go starving for our shot." Tom was anxious.

"Aye. Leave all now to Pitt. He will not fail."

At the given signal, anchors were raised. Canvas blossomed as yardsmen hauled upon the halliards.

The little fleet of laden boats set forth before a luffing westerly that they might succour their larger brethren. Under harsh St. Albans Head they sailed, past the white cliffs of Anvil Point, to run across the bay. Standing off from the towering ironstone of Hengistbury Head, out from the rough waters of the ledge.

Atop the aft-castle of the *San Martin*, anguish mounting, he watched the *Gran Grifon* fall astern the fleet. Flagship of the merchantmen. She had all canvas raised, yet in those light airs she could no longer maintain her station, her broad beam could make but little way against the running tide. An oath upon his lips and prayers within his heart, as the *Revenge* came from out the pack to pounce upon the laggard.

111

Burley cracked his knuckles in despair, as starboard broadside thundered into the hapless Spaniard. Past her prey Drake came, to go about, that larboard-side cannon would not be denied. Sharp crack as musketeers amongst the rigging took their aim and fired to take a further toll.

Would that Sidonia join the fray in recompense for the lost *Rosario*. Pride. Where was his Admiral's pride? At last!

The *San Martin* slowly went about. Her topsails struck in challenge, on course to where Drake plied. Now to engage! Now the flagship of Spain would strike the pirate Drake, whose very soul embodied all that which he detested. Enemy of his King! Enemy of his faith! He ran his right finger down his breastplate and then across in likeness of the crucifix. He prayed for battle, that he might prove himself before his God.

The coward! Damnation to his enemies! Oh the frustration. Would the English never fight as men? Through the haze of bitter tears he followed the retreat of the *Revenge*, away from her stricken foe. Taunting. Out of range of Spanish cannon.

" 'Oh those who fight and run away, may live to fight another day.' A pox upon him. would they but fight this day!"

The two fleets lay becalmed, the breeze of the morning now but a memory. Two hundred ships floated as flotsam at the whim of the tide.

All powder and shot was now unladen to where it was most needed. Excepting those quintals required to remain on board.

Flemyng had climbed aboard the flagship *Ark Royal* to make his report, as Hawkyns had so bid. For the taking of the payship was of major import and must be addressed in proper form.

"Sir Edward Hoby, your servant, sir." He gave half bow, Tom returned, taking a quick glimpse about the cabin, would that his might contain such comforts. But what manner of man was this? Knighted by his Queen, doubtless of same age as Richard, yet to reach his thirtieth year. Fine clothes, clean shaven save for the fluff above his lip. More the stuff of scholar than of soldier. If so, how came he by the bruised and inflamed scars that so enlarged his cheek?

"Thomas Flemyng, of the barque *Golden Hind*, come to render my account of the taking of the *San Salvador*," he said.

"Tom, is that what you are called?"

"Aye, by my friends."

"Then Tom it shall be, since friends we shall become," he replied in easy, educated tones. "I trust you have no objection?"

Tom made no response, other than to himself: be wary, Tom, be wary, lest his smooth tongue baits the trap.

"I am secretary to my kinsman, Lord Howard, and wish to note the detail of your taking of the Spaniard." He paused, his head cocked upon side. "Are you not the pirate of whom I have heard tell? Yet, so young to be employed in such a fashion?"

Tom blushed in anger. "Privateer, sir and what I lack in years I have in learning and experience."

"Tush. No need to bandy words, sir. For remember if you will, I address you as my friend. By your deeds you are in good grace and if there was misdemeanour, now it is forgot. I do but tease, sir."

Tease or not, Tom knew he must take care, and not rise to this man's chaff. Had not Hoby placed him on his guard and let it be known he knew his past?- Now his turn to disconcert, to thrust and then to parry. To fence with words.

"An honourable wound, sir?"

The secretary paused. "Upon my cheek? Damn me, no sir. A skirmish of the bedchamber not one of the sea, and come to think on't, sir, directly of your causing."

"The bedchamber? My causing?" he said in question form that begged Hoby should continue.

"Ah, but she was a fickle maid." He laughed in genuine amusement whilst fingering his swollen cheekbone. "Indeed it was a tavern at your harbour-side that it came about. I was armed with a warrant for your arrest whilst on a commission for the Queen." He continued without pretence at his connections. "Making report on our preparedness to meet King Philip's threat, I was seeking to know which ships we might have for our defence. At the tavern where I was lodging there was a comely serving wench."

"Daughter of the landlord. Her name is Rebecca."

"I recall not the name but her form, ah, the sculpture of her breasts still lingers in my mind."

"Say no more, sir, say no more," Tom laughed as Hoby continued to touch where the wound was tender. "But see you take care not to make mention of your triflings before my bosun."

"That is hardly likely."

"Maybe not, but beware. Should he learn 'twas you that tampered with his maid, surely he would feed you to the crabs."

"Ah, but she was inviting, and had she succumbed, I would risk the wrath of your bosun or twenty more besides, for it would be worth such dalliance, I do declare!"

"But for all your fine feather," Tom replied, a smile in his voice, "she failed to yield to your advance?"

"To seduce is but a question of timing," he lectured with wagging finger. "Timing and opportunity."

"How so?"

"When the maiden heifer is a'bellowing for the bull, she cares not overly whose red rod it be, as long as she be served."

"Ah, but maids are not as beasts and must be wooed. Leastways," Tom grinned, "those of Mousehole must, as you yourself have proved!" Tom warmed to his companion.

"I do but partly jest, for there is many a fine lady graces the court that has long forgot the meaning of the virtue that Cornish maid possesses. Your bosun has good fortune in the love of such as she. I trust he is young and strong?"

Tom nodded his reply.

"Then feed him well on good red meat for when she has the taste she will demand all such strength he has."

"Shell fish, sir! Oysters from our Cornish coves!" They laughed aloud together. A bond was forged and Tom was made at ease.

"Now to business." Hoby pointed to a stool and they sat down each side of an oaken table, Hoby taking quill in hand. "Were you given orders?"

"Aye, sir, by my vice-admiral, John Hawkyns."

"Who is also your kinsman?"

"Ours is but a remote relationship."

"To be Cornish and at sea together is sufficient, for all of you are pirates. And related? Then 'tis an even stronger tie." He laughed that Tom might not take offence.

Tom told of all they had achieved. The part that Richard Pitt, Mayor of Weymouth, would play, to ensure that whatever remained on board the hulk would reach its proper destiny. Hoby made his careful notes, punctuated on occasion by doubting grunt, then patent disbelief as the story was unfolded. Gradually his doubts were overcome as positive answer parried probing question until all had been revealed — except that which was concealed beneath the gunpowder, safe stored aboard the *Golden Hind*.

All enquiry ended. Hoby relaxed to lean back upon his stool.

"It is apparent to me, Tom Flemyng, that you are no bumpkin."

"Indeed sir, I pray not, whilst I am of the west, we too have men of learning. 'Tis the culture of the Celt."

Hoby raised his eyebrows in enquiry.

Tom laughed. "We relish debate, Sir Edward," he answered in explanation, "and thrive on controversy. Why, my father and brother are men of scholarship and learning, well read enough to surpass many a city intellect."

"I would welcome an evening in the company of such as they, uncluttered by court intrigue and the jostling for position."

"Then mayhap you will."

"Indeed, Tom, for should I need to know ought of Cornwall that is of confidence, I can call on you?"

"Indeed, sir, you may and in my absence, any of my family."

"Likewise, Tom, likewise. For 'tis good to have those about that one can trust, and so I feel safe within your company."

"That is a rare compliment, Sir Edward, for we are but newly met. Yet, I sense, we have more of common ground than the distance that separates us."

"And likewise, Tom, as I may call on you, so you on me.

115

If such influence I may have can assist your cause, provided it be just, then I shall be pleased to be of service."

And so the bond was made.

Chapter Seven

Friday 5th August. From haven and from harbour came the men of England. Little ships, big ships, to provision or to fight, willing to play their part. The two fleets lay apart. The English to replenish their armoury with the aid of that which came from Weymouth. The Spaniards, to lick their wounds that they might heal.

"See there, Teek, still more come to join with us. Makes one proud, not so?"

"Surely so, Master Martin; but 'tis difficult to command such a motley crew."

"Better one volunteer than ten men pressed."

"They come but to snatch their share of glory and hope for a share of booty."

"Curmudgeon!"

Teek turned to grin. "I do but jest. Who could feed those Spaniards such false intelligence as made them believe we would be defeated?"

"Those who believe only that which they want to hear."

"Aye, methinks that the Duke of Medina must now have cause for concern."

"But 'tis not yet won, Bosun. If he should link with Parma he could call a different tune; then it would be our turn to dance to it."

"But, Master Martin, he must still contend with the Eastern Squadron."

"Aye, Seymour and Wynter with Hollanders and all lie in wait ahead."

Tom's voice was heard. "What is that signal? A council."
Martin turned at the approach of his captain. "See, yonder

117

goes Hawkyn's skiff. And Frobisher."

Later, across the water, from the *Revenge*, came the sound of cheering. Another signal from the vice-admiral, a summons for his captains.

The skiff was lowered under the command of Teek and rowed in calm waters alongside the *Revenge*. A boarding ladder lowered, Tom followed his fellows aboard.

Directed by the ship's bosun he came to a great cabin, a sight that would dwell forever in his mind. Through the haze of tobacco, laughing, joking, he saw others of his ilk. Each, armed with a fine glass of wine or ale, was as richly attired as circumstance might permit. Rapier on left hip, poniard on right, they gathered about John Hawkyns, whose dour face lit with the warm smile of welcome as Flemyng made his entrance. He pushed through the throng toward his kinsman.

"Dubbed, Thomas! Dubbed by my Lord Howard. No longer Master Hawkyns! No longer will she be Katherine or Mistress Hawkyns. Eh Tom? Lady Hawkyns if you please. At last she will be satisfied." Tom had seldom seen him in such spirits. "Knighted, Tom!" he repeated.

"Deservedly so, Sir John. My heart-felt good wishes." Tom gave a small bow to his host and a servant placed a glass within his hand. He raised the wine. "I raise my cup, sir, and drink your health and that of Lady Hawkyns."

Sir John made acknowledgement with his own glass lifted.

"Others too, Tom. Frobisher and Howard. I tell you, spirits are high. Why, even Beeston of the *Dreadnought* and him of eighty-nine summers!" He sipped to savour both the wine and the moment.

The old sea-dog placed his arm about Tom's shoulder in rare gesture of affection. Then softly, that none other might hear, "How fare the riches? Enough to fit my new found rank, eh?"

"Safe and sound, Sir John," Tom quietly returned. "All safe and sound."

"And your share?"

"Well, Sir John, mine too is fit for a knight of the realm!"

Together they laughed aloud at the shared secret.

"Gentlemen," the hubbub ceased at Hawkyn's raised voice. "Lord Seymour has been sent to join with us. You witness our forces strengthen daily. Thank God, Tom Flemyng has replenished our ball and powder. Yet all is not over. Should Parma link his soldiers with the ships of Medina Sidonia . . . " His voice trailed as he shook his head at such a prospect. "But we shall pen those sheep of Spain and we shall make sport! Keep careful watch. Now return to your commands and await my signal."

Saturday.

"See how grows the pack of English dogs."

"Mongrels, your Grace, naught but common curs."

"Yet common curs can bite or, when confronted, turn and run with tucked-in tail. No news of Parma, Burley, no news. We will soon be desperate for provisions. Domingo Ochoa has been sent ashore, charged to entreat with Parma and to bring round shot and fly boats for our needs, for there is little left within our lockers."

"I wish not to heap on further misfortune, but should the weather worsen yet again," Burley paused, "our soldiers are cramped below. Poorly victualled, and this swollen sea sickens them greatly. They will weaken further lest we find calmer waters. Else they be unfit to fight."

Through the drizzle's murk the command came. A council aboard the *San Martin*. With anxious eyes Burley noted his Admiral was confused, which way would his decision go? Wavering and quavering before the onslaught of the proffered council, as wise as the last man to speak. Then the advice of the English pilot was sought. Stucley, he who knew every current. Every channel. Ahead, he told, were the shoals and ill-favoured currents of Flanders. No haven there. No harbour. There lurked Seymour and his squadron of the east. Waiting to pounce.

The decision was made, there was no other option. At Calais, the greater ships would veer off course, drop anchor in a seaward arc, a shield to the lesser vessels anchored closer to the shore. With such a sudden deception mayhap the English fleet would sail past, and thus leave Spain to windward, and grant to them the advantage of the weather-gauge. The combined fleets of England would then be to their fore,

119

giving Sidonia the chance to attack on such terms he could decide.

Into the wind they lay, sturdy wooden walls of Spain, protection from the English cannon.

Through the northern haze of evening topsails came to view. Seymour, Admiral of the narrow seas, come to join forces with his Lord High Admiral, announcing his presence with a broadside.

Through the damping dusk Burley saw the English pinnace. Sails filling in the light airs as she left the lee of her flagship. "Would that I might know the message she carries," he thought unto himself.

The orders were written, signed with a flourish by Edward Hoby, to be delivered to where the *Angel of Hampton* lay, command of Lawrence Prowse, then to John Young of the *Bear*, part of the Western Fleet. Time-worn ships, sea battered; yet soon their time would come, their part to play, to take the centre stage.

The message delivered, Pentreath took her about, to feel the deck heel beneath him as the wheel turned and sails filled, as the *Golden Hind* returned to her post, off the *Victory*, to await further orders.

The English fleet were anchored off, outside the range of Spanish cannon, watching and waiting, daring the Armada to break and run beneath the clearing sky.

Midnight was approaching. What was this cortege that slipped so silent by, no lanterns, no sound? Eight ships of England. Teek gave an unvoiced cheer. Ships in line astern eased their way toward the crowded fleet of Spain.

Fretfully Burley paced the quarter-deck, his soldier's senses warned of danger. It was too quiet. The soft slap of the sea, the occasional order shouted from a pinnace, one of the screen of little ships, first line of defence; the sigh of the wind through the shrouds, the low voice as a sentry made report, was all that broke the eerie silence of the night.

Above, from the masthead, a sudden shout of alarm. He

forced his eyes to strain into the darkness. Screams and shouts of terror all about.

One, two, six, eight glowing embers pricked above the water. Fire ships kindled. Laden with combustibles. Old spars, cordage. Sails besmeared with pitch and wild fire. Fire ships sweeping toward them. Ember became blaze. Angels of death, helms lashed, wafting upon them aided by west wind and spring tide. Fire, the fear of every seaman.

"God's curses upon them," Burley roared aloud.

Havoc. Panic and confusion, as galleon slipped anchor and galleass cut cable. The protective arm of the wooden wall was broken, scattered in disarray, as each made way as best they might for the safety of the open sea.

Monday 8th August. The wind rose with the dawn and lightning flickered as Burley cast his eyes across the heaving grey waters. Where was it gone, the invincible Armada? Scattered about the surface of the sea!

Near the distant shoals a galleass wallowed, surely the *San Lorenzo*. Her rudders earlier damaged: the capitana with treasure aboard, unable to prevail against dual onset of rising wind and tide.

Thanks be to God the *San Martin* and her four galleons were now safe anchored. But what of the other ships? From the bows a recall gun was fired.

Trumpets pealed their orders. From the foretop of the *Ark Royal* proudly streamed the Standard of England. Dripping anchors were slowly raised, and canvas filled as the English fleet took up formation for impending battle.

"What think you Lord Howard is about?" Martin pointed to where the flagship led the squadron towards the great galleass, now tip-tilted, careened upon the shoals.

"It seems he goes to take what he so far lacks, a prize! To Drake the *Rosario*, to Hawkyns the *San Salvador*! That is a rare great galleass that has grounded. Steady as you go, helmsman. Follow in the wake of Sir John. Take heed of no other."

121

f

He pointed to where the *Victory* sailed, the flag of St. George flying from her masthead.

Tom gave commands. "We go to engage. Richard, send me the bosun. Make sure the gun decks are prepared."

"Aye, Captain," replied his uncle with quick smile.

"Teek, to your locker. Raise our Cornish pennants to the main top and fly those from the *San Salvador* from the starboard halliard, then await my signal, 'tis time we played our part. Be ready to change course as I may direct."

Teek grinned at the prospect of action and touched a forefinger to his stocking cap. "Let those galleons know the stuff of Cornishmen, eh Captain?"

Tom nodded. His attention lay ahead where the flotilla sailed in line, anxious lest they lose their station.

Ever closer came the *Revenge*. Pray God she would close that they might grapple! But Burley doubted his prayers would be heeded. Now but half a musket shot away, once more his men were roused, hooks ready to be swung.

From her foretop flew the flag of England: the red cross of St. George. Drake himself had come to challenge the Duke of Medina. Eager hands gently swung the grappling irons ready to sling overboard, to clutch the Englishman where'er they might. To clasp and hold, then haul together that they might board.

Temper overcame frustration, the *San Martin* shuddered at the impact of the shot as the *Revenge* unleashed her broadside. Then the heel of the recoil, as Spanish cannon replied in kind and English ships sheered off toward the open sea, in pursuit of other prey.

"Cannon ready and primed." Richard called his replies, "See there, Martin, Frobisher has struck his topsail and goes to engage."

"There is no love 'twixt him and Drake, he intends to show what Sir Francis starts, Frobisher will finish."

"Or mayhap he too seeks a prize? See, 'tis the Spanish flagship, has Drake left glory for the Yorkshireman?"

The *Triumph* lay near enough alongside. Yet not close enough! Broadside roared on broadside. Muskets cracked and took their toll. In the shelter of the gunwhale Burley crouched; Spars and rigging fell about him, gunsmoke and rain showers conspired to cast a pall above the threshing sea, grey cloud hung low above the masthead. Nature had made her mood in keeping with the carnage.

Each musketeer aimed arquebus at his enemies. Take aim! Fire! Temper overcame frustration, as curses were thrown across the water and returned, so close beside were they.

He raised his head. Blessed relief. Gunfire heeded, Spanish pride responded, other ships had come to their Admiral's aid, but punishment such as this could not be long endured. Spanish voices shouted challenges to the Cornishmen to fight close in. A cheer was the reply as round shot struck home from the *Victory* and her squadron. They were close to the kill, for Spanish powder and ball was near exhausted, no longer could they return the cannonade.

Was it answer to their prayers or God's anger at the foolishness of men? The great rolling swell heaved in ominous omen, beneath heavens black with anger. Thunder's roar drowned the sound of cannon as lightning flashed in further portent of unremitting danger. Rain pelted in horizontal squalls as the south-west wind became a gale, and the English fleet called off their action.

Blessed relief. Now could they escape as best they may.

A council was called and Burley summoned to attend, that Sidonia might report unto his captains. With the Armada so long delayed, Parma had dispersed his soldiers for want of provisions. Flat-bottomed boats hurriedly built of green timbers were warped, twisted and unseaworthy. Too close confined, his men had contracted the fever, he could give no assistance.

Thus they must sail northwards. The gathering English fleets behind, both east and west united. Seymour and Drake combined.

With ball and powder gone they could no longer stand and fight. Northwards, only northwards. With English pilots aboard to set the course. Around the ragged coast of Scotland must they track and then along the alien shores of Ireland, thence to the Spanish coast as quick and best they might.

Yet wind and sea conspired to drive them ever shorewards. Clearly could the foam breakers be seen, beating in rhythmic motion on the sand shoals.

He heard the fearful tones of leadsmen, calling the ever-decreasing depth beneath their keel. It was certain. The flag-ship must surely founder. With primary anchors cast loose at Calais, lesser hooks could find no purchase, only dragging in the shifting sands beneath the sea.

Soon, mused Burley, all record of their being would be gone. As if they never were. His thoughts turned to escape.

A messenger came with a summons to attend upon his Admiral, where others of his rank were gathered. They listened in the presence of their priests, as Sidonia made known his thoughts. He declared he had made his peace with God, shriven by his chaplain and adjured all should likewise be prepared. They too must pray at this time of direst need for Him to intercede. With anxious eyes Burley looked upon his Admiral. Was there nothing which could be done? So did he join with others to implore the Duke to board a pinnace whilst time allowed and thus save himself. So did they prevail but without success. Sidonia would not do so, rather would he die in defiance of his foe.

"God alone, my friends, will deliver us," he paused, "if that so be His wish."

In desperate straits Burley attempted a further ploy, "If your Grace refuses to be saved, what of our blessed banner? I must protest, your Grace, lest it fall into the hands of heresy."

But Sidonia would only give wan smile and shake of head in gesture of dismissal.

They knelt to pray that God might heed their plight. Had not the elements aided their enemies since first the venture was begun? They prayed God to deliver them from the heretics, and the threatening surf in order that they may continue in His work.

There came a crack of canvas from above; a hint of a heel, a slight shudder through the ship. Burley raised his head and

124

crossed himself. He and others gained their feet, to jostle and make topsides upon the aft-castle and clutch the mizzen shrouds, lest they stumble on the heaving deck. Shouted commands and whistles were heard amidst cries of praise.

A miracle! Prayers were answered. God had spoken. The gale subsided.

A fresh wind sprung from the southern quarter to blow them north into the open seas. Ships swung round. Dripping anchors were raised, sails shaken out, as they headed for safety. The hungry shoals of Flanders left behind with appetites unsated.

North they sailed coursed by the English fleet, some eighty ships of Spain so Burley counted. Was it but three months since they had departed? Three long months ago, when there had been one hundred and thirty of their number?

It was Thursday, the eleventh day of August when the Duke of Medina Sidonia called a council of the captains.

Once more Burley was to listen to the threats his fellows made, to turn again and face the English foe and reach for the hand of Parma.

With cannon that could not be fed? Better round the cold coast of Scotland. Keep off the rugged shores of Ireland, lest you fall prey to their twin evils, the malice of the hidden rocks or the vengeance of the Protestant army. Make west, far into the ocean then south-east to the safety of their homeland. The course was set.

The north wind ordained that which they must do. Their heavy ships could not steer so close the wind as those of England, and thus to go about, they would make but little headway.

"See, battered as they are, still do they not lack for courage."

"Their flagship falls back."

"Ah, and has struck her topsail."

"By St. George, Hawkyns will accept the challenge!"

"He is too wily a fox. Why should he expend scarce ball when seas and rocks will serve instead? Besides, chance

125

shot could provide them with some solace. We have lost but one ship and that of little consequence. Why sink more? 'Twould be foolish to engage at this stage of the game."

"Ah, Tom, and has it not been resolved that come the Frith we shall return? I now long for Cornwall."

" 'Tis true I do suppose. For their ships are riddled by our cannons, and must leak horrendously. They are not made for the waters they will encounter. May God give mercy to them. They have had no respite. You recall how pitiful was the *San Salvador*? That was before shot was fired. What must it be, crammed 'tween decks in those sickening seas? Soldiers, never been afloat before. No food. The fever. The sickness. The vomit. Ugh!" He shook his shoulders at the thought.

"And never to have fired their muskets or swung their swords in anger."

"May He have mercy on them."

"Had they linked with Parma would they have been merciful to us?"

"I pray God we shall never learn the answer to that riddle."

"Amen."

Monday 22nd August. At last! To anchor in safety. They of the western fleet lay in the lee of the downs, off the coast of Kent, betwixt Deal and the Goodwin Sands, to await a shift in the wind that would waft them westwards through the narrow seas to the broader waters beyond: and home.

For now they must take advantage of the delay to change their ballast and pump their bilges, for the water they had shipped was fouled and would foment the fever. Damp broom was burned that the smoke might cleanse. Richard bargained with the hovellers that plied from their boats, that they would bring sweet water and fresh victuals.

Under the vigilant eye of Teek, men set-to to make good the damage. Wild seas, strong winds and shot had wreaked their share of harm.

Now must Tom make his reckoning. An inventory of loss and damage. From the jotting he had made, Martin recited to him the measure of the injury for which to indent,

126

that the costs might be recovered.

Quill in hand, Tom made precise notes as his uncle called to him. Cordage, lengths lost and cost. Masts and spars broken or splintered. Anchors that fouled in a rocky sea-bed, and so were cut and cast away. An account of money. His money. To victual and to pay his men. How he did detest this clerking. Rather would he hold a sword than the wing feather of a goose! He paused and lifted up his head, but tonight he would be jubilant, for he was required to attend aboard the *Revenge*. Had not Sir Francis sent an invitation for an evening of account and celebration? All his peers to be present and sure to be in fine fettle. Was it not now their victory night?

The steep sides towered above as he clambered up the boarding ladder. From the poop deck a silver trumpet sounded a welcome aboard. He was immediately ushered to the Admiral's cabin.

The air was thick with pipe smoke. With pewter pots charged with ale, cordiality became joviality.

The privations of the previous weeks lay behind. Now they might relax awhile and relish their exploits, regaling each other with tales of prowess and of bravery. Deeds lost in the smoke of battle were recaptured and embellished with the ale. Chaffing in friendly merriment.

A figure eased through the throng, sturdy yet commanding. Sir Francis Drake came to Tom's side. Alert brown eyes fixed in questioning look.

"My cousin Hawkyns tells of the strange tale of the *San Salvador*. I would wish to hear it from your lips, Tom Flemyng." Then louder. "I pray you to listen. Whilst we all may have stories to relate, there is none so uncanny as that which Flemyng is to tell. Come sir, come we wish to hear."

An awkward silence as around him his fellows were crowding, now the chatter had ceased and Tom had centre stage.

"You are under your Admiral's command, Tom. Steer a straight course as I have always bid you." It was Hawkyns who spoke and gave a wan smile with hidden meaning to his words.

Tom coloured, drank deep for the courage of the ale, then, in rich voice began to tell of how Sir John had ordered him aboard the wreck, to take her to safe anchorage.

" 'Twas not without difficulty, for my barque is of but fifty tons and the *San Salvador* some six hundred I do suspect. Water-logged and rent asunder, seams open, taking in water, stern-castle splintered and smouldering, her masts gone. A reeking wreck, and the crying and the moaning of the wounded and the dying." He shook his head upon his breast as he recalled the scene. "But, gentlemen, above all was the stench. 'Tis the smell of it all that lingers in my nostrils that I shall carry to the grave."

"Was she not the payship?"

"Aye, so later I was told. Yet was she well armed. Some twenty-five cannon did she carry. And men, near four hundred, soldiers mostly, as well as mariners, together with the Paymaster and his cohorts. Yet near half were killed, or drowned. For as they burned they threw themselves upon the waves." A pause, another draught.

"What of the cause?"

"That is a matter of amazement. For aboard, I did discover, had been a German gunner, and as was their custom he took his wife with him, perhaps in the likeness of a youth, for to smuggle a woman aboard was against the orders of the fleet."

"Was she discovered?"

"Aye, so 'twould seem. Perhaps it was the sickness of our short seas that in cleansing off the vomit she revealed her womanhood, I cannot tell, but discovered she was. It would seem that there was a captain aboard, the commander of a company of soldiers, Pedro de Priego by name, to whom her presence was reported."

All eyes were upon him as he sipped once more from a pot new charged. "Her husband was beaten by Priego who claimed the gunner was not aiming true. I wonder, that since he was of the German race could it be he was a follower of Luther? So desired not to see the Prince of Rome prevail. Thus might he deliberately fire, to miss?" Tom looked about him.

128

"Envisage the despair of the gunner, pressed to serve on board a ship of Spain, amongst those who could not speak his tongue." Drake added weight to the words of Flemyng, nodding for him to continue.

"Aye, sir. His wife betrayed and so it was believed de Priego presumed upon his rank, to take advantage of her womanhood."

"The 'droit de seigneur' some foreigners practise?"

"Yes sir, to become a plaything at the mercy of a Spaniard's whim. To be discarded when the novelty was worn, that others might savour her body. But, as for the gunner's act. The piece was awry, he claimed, consequence of wetting and therefore must be discharged. Within the cramped spaces of the gun deck anger and anguish were to combine and overcome his reason. He must avenge his honour and his God. His wife was despoiled by one of Rome! The cannon was fired. Some who bore witness were by a miracle saved. He deliberately plunged the port fire into a powder keg, then threw himself to the mercy of the seas. Keg after keg was fired, and the ship near completely lost."

"And doubtless would have been, without your skill." It was rare for Hawkyns to give such compliment.

Came a voice from the fringe. "But what of the treasure?"

"Treasure?"

"She was the payship of the Spanish fleet was she not?"

"She was relieved of men and ducats before she was taken."

"And there was no time to pick her clean, you Cornish pirate?"

"Sir, a Cornish pirate do you call me," slowly his hand went to the dagger at his waist. "Pray, do you insult, or flatter me? What is your intent?" He made mild enquiry. "Take care on your reply." Then in voice both loud and deep, "lest I spend the best blood of your belly!"

Drake's fingers flashed to grasp the wrist of his young captain. "Silence," he roared, then to Flemyng: "Not so hasty, my young fighting cock. You have won your spurs; now you must accept the banter of your fellows."

"Forgive me, sir."

"But found you treasure, Flemyng?"

Tom faced his Admiral.

"Sir, the orders I observed were strict and simple. The hulk must be taken to a place of safety. She was heavy laden with much needed shot and powder. There was but little time to make an exploration. I left her in the charge of Mayor Pitt of Weymouth town, a man not without honour, as I am told. Then with all haste did I return to the fleet with lesser boats in consort, all heavy, laden as we may to replenish the cannon. I only retained that which for myself was required."

"Aye, Sir Francis," Hawkyns spoke, "Tom Flemyng followed my orders in all respects. Mayor Pitt has undertaken to salvage that which he may and make a distribution in accordance with custom."

Tom nodded in agreement. The doubters were nearly satisfied.

The following day, he brandished quill once more. The clerking was near complete, thanks be to God. But his head was thick, the wine and ale were stronger than he had believed; however the evening had been a merry one, leastways that which he remembered.

Would that there were an interruption. A brief reprieve, for he was in no mood for figuring. As if in answer to a prayer, he became aware of a commotion without his cabin. Voices raised in anger.

Martin rose to fling wide the door. A tumble of men, three struggling figures in a heap. He plunged into the fray to hoist two seamen by their throats to hold them firm and pin them against the planking. The third was Teek, who slowly rose and brushed his knees.

"Thank you, Master Martin."

"What manner of nuisance is this, Bosun?" Flemyng enquired furiously.

"Begging your pardon, Captain." Teek touched his forehead to stammer his reply. "Thieving, sir."

"Who has stolen?" asked Flemyng, his anger mounting.

"Not me, Captain, not me!"

"Silence, Nankervis and stand you still. Bosun, stand back to the door, that Master Martin may release them. We will make discovery here and now. Who do you accuse?"

130

"The yardsman, Nankervis, sir."

"So be it. And Boase?"

"He is the one aggrieved."

"Did any bear witness?"

"Aye sir, Pentreath the helmsman."

"Then," testily, "fetch him hither that he may testify."

They waited until the bosun returned with helmsman.

"Pentreath, await outside on my orders."

"Aye, sir."

"Sir, sir!" One of the sailors spoke up.

"Silence, Nankervis. You shall be given fair chance."

"Yes sir . . ."

"Silence I say, or be put in chains, I care not which. Martin, here is my Bible. Boase will swear on't."

The sailor repeated Martin's words.

"Now, Boase, tell me of this affair and remember, God is your witness."

"Captain, I was full of gripes so Bosun gave me leave to go below. Upon my cot I lay, my head pillowed on my sack of sail cloth in which is all I have, honestly gotten and according to my due. My belly aching and eyes tight closed, seeming as asleep. Then I feel fingers fumbling, a hand untying . . ."

"Not mine, Captain, I swear . . ." Nankervis fell silent as Martin's fist thumped his ribs.

"Continue Boase."

"I turn, half-roused to roll over once more as if in slumber. Hands I feel again. I squint, eyes half open in the gloom, a figure looms above me. I makes a grab for him." He jerked a thumb where stood Nankervis, "and holds him by the wrist and yells that others may bear witness to my plight."

He paused a moment to see what effect his words had upon his captain, who returned unblinking stare. In less certainty Boase continued.

"Pentreath hears us and makes a grab for Nankervis, who hits him in the mouth. Bosun, hearing the struggle and noise withall, catches hold of me and Nankervis both. Threatens to feed us to the crabs and," he shrugged his shoulders, "here we be."

"Was aught taken from your sack?"

131

"No, Captain."

"Was the knot about its neck untied?" A pause. "Before God, Boase."

A seeming reluctance. "No, Captain."

"Nankervis." The prisoner raised drooped head. "Have you a question?"

"No," in sulking response.

Flemyng nodded in conclusion. "Bosun, admit Pentreath."

With doff of red stocking cap the helmsman entered. Under oath he swore to tell the truth.

"Did you witness Nankervis put his hand into the sack?"

"No, Captain."

"Did you witness Boase grip Nankervis by the wrist?"

"No, Captain. I saw little of the struggle, but heard Boase call for aid and accuse him," he pointed at Nankervis, "of stealing. I separates them and yank them to their feet, for they were wrestling on the deck. For my trouble one or other gave me this as present." He pointed to his lower lip, swollen and blue with bruise.

"Which one struck you?" A pause. "Remember your oath, Pentreath."

"I know my duty," responded Pentreath. "In truth, Captain, 'twas dark and with two pairs of arms flailing, I cannot tell for certain."

"Have you any more to add?"

Pentreath shook his head. "Then comes the bosun and that was all."

"Nankervis, have you aught to ask?"

The yardsman made a mumble.

"Yes or no?"

"No."

"No, Captain," Martin prompted.

"No Captain. Saving . . . "

"Saving what?"

"I am innocent, Captain." He reached out to place his knuckles upon the table to plead with his eyes.

"Stand up and render your account."

"My duty was ended. In my sack I have both knife and bone on which to scrimshaw. To while away the hours, Captain, as trinket for my Mam. In the gloom I dropped the bone close by where Boase lay. As I knelt down to retrieve it Boase grabbed me and cried aloud I was a thief."

"Why?"

"I know not, save Boase was dreaming and awoke at my presence, to start and believe he was robbed, Captain," and his voice rose, "I am of Pensans and others are of Mousehole." He stopped.

"Continue, Nankervis."

"They are of the Protestant faith whilst I am a Papist, as was my father before."

Tom waited that the yardsman might continue.

"I am loyal to our Queen, Captain. But they plot to render me discredit. Captain, I am innocent. I beg you to believe me. For I have taken nothing that is not mine and honestly gotten."

"Because I caught you by the wrist when you thought me asleep. Else you would have stolen my share of the booty," yelled Boase.

"Enough! With God's guidance I shall decide this matter. Bosun, I would see the sack Nankervis has and what may be hid therein. Take Pentreath as witness. And search about his berth that nothing is concealed close to." Fingers raised in salute, Teek and Pentreath went their way. Boase and Nankervis still stood before their captain, and glared upon each other.

Martin stood, broad back against the door, ever watchful, ready to part the men.

All was quiet save the creaking of the timbers and the scratch of the quill as Tom resumed his task.

A knock.

Martin stood aside as Flemyng looked up and called to enter.

"Have you seen within the sack, Bosun?"

"No. Captain."

Flemyng nodded his approval and rose. "Then empty it slowly that all may see." Upon the deck Teek spilled the contents. A heap of odds and ends. All that Nankervis possessed. Articles of meagre clothing and of toilet. He shook the sack and felt within, where from the bottom a kerchief tumbled, tied at all four corners. But sign of knife or scrimshaw there was none.

"Untie the knot."

Within the cloth were coins and an oval medallion. Christ figured upon one side and upon the other, the likeness of the Virgin Mary.

Flemyng raised questioning eyes.

"Emblems of my faith, Captain."

"Aye, and stolen from a Spanish corpse. Found you aught else, Bosun?"

"No, Captain."

"Then search him."

Cornall stepped forward, Nankervis lunged for the doorway, blocked by the daunting form of Martin, who in flowing movement spun the prisoner about to force his arm high behind his back. Left forearm locked tight around Nankervis' throat in choking iron grip.

"Search away, Bosun," Martin grunted whilst Teek felt for knife or hidden purse, but none was there to find.

A struggle. Martin held him ever tighter. Nankervis, his head now forced back, his body arched, chest thrust forward, that rent his worn shirt open on his breast.

"What is that thong about his neck?" Teek tore the cord that broke, loosening a golden ring to roll across the deck to lie at the captain's feet.

Tom reached down, to crouch, then hold a ring upwards to the light to catch and wonder at the lustre of its beauty. In an ornate setting of gold, a stone the size of a thrush's egg was held between his thumb and forefinger. He rose to proffer it where Martin might better see as he restrained the struggling man.

Flemyng returned to his chair. "Never did I suppose to see a black pearl exquisite to this degree." Upwards again he held the pearl to gaze in awe as Martin relaxed his hold on the now-sullen prisoner.

From a cupboard Tom took a small box covered in brass filigree of Moorish style. He placed the ring within and returned it to its place.

"Bosun, now know you aught of where the scrimshaw is?"

"No, sir."

"Nankervis?"

134

"Mayhap others have cast it overboard."

"The scrimshaw is your silent testimony of truth. Did you make good search, Bosun?"

"We looked about but no sign could we find."

"Nankervis, the cards are stacked against you. No scrimshaw. Yet a Spanish medallion from a dead man's throat. And a ring, a Spanish ring. A ring of great value, off a dead man's finger!" He paused, his eyes fixed upon the prisoner, who cast his downwards without response.

"A dead man aboard the hulk, when you were of the prize crew." He looked up at Martin who nodded in affirmation. "And all that was aboard to be divided in accord with custom?"

"Those were my orders, Tom. And I too have never seen this ring before," replied Martin.

"Anything to say, Nankervis?"

"Nothing, since I sense your mind is made. Yet I contend this is a conspiracy by those who wish me ill since I am a follower of Rome, but no traitor to my country or those with whom I sail. 'Tis they who will be damned. Not I. That ring is mine by right."

"What right?"

"If I told, you would not believe."

Flemyng listened to his words. Then paused in thought awhile.

"So be it, for to believe you I cannot. All is written against you, both human and dumb object. I find you guilty of a foul deed, that of attempting to take from your fellow sailor, and of stealing that which was to have been shared. You have betrayed their trust and the trust placed in you when serving on the hulk. The punishment is decreed for such an act. You will be held in chains until we are off Mousehole. Your hair will be shorn and boiled pitch poured over your head then to be covered in feathers. To congeal. Then shall you be towed astern, into the harbour and if not drowned, set free that all might know the form of man you are."

Nankervis shook as he envisaged his plight to be, whilst his captain pondered, to thoughtfully propose: "Or else I can, should I so desire, replace such punishment with a flogging."

The tan of his face was gone to grey. He shrugged free from Martin, who let him slip without restraint. Then, with dignity that all did note: "I have no guilt. For as my maker knows I have done no wrong in this regard."

Flemyng let him speak.

"I am an honest seaman and will not be so shamed." Then with a scream. "Flog me. Flog me you bastards and be damned." In quiet tones. "The guilt and the shame is upon your head and I pray that you and yours will be burned for the heretics you are." Then to Teek. "May you burn in the fires of Hell!" His voice was choked with a hiss as Martin's arm once more encircled his throat and staunched all further utterance.

The men gathered at the mainmast to witness the punishment. A sombre, silent circle that their captain addressed with recital of crime and punishment, this was an example of what would await should they be similarly tempted.

"Yet this punishment will suffice, none further will you inflict. Should a similar deed occur . . . " He paused and looked around the assembly and with shake of head, "the guilty one may expect less mercy."

His wrists were lashed above his head, his lean and muscled back was bared, his legs astride, braced to receive his punishment.

Flemyng stepped aside, the bosun was ordered to proceed.

Men, hardened by the sight of pain and bloodshed, could scarce forbear to wince at the song of the rope's end. Thirty times it swung, from bruise to graze and criss-cross cut, deep into the fragile flesh. Between each stroke came the muttered words of prayer, an appeal to Christ crucified. That he, Nankervis, be blessed with the faith, to bear his pain with dignity.

Later, alone in his cot. Tom's busy brain denied him sleep. It was lonely to command, to make decisions only a captain can make, lonely to convict, to be both judge and jury. Yet surely the man had been guilty? All evidence did point to it. Nankervis too was alone. No friends, no family to lend him support. Good seaman. Handy in a fight. A Papist, loyal to his country.

"Dear God, why do I doubt? 'Tis too late to be uncertain.

Yet these thoughts do nag me."

Tom reached for the cupboard, for the little box of filigree Fernandes had given upon his birthday. Nestling upon the velvet lining, caught in the moonlight gleam, the soft reflecting lustre of the black pearl. Many hours later, sleep overcame him.

In the morning the sun was easing through the haze to shine upon a sea of unruffled calm. Devotions were ended, they had broken their fast. The inventory was complete. Yet neither Tom nor Martin could adjust their mood of gloom. Tom looked upwards where gulls circled the masthead to scream their accusing cry. Why did he feel this sense of guilt? Of shame?

"Shake yourself, Tom. Do not brood so!"

"Aye, Martin and so I must. Yet could I but be sure."

"Nothing in life is certain. Only death is sure." He gave a hollow laugh. "And even in death we do not know which way our souls will fly, up or down. Yet that Nankervis is a thief there is no doubt on't."

"May be so, may be so. Yet can you sense the gloom about the ship? The men have no stomach for a flogging."

" 'Tis true. There should be jollity aboard. We have won a great victory and should rejoice. When duty is done, give the men ale. Let them sing and dance."

"Yes, my uncle." He rose and stretched. "That is then decided. We will have our celebration. A touch of merriment will not come amiss."

Dusk was falling as Nankervis stirred. Sleep had firstly overcome his pain, to nourish his battered body, but nothing could ease the hurt that burned within his brain. But he had made his plan. At the galley, midst ribald laughter, he had accepted the dregs they dished him, lumps of fat mutton without sign of flesh beneath, the skilly and the grease of which no other would partake. Some had he stowed within a rag. For he had need of it.

From top-sides came the sound of laughter, that he too should share. The patter of bare feet dancing, and the sound of singing. Painfully he rose in the concealing dark, silently

137

he fumbled his way aft, to crouch and listen.

No sign of danger as he crept toward his captain's cabin. No one to witness. No watch set.

Slowly, silently he prized open the door, to ease his way toward the cupboard and the filigree box. To grope, and fumble, then to clasp the treasure. The black pearl! The box was replaced. To take that was to steal.

From the rag he took the mutton fat, to mould it around the ring, into a rounded pellet. His hand to mouth, he warmed the grease within his saliva, and bolted the gem at third attempt.

Now it was safe within his belly. No one but himself would possess the jewel he vowed. He closed the door soft behind him, to make his way forward from shadow to shadow. Hidden by the capstan's spindle he stripped and placed all he owned within his sack of sail cloth, well greased with fat, and knotted the string tight. Over the gunwhale he slid. Had he judged aright? Had the tide ceased to ebb and was it now slack water? Sack tight-gripped between his teeth, hand over hand down the anchor's cable to plop into the water, to swim shorewards and unseen in the calm of the summer sea.

The morning watch reported the man was missing.

"Nothing of great moment, Tom, to have a thief jump ship. Take no heed." So Richard advised in reassuring tones.

"Aye," agreed Martin. "And as for the ring, it was never really yours, and what you have never had is never lost. Leastways the wind has shifted and Weymouth beckons."

"Weymouth?"

" 'Tis the prize that beckons, Tom."

"Aye and the Mayor's daughter!"

Soft winds and sunshine ushered them on their way.

Elsewhere the gales were worsening. Too long had Burley been used to warmer climes as cold and damp ate the marrow of his bones. Thank God he had escaped the fever that afflicted so many of his fellows. What little water remained was rank, the food fast putrifying. Only the rats did multiply and thrive. Pray God he may yet again set foot upon his adopted land.

"So this, Master Keigwin, is your brother?"

"Indeed so, sir."

"And therefore this must be your pirate nephew?"

"Indeed, Mayor Pitt, I trust they do not disappoint you?"

His jowls wobbled with his chuckle. "I must confess I had expected a more fearsome fellow."

" 'Tis true." Richard's hand reached for Tom's shoulder. "He is seemingly tender and mild of manner, I fear he learned his wicked ways when but a lad. Is it not so, nephew?"

" 'Tis well you jest, Dick, lest I would let my sword answer for me."

"Come gentlemen, for I have looked forward to this time. Let us then first to business and afterwards pleasure. Come."

Their host ushered the three before him into a room oak-panelled in the pattern of linenfold. Across a carpet-strewn planked floor, a merry fire blazed a welcome upon the open hearth. A panel opened at his touch, in the recess behind there sat a canvas sack, cord knotted at its neck. The Mayor struggled to hold it in two hands and shake it next to his ear that all might hear the jingle from within.

"A joyful sound methinks." He held it that Richard might receive. "You are the eldest, sir," he smiled, "I trust you share it fairly." He looked at Martin and Tom. "I have allowed you one third the spoils, gentlemen, and trust that does suffice. 'Twas well I acted swiftly." His eyes twinkled, as in lowered voice, "for their Lordships sent for an inventory and those two gentlemen that came were most displeased. For there was little left of which to make a list!"

He paused and for once his voice was earnest. "You must trust that what Richard holds is your true entitlement, for no one must know the part I played."

"No one will know, sir, saving Sir John Hawkyns, who too must have his share. But how it was attained is a secret we shall not disclose. Not so brother?"

"Aye," Martin responded. "And we do not doubt Mayor Pitt has given us our just dues."

"You need not doubt me, gentlemen," the Mayor smiled, "but there is no way of telling." He rubbed his hands. "Then that is settled and all are satisfied. Let us to our ale and to relate your adventures, 'tis time to eat. We dine on goose, Michaelmas goose. A favourite of her majesty."

"Aye and the goose is cooked for the King of Spain." quipped Martin.

"And here is my daughter. Jane, this is Tom Flemyng," Pitt effected the introduction. His bow to her curtsey. For a moment their eyes held each the other, until hers were lowered as modesty would dictate, a blush lingered upon her cheeks. Now were they met, each cup of expectation overflowing.

Chapter Eight

The casement at The Mermaid opened wide on the morning of Tuesday 30th August and Becky wiped her sleepy eyes, fair hair falling in confusion down her back and shoulders. Over the harbour she gazed towards the haze that veiled the outline of the Lizard.

"A day of silver," she mused, as the silver sun, played peep-bo behind silver clouds that chased above a silver sea. Her eyes once more searched the far horizon. The ocean was empty, save for the fishing boats manned by the old men.

Travellers to the inn recounted tales of battles fought and victories won, and of the Queen's address at Tilbury when the troops were disbanded. The Armada was put to flight and the fear of invasion vanished.

Little by little, as stories were confirmed by trader and by traveller, the folk of Mousehole began to realise the invincible Armada had been vanquished. As they awaited the return of husbands and sons pressed into England's fleet they began to deck home and town with garlands and with bunting, in celebration and thanksgiving.

Yet still they waited.

Becky sighed; she must wash and dress, and prepare the victuals for market day. Soon the stalls would be in place, gaily-striped canopies stretched upon timber frame as the street vendors argued over favoured pitches. Villagers would arrive to purchase, to seek news of battle and of family, to inspect with critical eye and caustic comment the goods that were on sale. Food and produce, poultry and livestock, baskets of woven withies made to order, pots of earthenware, skillets of iron, cheeses and hams from country cottage; services for sale, labourers for hire.

Silas, surly fellow with ear-torn terrier at heel, the rat-catcher, armed with ferret and with net, was twice paid to catch his prey — for the vermin would be sold to the pits for 'Spot' and 'Snip' to break their necks.

Cock-fighting and dicing for further ill-afforded wager was a part of the excitement, the noise, the colour, the smell of farm, of fish and unwashed humanity which was a market day in Mousehole.

Jenkyn Keigwin gazed up at the canopy above and blinked himself awake, drew curtains that contained his warm, wide bed and, perching on the edge, wiped away the sleep from his eyes with knuckled fist. He pushed his nightcap awry, yawned, and still only half awake, collected his thoughts. Every morning he wondered if this was to be the day.

Would the fleet return bringing Martin and Richard with tales to tell before once more plying their trade as fishermen and merchant? France would need all the oil and salted fish they could supply. Celebrations meant wine consumed and cellars to be replenished! His ships would return with full loads from foreign vineyards. There was business a-plenty if now they had but the men and the ships! And what of the *Golden Hind* herself? Would she be much damaged? Would there be a share for him of spoils taken from prizes?

Through the window he peered into the silver morning. Left, to the Mount and the Monastery, across to Porthleven, and right Mullion. But of sail there was no sign.

Dressed and breakfasted, the servants put about their work, he took his favourite stick and walked the village. Acknowledging, giving greeting and good-day with doff of velvet hat, his eyes restlessly wandered above the chapel-topped island to the silver sparkle of the wide bay beyond. Although messengers had brought news of a great victory, Mousehole would not rejoice until she heard from the lips of her own, and witnessed their safe return.

The great galleon made her weary way south off the west-ward coast of Ireland. She rolled in the heavy swell, aftermath of the terror of the gales that had pursued them around the

142

wildness of Scotland's coast.

With want of fresh victuals, the fever was now taking toll. Men were dying by the hundred, weakened by water now filled with a slime of green, biscuits a mass of wriggling weevils, and salt meat that was rotting in the casks.

The mistakes. Oh, the mistakes, thought Burley. Horses and mules thrown overboard that would have provided fresh meat for days. Had they but known. The mistakes — surely the greatest was to send ships built for warmer, calmer climes to fight in the cold and storms of England. How could they compare with the sea-faring agility of the fighting ships Hawkyns had built for his English waters? And their gunners as well. How they had battled!

Burley reflected. He was low in body, mind and heart. When would they sight the coast of Spain? He was sickened by the sea. Nothing but sea. Nothing but the sight of damned sea that had swallowed too many of his brave companions. But God be thanked for their English pilot. Without Stucley they would have come to grief off Flanders. Surely without his skill and knowledge they would have foundered on some rocky islet. He alone had led their squadron to these safe and calmer seas.

From Castallack to Raginnis they jogged. Sterns erect, pausing to scent and mark the granite rocks they passed, chided and praised each by name in Jacob's gruff tones as he trotted behind on long-tailed cob. These were the Keigwin hounds, bred by the Squire to while away the winter with sport upon the moors when seasonal storms put end to fishing and to trade. Testing his learned mind to blend pedigree with performance, aided by observation and by instinct, piercing eyes deep-set in weathered face, Jacob jogged, ever watchful for his favourites.

"Yeow, Pirate!" Leather thong cracked. "Get back to 'em, Pagan!"

With the danger of Spanish conquest now departed, the sons of the house soon to be home, his master would turn to his hunting to entertain and relax. He, Jacob, must ensure there was sport to be had. Horse and hound must both be fit; sheltered combe and hollow watched, left undisturbed for the lie of the red and fallow deer that had escaped the tinner's pot.

He lived alone in a thatched granite hut: catching the wild brown trout and eel from the stream and netting coney and game for his larder. He preferred the company of himself and his hounds to that of other men. Daily he trudged his solitary way from Newlyn's combe to his beloved pack and the stock he tended.

Pink tongue lolled through open jaws, Merlin grinned upwards from the offside of his mounted god as he jogged along in pride of place, no other hound dared dispute him. As one might croon to a much-loved child, grey beard leaned down and spoke terms of endearment never wasted upon human soul. Jacob raised his eyes to peer seaward from his clifftop vantage and checked his horse's stride. In the blue of the sea was the set of sails that even his landsman's eyes well knew. His master's sons were at last returning to their home.

"Tommy!" Jenkyn called to his wife, a pet name rarely used. "Tommy, put on your finest bonnet and cape. Come with me."

"Why Jenkyn?"

"Because, dear wife," he spoke with urgent glee, "your sons will expect it of you."

"The *Golden Hind* — she is within the bay?"

"That she is and soon to be upon us. Quick, tell the servants to prepare the feast."

The tide had helped her round the Lizard Head and she raced for the harbour entrance where the folk of Mousehole were running to give greeting to their *Golden Hind*. Upon the harbour wall they gathered in excited hubbub, some crowded aboard the fishing boats to be taken to the island, to scramble ragged granite, where the chapel sat on precarious perch, each determined to be the first to cheer their welcome back.

Thomas stood alongside Pentreath at the helm.

"Come, Tom, let us give them a show!" Richard called from amidships as he peered towards the island.

"Aye then, Richard. Master Gunner, prime the cannons and

run them out. Give blank broadside when I give the order! Bosun, run up the masthead pennants."

Cheers surged from those ashore to see the flying flags of Cornwall and England. Tattered and torn they might be, their brave colours faded by salt and sun, yet were they not the emblem of freedom? Those of the *San Salvador* too were raised. Tokens of victory for all to share.

The *Golden Hind* came to the north of the island. Martin shouted the order and the broadside of three cannon spoke with roar of thunder. Again the command, the other broadside fired. Cheer after cheer rang out. The gathered throng shouted and waved in the ecstasy of their welcome. Mainsails reefed, her head came round against wind and tide, to anchor where oft she had before, and await the water that would take her into the safety of her harbour home.

Thomas grinned to his uncles, and bid Teek take them ashore, whilst he remained on board to ensure that all was shipshape; that gold and silver coin remain safe hid amongst the barrels of powder, on the morrow to be taken to the warehouse on the wharf.

As they neared the shore, boys and girls rushed waist deep, to pull and beach the skiff, to ply the brothers with a multitude of questions, nearly to unship them in the excitement of the moment.

Smiling at their antics were Jenkyn and Thomasine. With the dignity it behove them to uphold, they waited upon the shingle.

Head held high, Thomasine fought the tears that struggled to escape. Pride forbade her to display emotion before the people of the town, but each of her sons felt the warmth of her embrace. At last God had seen them safe returned. Her prayers were now answered.

Jenkyn proudly clasped his sons and held them to him.

Thomasine, with mother's care and fond concern, asked as to their welfare and of Thomas. Reassured, she enquired as to the men. All had returned safe and sound, save but one, Nankervis.

His fingers touched to his stocking cap, the bosun asked might he be allowed ashore, to return forthwith to do his part on board.

g

"You have business?" In response to the bosun's embarrassment, Martin laughed and nodded his dismissal.

Teek touched his forelock to the Squire and his lady, and with a grin quickly vanished amongst the throng.

Across the yard Becky carried wooden buckets with water for the nags. All day she had been kept busy in the inn, serving hungry travellers. Here, in the comfort of her friends, she might relax, her fears be dispelled. Lost in her thoughts, she opened the stable door to look into the dark inside. Fat quarters and swishing tail, the pony's nose, deep-thrust into sweet-smelling meadow hay, newly-strewn along the manger. Artlessly she leant to stroke the stable cat that brushed and mewed about her ankles, nagging for her dish of milk. The pony turned and leaned a sleek neck over the stable door to nudge his tabby friend beneath. In soft voice, rich with Cornwall's tones, Becky chided and confided to those that would not tell.

Under the entrance arch he stood, unwashed, unkempt in soiled clothes of wool and canvas. Hands on his hips, his mouth slashed in a smile in the tangle of his beard. Softly Teek stole towards her from behind, his arms flung about her, to lock his hands across her soft warm belly; as she struggled to turn, pink pointed tongue flicked through white teeth to lick the tempting lobe of her ear. Vainly she struggled against his grasp. Soft kisses upon her neck combined to fill demands of love and passion.

He relaxed his hold upon her. Becky turned with widened eyes to fling golden arms about her lover's neck. His face pulled down towards her, to accept her unbridled kisses of love and greeting.

Later, each reassured of the fidelity of the other, Becky ran to her room to don her Sunday frock. Teek returned to duty, to his ship and his captain.

Made fast fore and aft inside the quay, the *Golden Hind* would take the ground when the harbour emptied. The men were summoned one by one before Tom to receive his thanks and silver coin with which to enjoy a brief time ashore; their due reckoning to be made upon the morrow.

A messenger from the Squire rode to Madron to tell Nicholas and Elizabeth of their son's return, and bid them join

146

the family in celebration. In the Manor, Thomasine and Mary took stock of the pantry and planned the repast to come.

Gravy soup from the shin of ox, vegetables and herbs fresh-gathered from the garden. Fish pie. Pilchards with pears steeped in mulled wine, baked in pastry upon a bed of artichokes and autumn fruits. A leg of lamb spit roasted, then stewed with sweet rosemary and capers.

Yesterday she had prepared a stew of venison, all the better for the keeping. The haunch of the stag whose carcass was now hanging in the pantry, brought to bay upon the moors. A fricassee of young, plump pigeons would surely please: and cheese from the farm and home-cured hams, salted in the leads benched within the dairy, a syllabub of rich cream on brown bread; served beforehand. Thomasine would protest her love through the stomachs of her menfolk!

Handshaking his thrusting way through the crowd gathered around pedlar's pitch and market stall. Tom entered the darkened portals of The Mermaid.

Adjusting his eyes to the dull light, he shouldered his way past the customers to the foot of the stair. He called for the landlord:

"Trewhella, where in God's name are you man! Trewhella, I have no time to waste. Come here about your business! Ah, there you are," as Trewhella stumped down the wooden treads, hand outstretched. "Are you so fat and rich you no longer need my custom?"

"Nay, nay Captain, 'course I do." He grinned his greetings. "And sir, 'tis good to see you safely home." He shook Thomas's hand in warm affection. "How may I please you Captain?"

"Well, Jan," for since boyhood he had known the landlord, "my bosun tells me he is courting your daughter Becky, and a fine lass she be. Though what sort of a catch with you for a father — I know not!" He smiled at the older man to show his teasing. "Landlord, Cornall is a good man, a brave man and no fool. He will have some silver too as consequence of our adventures. With your permission he will make her a fine husband. I have said my piece. Now to business. There will be celebrations tonight for we have much in which to rejoice.

147

Here is some silver to pay for ale and victuals for my seamen. Stand no nonsense for so much salt air and salted beef has given them fair thirst! Let them cause no harm. But should they do so, alert me to the reckoning."

"Why, thank you Captain, I'll see them right and no harm done."

Jan Trewhella escorted him to the door, Thomas nodded a farewell and strode at last to the Manor. His duty done, his men well tended, now might he relax in the comfort of good family company.

One by one and in noisome groups the men of the *Golden Hind* made their way toward the tavern. The barque now leant against the harbour wall, the tide ebbed from beneath her keel.

Teek climbed the harbour wall amidst a lingering crowd of onlookers, as with curiosity unquenched, they regaled him with questions as to the battles and the action he had witnessed, anxious for details of blood and gore.

Seamen sat upon settle and stool within the inn as the darkness crept its relentless course. Oil lamps were lighted and rush lights glimmered. Logs were thrown upon sea coal for sparks to shower in upward cascade in the open hearth of The Mermaid. The dusk leant greater magic to the boldness of the stories exchanged for foaming jugs of home-brewed ale. The seamen vied with each other in the telling of the tales. The bloodier the story, the more extravagant the adventure, the more ale there was to pass parched lips. Simple countrymen, eyes agog, rubbed shoulders with sharp-witted trader as they listened in eager awe to the boldness of the deeds of the dauntless crew of the *Golden Hind*. Men who, it seemed, from their diminutive barque alone, had muted the might of Spain with but scarce assistance from the English fleet.

Teek looked about for Becky for he had not seen her this last while. He rose and eased his way through the noisy throng to the quiet of the starlit stable. A shadow moved. The gentle rustle of a skirt. Her arms wide held, to receive him in soft embrace. They clung together. Their lips hungry for each other. In the warmth of the autumn evening their bodies tight-pressed in the understanding darkness.

Becky sensed his manhood rise against her loins and clasped him ever more tightly to her. At last, she gently took his arms from about her waist and holding his roughened palm in one hand, held finger of other to her lips, and led her lover up wide granite stairs against the stable to the hay loft door.

Below the revelry continued, whilst Teek and Becky lay in each other's arms, the soft sweet-smelling hay their pillow, and their bed. They lay together, secure in their embrace, safe in the knowledge of their love.

A curious moon shone its rays through a cobwebbed window, peering at the maiden, asleep in a strong man's arms. Gently Teek roused her.

"Come Becky, it is time for me to return to my ship and you to your bed."

Carefully and silently, they closed the loft door behind them, whilst from across the yard came sounds of revelry and voices joined in song. Twin passions vented, tenderly they embraced and kissed goodnight, as reluctantly Becky stole away, unseen. She to her bedroom, he to his duty: to relieve the watch on board the *Golden Hind*.

Until first light he must keep watch, he gazed heavenwards at the cloudless sky, pinpricked by myriad stars, his thoughts of Becky, her handsome features and golden hair. She of the trusting innocence and shapely, lissom body that had pleasured him so greatly. He sighed and shook his head almost in disbelief at the wonderment of their loving. With an eye that seemed a-wink, an all-knowing moon pried down upon the harbour scene and the lone figure who looked landwards, waiting the snuff of a candle that shed soft light in a bedroom of the inn.

This had been his first time with a woman. The harlots that haunted the quayside taverns, they of painted face and blackened teeth, had left him untempted. They with the slatternly ways, wanton demands and promise of disease. He shuddered at the thought of such creatures.

Her lips puffed upon the candle. Now in her truckle bed she lay, hands clasped behind her head, gazing upwards wide-eyed to the low ceiling above. Her mouth smiling in sweet contentment as she recalled the magic of each moment

149

in the hay. Not only was she nearing seventeen, but now she was a woman. Now she could begin to comprehend a woman's feelings. Uncertain feelings she had tried so hard to stifle. Teek had been so kind, so gentle. Were all men thus? Could all men give such ecstasy to a maid? She sighed and snuggled further down the bed.

A sudden frown disturbed the beauty of her features. Had she satisfied him? Could she have done more for his pleasure? There was so much to know and no one to advise. "Please God, may Teek and I learn together that we may please only one the other." She turned to close her eyes and bathe in the all refreshing sleep of love, new requited.

Dawn saw the barque dried out, tight against the granite wall. Sore-headed sailors lifted and carted barrels and stores topsides, to be lowered overboard where the iron-shod gurry waited on the shingle to be towed to the warehouse by a shaggy pony, taciturn Jacob at its head.

The brothers saw to safe stowage of powder and shot, whilst Teek and his captain remained aboard; recording and noting that which contained the Spanish coin.

As the calm, making sea gently returned through harbour mouth, Tom ordered warps to be layed from the barque's bows and turns taken around the stone pillars set beside the slipway. Thus lightened, she lifted with the incoming tide. The warps were shortened as she rose, with high water her bows were near the edge of the wharf.

Wooden legs were propped around her as she was made secure with lines from ship to shore, there to be left high and dry as the waters retreated.

When all was unladen and the men departed, Keigwin and the three inspected their prize of gold and silver covered in the grey black of the gunpowder in which the coin was hid.

At the far corner of the warehouse, Keigwin ordered his sons to roll away the hogsheads of wine, stacked high upon the dry floor of hard-packed earth and stone. Shirts removed, unaccustomed to their labour, the three sweated and strained to at last reveal the grounding stones, foundations of the granite storehouse. Eager fingers sought purchase upon a smooth rock, and heaved it free, to reveal a low cavern beyond. The kegs of gunpowder were then placed within, the stone returned, and the wine stacked as before — that none might guess the secret that was hid.

Their work done and night descending, cautiously they opened the wooden door, Martin peered into the gloom. He beckoned his father forward as they returned through the stableyard, thence to the rear door of the Manor, secure in the knowledge that no one had seen.

The barque was left secure at her moorings with Teek and Pentreath sleeping aboard and keeping watch in turn.

By mid-morning the sea had drained from the harbour. The timber legs held the stranded barque upright as Thomas and Martin tested the state of the planking inch by inch for damage done by Spanish shot or gribble-worm.

With Teek in attendance the knot of men pored over their pride and joy upon which depended their lives and their fortune. Sprung timbers to be repaired or replaced, fresh pitch to be painted upon her. Only now could they assess her hull, and the damage caused. There was much to do, for winter would soon be upon them. Until the advent of spring, winds and savage seas would deter them from sailing in these wild waters.

The shortening days passed swiftly. A core of seamen were retained, the remainder paid off, to work the tin streams, with promise of re-engagement should need arise. On hands and knees seamen reamed out the deck seams with caulking iron. Driving fresh oakum home with mallet-struck chisel; that again might the privateer endure the wash of sea upon her decks without fear of taking water.

Martin had joined Richard to assist with the fishing in the calm of the Indian summer, for there would now be few fine days and fish would soon be scarce. Trade lost must be made good. Pilchards had to be pressed, mackerel to be salted down; trade with foreign merchants to be regained.

During this time Tom had been home to Landithy, enthralling father, brother and the doting ladies with stories they had prised from his reluctant lips, but he was pleased to return to his *Golden Hind*, the world and the men he knew and the life he loved. Teek smiled as his master clambered aboard, fingers touched his forehead in gesture of greeting

151

and respect.

"Come now, Bosun. Have you completed your chores of the past days?"

The work was nearly complete, save for the replacement anchor and sails awaiting return from the attentions of the sailmaker. New spars and sheets had been run up and Martin had already dealt with the ordnance.

"The ballast, Bosun. Have you taken on fresh shingle?"

"That we have, Captain, and await you and the weather to take her out to check her trim."

"I shall remain aboard until we have done so. We must still be wary lest the Don seeks to salvage some lost pride. Where can he strike more easily than here? Always, too, there is the Turk to consider. For with the Armada gone and our ships refitting, he might yet be tempted to seize our ships or men. Always be wary of the Moor, Bosun. Now be off with you, lest that pretty sweetheart of yours accepts favours from some lusty stranger!"

With grateful gesture Teek took his leave, to go below and change into his shoregoing clothes, upon his belt he fastened his purse and dagger. He ran up to the bows, swung hand over hand along the land lines, and dropped lithely to the shingle, to stride along the wharf and through The Mermaid's welcoming door.

"Landlord Trewhella, my duties on board are done for the day. It would please me to walk with Rebecca if you would so allow?"

The delivery of wine was not forgot, and his captain's kindly words had also found their mark.

"Sit yourself down, Master Cornall, and sup some ale whilst I tell my Becky you are waiting on her." He winked and beckoned another wench to attend to Teek, whilst he disappeared up the open stairway.

Teek did as he had been bid and sank a draught of ale before the fireside in the parlour. And waited.

Upstairs, in mix of excitement and confusion, Becky attended to her toilet.

Another foaming jug arrived. Teek waited.

What should she wear? What colour would please him most?

152

Teek waited.

She donned a dress of pale blue linen and bonnet of embroidered velvet, which she herself had made in likeness of city style. Her wayward golden hair tumbled from beneath, near to her waist.

The mug raised to his lips, was held there to pause for brief second, as Becky came down the staircase to smile and wave her greeting. She was worthy of all the waiting!

He rose and thumped the earthenware mug hard upon the board. "My robin, but you are a right beauty."

Trewhella, wiping hands upon his apron nodded fatherly approval.

Proudly, possessive of his capture, Teek grinned down at her, as she smiled upwards to him, shyly to take his arm. Together they departed the tavern and walked the busy road, that all might bear witness to their courtship.

Land at last! Their homeland sighted! Closer they came to the broad, welcoming estuary. Soon clean water and fresh victuals, and the needs of sick and dying would be attended. The Atlantic swell had eased and the blue of the sea sparkled with silver in the midday sunshine. To starboard the high hill of Cabo de Lata, clad in the black-green pine, to larboard the great spit of sand where white gulls and advocets preened. Beyond, low-wooded landscape, this was not the Corunna they were seeking, but Santander.

No matter, it was Spain, it was shelter and he was safe and still alive. But only just, for typhus ran rampant below decks.

Upon the shallow waters boats netting fish and shrimp on the incoming tide stopped harvesting their rich reward to gaze in wonderment upon the gathering of great ships. They had departed Corunna in form of proud procession, as a queen in full majesty of pomp and splendour, to head her entourage of admiring courtiers. So recalled Burley as he stood upon the forecastle. Now the *San Martin* was returning as a raddled whore to lead her troupe of pockmarked harlots, dressed in rags and tatters — remnants of a faded glory.

153

A cannon fired, to summon aid that would haul her to safe anchorage.

Around his neck hung the medallion. In his palm the silver cross that once had belonged to his father. He held aloft the crucified Christ and closed his eyes, to thank God for his salvation. Upon this emblem of his faith, and on his father's name he swore a solemn oath. He, Richard Burley, would strive to avenge his Maker and His earthly servants, the Bishop of Rome and his sovereign King. He would dedicate his life to their service. Vengeance would one day be theirs. Those who had ordered the execution of Queen Mary would suffer the fate of all heretics. Their evil would be exorcised. Their souls cleansed by fire, tied to the flaming faggot, as so many of his countrymen had been, on the orders of vile Elizabeth.

Chapter Nine

The hammering on the door of Landithy Manor alerted the household. The maid servant cautiously opened the yard door to peer without.

"Who is that, Joan?" called Elizabeth.

"A lad with a letter for the master, Mistress. Says he must deliver it personally."

Nicholas himself entered the hall. "You have a letter for me?"

"Aye, sir, if you are Squire Flemyng."

"Indeed, no other, so please you give it me. But first tell me, who is your master?"

"Why, sir, your kinsman, Sir John Hawkyns."

Nicholas nodded his reply. "Joan, see the nag is fed and watered, then provide the lad with victuals and ale for by the sweat and smell of him he has travelled far enough." He waved his hand in dismissal. To call after, "And attend whilst I draft a reply."

A bob and Joan turned with the youth and took him through the yard to fuss within the kitchen. While he enjoyed a repast of cold meats and home-brewed beer, Joan wheedled such news she might of Plymouth and the family he served.

"Elizabeth," Nicholas called his wife, "John Hawkyns comes to visit us this four weeks. Lady Katherine is coming too, for she has been ailing and needs some cheerful company."

"Then, husband, the girls and I have to prepare, for they will want some considerable attention." A frown creased her brow. "There is so much to do. But what a merry-making we shall have! Pray enquire how many will be in their party and as to when they wish to depart."

Nicholas retired to his study and read the letter again before drafting his reply with care. Sir John was now a man of some considerable consequence.

There would be feasting, playing and story-telling. A hero of the Armada would expect it of them. They would use such opportunity to entertain their friends and display their rank and kinship with he who had been newly knighted, a hero of his country. The old rascal would doubtless relate tales of his exploits in Sierra Leone against the Portuguee, and of the Indies too. Tales of trading, feuding and fighting with the Spaniards he so detested. They who were but little travelled could learn much from him and his journeys of adventure. Even Jenkyn Keigwin, Merchant of Mousehole, would stand in awe of Hawkyns, the merchant-venturer. Flemyng would sit back, an auditor in the verbal play: both were men of religious conviction. Would Jenkyn hold in contempt the traffic of slaves that was the bedrock of the Hawkyns' fortunes? Slaving was now forgot, ended in disaster some thirty years before. Yet the stories would remain fresh and entertaining, embellished over the years. This would be an event to be remembered, and not merely a social visit; for the victor was coming to collect spoils that were hid in the Keigwin storehouse!

Elizabeth tapped gently on the door before entering her husband's sanctuary, a glass of sac on a pewter tray, excuse for his attention. He took it from her with grateful nod as she sat herself upon cross-legged stool. He took slow sips, watching her thoughtfully; knowing she was both anxious yet in pleasurable anticipation of the visit.

"My dearest. You and our daughters have truly an occasion upon which you may excel." He sipped in meditation. "Your talents to be used to full effect. We must have much feasting and jollity. Music, and dancing, aye and sport. We must not allow Lady Katherine to suppose that we at the tip of Cornwall are backward in our hospitality. 'Tis for you, my dear, to show that we know how to pleasure our guests as well as those who live in those up-country fashionable establishments. Tom and I will arrange the amusements without, whilst you and our dear daughters look to the dancing and feasting that we shall enjoy within."

Amidst great excitement Elizabeth called her girls to her. Elizabeth and Mary seated at their mother's feet, hands clasped around raised knees, listened in rapt attention to that which she proposed.

"There is to be a party?"

"Dancing?"

"Yes, my dears, many parties. We shall have to look our best."

"But how shall we know the fashion?"

"By calling upon the dressmaker, our gowns must be to the fashion of London."

"We shall be grand!"

"And I shall sing, and Elizabeth shall play."

"And we shall dance!"

In the peace and quiet of his study, Nicholas made his own arrangements. Firstly a message to Mousehole, that the family of Keigwin too might be informed of the impending visit. This done, he summoned his sons to hear their opinions as to entertainment.

"At Oxford," John had only recently taken his doctorate at Oxford and was proud of his academic learning, "it is to my certain knowledge that persons of degree seek amusement in subjects that stimulate and exercise the mind."

Thomas sighed. John's ecclesiastical nature was a contrast to the life of adventure and danger that he, his seafaring brother, was pursuing.

John continued: "A mystery play perhaps, for by all that is holy, what better than a play about a saint of Cornwall triumphant over the Devil! This may be related to our Cornish captain's triumph over the evils of Spain!" He rose to his theme. "By all the saints, we shall remind the folk of their history. We shall set an example to them. We shall show that gentlemen acknowledge the benefits and deeds of the Church: that, armed with righteousness and truth, the humble too may expel the devil that lurks in the soul of each — just as a maggot may devour the heart of the apple so rosy from without but hollow and rotten within!"

Nicholas nodded approval at his son's eloquence.

"By Hell's fire, this be sport for women! What scurvy entertainment for a hero of England! Come, brother,"

Thomas retorted, "our guests can hear you and your kind preaching fire and damnation any Sunday they choose! We are all men of God and are His servants. Sir John has served Him in battle, amidst ball and storm, not from the safety of the pulpit! He needs no lessons taught by a sheaf of itinerant prattlers, preached from the deck of horse-drawn cart! He seeks pursuits of a manly nature!"

"Enough!" Nicholas smiled. The scholar and the soldier, the opposites of the Celtic character. His sons had always argued relentlessly as brothers do but, should an outsider criticise either one, he would find argument with the two.

Thomas and John looked to their father.

"There are points in each of your arguments. Therefore, John, you will prepare your miracle play based upon the life of a Cornish saint. Whilst the moral must be told, let it not be lost in profound language too obscure to comprehend and," before John could reply, "ensure the players are well versed and do not forget their lines to cause merriment where none should be."

"But Father . . . "

"Never fear Thomas, there will be cards and story-telling and wine enough of an evening. There will be hunting for the stag — a manly sport, the ladies too may follow. A tournament perhaps. Not the tilt-yard of the city, but with a test of skill and strength with the longbow betwixt men matched from St. Madern and elsewhere. Sir John shall present the prize. A horse race perhaps, along the shores of Marazion that all may witness and wager upon. I care not for cock-fighting or bear-baiting but prefer contests wherein men may match their mettle. Together prepare a plan and arrange what I have said."

"Surely Father, but I shall have so very much to prepare," replied John. "For if we are to present a play of mystery or passion for Sir John and his Lady there is but little time if it is to be played in a manner as befits their station."

"Do as you will, John. Such a festival will I know be safe in your hands."

Time flew in the Flemyng household. Nimble fingers stitched

and sewed. New dresses were designed with high ruffs of cambric, starched in the style of Holland to frame the head and emphasise the hair, the neck left bare save for an elaborate necklace. The rich embroidered stomacher, deeply pointed, was the style of the day and the flamboyant broad-spreading farthingale that swept the floor beneath, emulating the style set by their sovereign. Hairstyles were fashioned and discarded. Dances were privately practised, the stately peacock-strutting of the pavan at contrast with the leaping and whirling of the gavotte. Sonnets were sung, madrigals rehearsed — the ladies of the household determined not to be found wanting in their social graces.

The moon was fading in the watery grey sky of late October. Early rising rooks flapped in their flock in search of fresh feeding. A shape moved slowly down steep slope of the combe and paused, before crossing where granite slab bridged the rushing stream stained brown from the autumn rains that washed the moors above. It climbed the bracken slopes towards the hanging woodland of grey-green lichened oaks, whose stunted trunks leaned from the western wind. To stop once more, silhouetted against the fading moon, the outline of a grazing horse, head downward bent upon the steep incline.

A shadow moved at the woodland's edge. In the soft light of the wakening world delicate nostrils scented the morning air. The proud head erect, crowned by antlers of twelve points. The red deer, a royal stag, listened and watched from his vantage.

The pony stopped its upward path to graze amongst the dew-dropped ling and bracken. Jacob set the stake firmly in the soft mound of an ant-hill. For it was he who by dawn's first light, carried the stalking-horse, fashioned from withies that he had plaited to cover with hide in likeness of the wild ponies that grazed the granite moorlands. For only by such stealth and fieldcraft could he gain advantage of his wary prey, off at first hint of danger. For only thus could he determine where stags and hinds might be harboured on the day his master wished to hunt. Without his cunning many an unrewarding hour would be spent upon the moors and combes. It was his duty to provide sport for his master and those that followed his hounds. It was his duty to provide venison for the Squire's household. This king of beasts he had watched and known since but a yearling. Now in his prime, full grown, he would provide a fitting quarry for the hunt to be held in Hawkyn's honour.

Careful not to alarm the stately stag, he retreated to the dead ground of the hillside between wood and stream. His face softened in unaccustomed smile at the thought of that regal head. A fitting challenge for him and his hounds to pit their skills in the science of the chase. The art of venery. The thrill of the hunt. In wide arc his loping stride carried him past the timeless standing stones planted by his Celtic forebears. They too had hunted the deer across these same windswept moors, for hunting was as old as man. He pondered. His ancestors would have hunted their quarry to feed their tribe. But surely too, the blood had coursed through their veins in the excitement of the chase. The kill itself provided no satisfaction, only the prospect of food and feasting. The chase was the thing. The age old battle of survival between the hunter and the hunted.

The day arrived. Elizabeth looked on with motherly pride as her family was presented to Sir John and Lady Katherine. Wine, sweetened and spiced, was taken whilst the ladies regaled each other with stories and gossip of family kinsfolk. The changes of fashion, the extravagant style encouraged at court, the problems of starching the intricate ruffs, how best to colour one's hair, fair or red, in accord with the fancy of the moment; the powder and paint most effective, and the potions used by those of fashion. The girls listened agog as Lady Katherine held forth. Her confidential tones put them at ease and encouraged them to comment and to question their guest.

At the far end of the room, Nicholas Flemyng and Sir John were in deep political discussion about the opportunities now open to an England elevated to a world power upon the defeat of Spain. Due to the navigational achievements of

Drake and his fellows trade routes were now open to merchant venturers. There were the spices and precious stones of Africa and India; sugar, tobacco and gold from the Americas. English settlements must be created, to profit the bold, bringing wealth to their mother country. The younger men listened in to the conversation in awe as Sir John outlined his vision of the future.

"The fullness of the Earth is there for the taking." He looked at the boys. "Drake has shown you the way. Our navigators are now the equal to the world. He and myself, have given you an example to follow. The ships I designed are now of the finest. The challenge is there for young men to accept. Go and make yourselves rich and your country the greatest nation upon earth. You, Tom, you have shown your worth, your pluck and your seamanship. Drake, Cumberland and I can do with men such as you in the service of our Queen. Challenge the Don wheresoever we can find him. Aye, and I will see to it you get your just reward, never fear. Now," looking at Squire Keigwin, "on the morrow do we, Jenkyn, resolve the matter of the silver of Spain that even now I trust is safely hidden in your warehouse?"

"We do indeed, Sir John. Will it please you to ride to my home at ten of the clock and dine with me, following an appropriate distribution?"

"And who sir, decides whether or no the 'distribution' be appropriate, eh by Jove?"

"Never fear, Sir John, we shall apportion according to each his deserts."

A summons to dinner prevented further thorny discussion.

The morning of the following day, they strode across the shelter of the stockyard. A gaggle of geese, raucous watchmen outside the warehouse door, waited to alert the household at the advent of strangers.

Tom slid the bolts back from their hasps and opened the creaking door. Arm outstretched, Keigwin ushered Sir John into the dark cavernous barn; Martin and Richard followed, each carrying canvas bags.

"You fellows, show Sir John where the treasure lies,"

Jenkyn spoke in muffled voice that could not carry beyond those present, cautious that even his most trusted servants should not hear. Together they rolled the heavy wine-filled hogsheads to one side in the gloom of the corner. The granite boulder then heaved aside to reveal the cave behind. Strong arms carried the kegs to the centre of the warehouse, into the only light just cast by the door left slightly ajar.

"Is that all?" asked Jenkyn.

"Aye, father, six we marked and six there are," replied Martin.

"How do I know that is all?" demanded Hawkyn.

"Because Martin has told you so, sir, his word on't is enough," Tom replied with hackles raised.

"Spoken like a man, Thomas," his commander replied. "Martin's word doth indeed suffice." Then with thought, as if to justify his query, "Mind you, there's many a fine gentleman whose word I would suspect, I can tell 'ee."

Keigwin and Nicholas Flemyng moved to the yard outside to keep watch. Inside the barn, carefully they eased open the wooden lids as with sleeves rolled over elbow they delved into the grey black dust of the concealing gunpowder to retrieve the shining Spanish coin which they poured in shimmering cascade into the mouths of the sacks. Finished, they rolled the barrels into the yard and tipped them upside-down, lest even the value of a penny piece remained unretrieved.

"Proper job," muttered Martin, as his nephew hoisted a heavy sack over each shoulder, and strode across the open yard to the back hall of the Manor of Mousehole.

Up the staircase they went, to the merchant's study. The bags stood dumped and leaning together upon the oak-boarded floor.

"Martin, pour wine, or ale according to each his need." Keigwin then spoke to his eldest, Richard, who went to a handsome cupboard to produce a silver tobacco box complete with ladle, tongs and priming iron.

All eyes were now fixed upon the drawstrung sacks. All was quiet save the sucking upon pipe stems until Hawkyns broke the embarrassed silence.

"Tell me gentlemen," he spoke in quiet tones, "how do

you propose we divide?"

Jenkyn well knew the wiles of Hawkyns. "Nay, Sir John. 'Tis your privilege to give us your judgement on the matter."

A pause as Sir John looked with close-set eyes upon the bowl of his pipe and tamped his tobacco tight. "I have had graver matters to dwell upon and have given this but little thought," he lied, drawing upon long silver stem; his forehead in thoughtful frown. "It was my ship that boarded her. 'Twas I that appreciated there was coin still aboard." He pondered a moment. "I do realise that 'twas young Thomas who brought her to safe harbour, but again, only because I trusted him as a kinsman and ordered him so to do. Thus I say: three fourths be mine, and one quarter between ye. Divide your share as ye will," he completed with an air of bountiful goodwill.

He sat back midst clouds of smoke, a benevolent, patronising smile upon his face. Tom opened his mouth to speak but caught his father's warning glance, as Jenkyn Keigwin rose to his feet, pipe stem pointed at the reclining Hawkyns, and spoke in the soft mild tones of deception.

" 'Tis fine, Sir John. Now it only behoves us to acquaint their Lordships of our decision for them to claim their part."

Hawkyns sat erect, "Take a reef or two, Keigwin," he blustered. "Me thought the value of the hulk should suffice as their entitlement. There is no need to tell them of our arrangement."

"Surely, Sir John, would that not be deception?" he mildly enquired. "What would be the outcome should the Lords of the Admiralty know that you ordered Thomas to bring the coin to Mousehole? Let us not argue." In sterner tones of finality: "Tom has taken the risk. We take half — or none. That is fair to each, since if we take none, we shall have to inform their Lordships of how much we have counted and entrusted to you, that you may account to them for what they claim is their due."

"Aye, Father," from Richard, "and 'twas I ensured that Mayor Pitt delivered us the proper share of that which he discovered."

Nicholas removed his pipe and grunted approval as Keigwin looked around the room for support.

"Aye, Grandfather," said Thomas, "that would seem to be honourable to all. To their Lordships and Her Majesty the hulk and what else they may discover. To us half the gold and silver. Providing Sir John is to entrust me with more ventures of this kind."

Old campaigner that he was, Hawkyns knew himself outgunned, but was determined to go down fighting. "There will be other days and other ways when we shall need each other, be it trade or facing common foe. I know not. But I accept. However," he wagged his forefinger at Jenkyn and his voice a-smile, "they do tell me you keep a remarkable cellar," looking at his goblet, "as is presently evidenced. They do tell me this was complemented by some that you acquired from a certain hoy, from Newhaven. Of that I should like to partake, sir. Be good enough to send me two hogsheads if you will. We will then call our trade fairly balanced, Jenkyn Keigwin."

"You are a hard man with whom to deal, Sir John. Ah! But you have bested me yet again! I shall be graceful in defeat. So be it." Jenkyn offered his hand to Hawkyns as the two men stood to clasp each other breast to breast. Each satisfied with the result.

"Richard, you forget our guests, my boy, more wine if you please. Let Sir John sample some of that soon to be his own. Fetch my merchant's beam, Thomas, that the coin may be fairly weighed and balanced. Later we shall divide our half share between us; according to the reward we each deserve. But not today. For tonight we go early a-bed. Tomorrow we hunt."

In the cosy warmth of The Mermaid, Teek sat in his now accustomed place, relishing the soft saffron cake that Trewhella had brought him. This was washed down his dry throat with gulps of small ale, in which bobbed toasted crabs, a delicacy of the inn. His eyes wandered hungrily.

"Is Becky about, Master?" he enquired of her father.

"I know not where she is, Teek. She has gone all day but said not where."

Teek finished his dinner and he waited. Trade was slack

and there was little to do or few with whom to talk. He poked the fire into a shower of sparks with the point of his toe, and watched them curl upwards into the chimney's throat. Yet still he waited. The sound of a soft step; before he could turn, her arms were around his neck. His rope-roughened fingers entwined in hers, the hurt left his heart and he felt good again in her presence.

"Hounds are at Madron tomorrow, my robin. Shall we ride there together to watch the folk?"

"That would please me greatly," she smiled at him, the love shining from her eyes. "I shall prepare cold poultry, fruits and ale. For should the weather be kind," a look of beguiling innocence, "we will eat out of doors in a wood-land — and perhaps rest amongst the bracken?"

A wink and teasing giggle.

Come the morrow all was gaiety as ponies and riding nags wended through the lanes to Madron, overtaking villager and urchin making their way to the meet. A day when people of the countryside met in common pleasure and excitement.

The hunt. Guests and visitors arrived at the Manor, hearty greetings called each to the other and, fussing the hounds, bid good-day to a sullen Jacob. Horses were saddled. Beautifully-attired ladies mounted their palfreys, determined to enjoy the sunshine of the day and the thrill of the chase. Mounted servants carried panniers of delicacies strapped to the cantles of their saddles. Elderly steeds that could scarce break from a trot, frisked like two-year-olds at the prospect of the chase.

Mulled wine was served to the gentry and strong brew of huff-cap ale to countryman and yokel. The burly figure of Squire Keigwin, seated upon his bay in the midst of his hounds received and returned greetings, with doff of velvet hat.

Merlin sat on his haunches beside Jacob's grey, occasion-ally throwing back his head to bay, a token protest at the delay. Like his god, Jacob, he was anxious to be away from the crowds and the chatter, anxious to be off on the line of a stag.

Astride their ponies, Teek and Becky kept a respectable

distance from the Squire, allowing their mounts to pick at the laneside verge. Yet Jenkyn's eyes noted all, and with beckoning finger he signalled for Teek and Becky to come closer. Over the heads of others he called to them, " 'Tis good to see a sailor astride and taking exercise. Me thought you were spending all your time in the safe harbour of a certain inn, Cornall."

Those mounted close by turned to see whom he addressed. "Well, if that be the pretty maid that is the cause, I can well understand. Good fortune to you both. I heard as you were well matched, and so it would seem." He doffed his cap, giving half bow and warm smile to a blushing Becky.

"Thank you Squire," returned Teek. "May you have a hunt as befits this occasion, sir."

Keigwin nodded his thanks and appreciation. For he knew it was not easy for Teek to reply when so embarrassed. He trusted Teek knew that what he had said was meant in good heart.

Chapter Ten

As Keigwin attempted to catch his huntsman's eye, a foxy-faced fellow, with wooden staff and the homespun clothes of a countryman, elbowed through the crowd easing through the horses to Jacob's side. Keigwin squeezed his horse forward, to listen and to learn. The huntsman leant down, cupping hand to ear and nodded. So, the royal was still in his woodland harbour, lying up with younger stag, for company and for watch.

A call from Keigwin, Jacob turned, nodded and spoke to his hounds and wound his horn. Whips cracked, Martin and Richard riding forward, in accord with Jacob's orders. Alongside rode the boy Pearce. Tongues lolled, sterns waved. The field moved off behind hounds to fall in behind the Squire, vying for pride of place and vantage amongst their fellows. Some, anxious not to be seen beside those of lesser rank, wanted to cut a figure in the fashion and the show. Others cared only for the chase, for the danger, the excitement of riding a horse at speed across a wild country. Countrymen watching the driving of the pack, commented knowingly upon the wisdom of the huntsman should he cast them wrong. There were those who were wise in country lore, caring nothing for the show, who understood only the challenge — the speed and guile of the hunted stag duelling with the nose and stamina of hounds.

A motley collection followed behind the hunt. Ponies and carts carrying food and ales for the mounted. It was an occasion, a holiday, a day of festivity and enjoyment. The collation of cold poultry, brawn and hams, fruits and cheeses, fit only for the Gods or an Englishman a-hunting!

Jacob had sent Pearce on, to view the stag away. Richard and Martin were to make a broad sweep, right-handed, away from the woodland to signal lest the deer should run their side.

His arm held aloft, Jenkyn gave signal to the mounted to halt and cease their chattering, as Jacob encouraged his hounds forward with language few but they could understand. Into the damp woods muzzles down, sterns aloft, hounds worried and fretted over the moist scent-laden earth.

A lone hound's tentative cry. Whimper of uncontained excitement, a duet as a companion confirmed, the deep blood racing bay as Merlin joined in affirmation. The pack in joyful chorus as their music rang echoing through the oaks. The pair of deer rose from their rest, heads held high, ears flicked below lofty crown as flared nostrils scented the air. Daintily they stepped to the woodland's edge. The royal stamped a delicate hoof as the dreaded cry of the hounds grew ever nearer, eyes searched the landscape ahead. Quarters hunched as they both sprang forward to break cover together. The monarch of the moor headed towards the north-east to the high granite lands, the wind behind him where he knew his scent would carry least to his pursuers. His companion turned left-handed, near where Richard and Martin sat motionless, to let him pass to hunt another day. Their quarry was the royal. The king of the red deer that flourished in wild Penwith.

"I have no wish to follow, Teek," Becky reined in her pony. I do not understand the chase and I have no care for killing."

"I have seen my share of death, and but little of my sweeting, who is so very much alive. No ways do I wish to share her with those that hunt. I saw the look that some of the fine gentlemen gave thee and," he growled, " 'twas not the look they would give their sister." Side by side they rode wheresoever their ponies wished to take them. Where width of lane or open moor allowed, their thighs would brush and their hands reach out to touch or hold awhile.

The track narrowed, frowning bushes locked thorns overhead. In single file, arms held to shield their faces from the tearing branches, they squeezed forward to where a sunlit glade awaited and a spring rose to tumble into a crystal stream. Each had heard tell of the holy well of Madron, where since time began lovers had made their wishes known to the Great Gods on high. Now their turn had come, to seek their blessing and the gift and joy of procreation.

Teek slid from his pony's back and looped their reins over a low-slung bough to turn and catch Becky within his outstretched arms; clasping her to him in tight embrace. They stood before the well. Gently he pushed her bonnet from her head and untied the silken bow. Tossed free, her fair hair tumbled to her waist. Hand in hand they wandered to the water's edge, to tie a pale blue ribbon around the green, grey-whiskered lichen of a may tree's twisted arm, whereon myriad pieces of faded silk and taffeta were already knotted: a token to the pagan gods of many a lover's tryst.

They stood at the well's side. Silent in a silent world, fingers entwined, blue eyes gazing into those of brown.

Cupping his hands, Teek knelt to scoop the magic water into his palms to proffer to his love. Becky sipped and likewise followed, for him to drink from hers. Then they plucked rushes and tied them in the form of a Christian crucifix. If it floated the wish would be granted; if it sank, they would be denied. Twice times a cross hesitated — and slowly sank to twist and turn beneath the crystal running water. But the third cross swept onwards with the stream to float upon the water before the laughing lovers. Blue eyes brimmed, and strong arms of comfort took time to quell her tears. But Becky would not reveal the nature of the plea the ancient gods declined to grant.

Arms around each other's waist, her head upon his shoulder, they walked onward to the nearby Baptistry. They entered, there to kneel side by side upon the chancel step. There they made their vows, their God their only witness. Thence to the open air. To lay, together amongst the dampened grass hidden by furze, sprinkled in golden flower.

" 'Tis said that when the gorse is not in bloom, kissing is out of fashion."

"How come that to be?"

169

h

"Silly Teek, even in the coldest frost always the gorse has blossom."

"Then kiss me in proof."

She turned to cradle his head within her arms, her ripe lips wide upon his open mouth. He felt the press of her firm breasts upon his chest. He felt an urge he could do little to control, even should he so wish. He turned to roll atop the maid that both might vent their passion.

Panting and exhausted they tumbled apart. Side by side, they lay upon their backs, heads cradled in their hands, to gaze heavenwards and muse upon sweet thoughts of further pleasures yet to come.

At last Teek rose and stretched his arms above his head, to look down upon his love. " 'Tis time we called the banns and were wed in church."

"Maybe I am but a simple maid, dear Teek, for I believe within this holy place our God has already given us His blessing. To church we have to go for sake of our kin, else the gossiping crones will make much ado." She smiled at the thought. "But to thee, Teek, I am now married and so it will be till the end of time."

She rose and clung to him as tears trickled down her cheeks in the sweet sadness of her love. His protective arm clasped her to him whilst he stroked her hair. Tenderly he kissed her silken head. Then to search, to fumble and to fondle as their passion once again was roused.

Young Pearce had watched the stag leave his harbour. Cap waving above his head, he stood in his stirrups to holloa him away. Within the woodland the cry of the hounds rattled round and round.

The sound of his hounds was music to his ears. He listened. A holloa. The stag was afoot. Keigwin gathered his reins, his leather boots squeezed the flanks of his bay that needed little encouragement to break into a canter for the field to follow as their quarry made for the high ground near Boswarva's stone-topped carn. The stag ate up the ground beneath his cloven feet. From out the woodland pied hounds spilled with Merlin at their head.

170

Across the rugged hills he knew. Past the hollow stone of Lanyon Quoit, the hard-riding Squire and his field pursued their prey: up and down steep rock-strewn hills to leap or wade the streams below.

Richard and Martin, with duty done, cut across country to join the chase, as hounds pressed upon their quarry. The going and the pace began to take its toll as the field thinned in its pursuit; some to fall back, and drop out to await the arrival of victuals.

Thigh and back aching to the unaccustomed sport, Hawkyns' horse scurried down a steep incline. Why in the Devil's name had he accepted Keigwin's invite? He leant backwards over the cantle of his saddle, feet thrust straight-legged forward, firm into the stirrups, fearful lest he plunge over his horse's head. His mind raced. Damnation to honour! Damnation to false pride! Twin knaves that demanded he join the chase! May the gods prevent him from foolish fall before the followers. No cheap pleasure at his expense! He'd be damned, but he'd show 'em!

Head up, hands down, seated firmly in his saddle, Jenkyn Keigwin led his field with accustomed grace. Jacob, his guide, as onward they raced. A glance behind, there were Thomas and Nicholas, father and son at ease with each other, following the hounds with practised eye. To his right, Martin and Richard chaffing and challenging as when they were boys, riding stride for stride across the roughest country. He smiled in quiet satisfaction at the pleasure he was giving, the sport they were having!

Before them lay the Red River, in spate from autumn rains. To Hawkyns' relief Jacob halted upon the high ground, to view the stag as it entered the water to swim and to scramble up the opposing bank. The hounds were still some distance from their quarry but the gap was beginning to close as Merlin lead his pack into the swollen stream, to be swept seawards by the torrent before gaining foothold upon the far side. Jacob lead the Squire upstream where the huntsmen bunched to follow him, to cross a wide and shingle ford. Their quarry was making good lost ground as Merlin came to Jacob's horn, to cast in a sweeping arc, to hit off the scent of the hunted deer with whimper, then full-throated cry as

171

Jacob's voice encouraged them in their task. The pack once more with deep melody continued with the chase, the sound of Jacob's horn now ringing about the countryside.

Across the stream the followers fanned outwards as they crested the rising ground, greeted below by a patchwork of stone-hedged fields that they must cross; granite banks topped with furze.

Jacob and Keigwin took a pull, as sure-footed horses leapt to dwell atop the bank and safely down to gallop onto the next and repeat with practised effort. Stirrup to stirrup, they rode, their shouts of laughter and encouragement carried by the wind.

Leaning forward over his horse's withers, Richard led Martin into the next wall of rock. He would be first to bank the hedge: his, the honour to be first at the death.

On leaden legs he could rise to barely a trot. Mouth agape, tongue loose hanging, the once proud head weighed low. The cry of the pack grew louder in his ears. Soon he must seek sanctuary or turn at bay in some chosen place to face his enemy and die as bravely as he might. He jumped the hedges to the valley bottom where ran the river Hayle. Flanks heaved as lungs gasped the air in pain, that he might run once more. He swam the river and westward took some strides, to retrace his steps and re-enter from whence he had come, to spoil and confuse his scent, to trot and swim upstream. Trees began to overhang the water's edge, a crop-filled heron flapped upwards from his path, mobbed by marauding crows. Yet onward he drove himself; to stop, to look, to listen. His lowered muzzle touched the water's surface to gulp his fill, then to raise his head once more, alert for danger. Droplets fell, to freckle the water beneath.

Where the hillside eased towards the river the brothers saw the circling hounds upon the far side as they cast the river's bank, working to pick up the scent the water could not hold.

Forward they strove in glorious rivalry, kicking on their sweat-soaked horses. On to the next wall. Richard rose, to land atop the crumbling stone that gave a false foothold. He felt his horse falling and tried to kick free to tumble upon the sloping turf beneath. But the unyielding leather of his boot was trapped. He crashed beside his horse that rolled upon him, to rise to bolt down the boulder-strewn hillside, his rider dragged alongside. Martin drove his horse on, willing it to catch his brother's. Whipping and riding with hands and heels, up to its quarters now a neck, reaching left-handed to clutch the flapping reins with fingers locked in desperate struggle. He jerked his right rein to bring his horse sideways to the hill and to wrestle them both to a halt. Swiftly he swung from the saddle. Round the panting horses' heads he ran to release the swollen foot from near-side stirrup. Head downwards upon the turf, his brother's eyes were closed. Blood oozed from the torn face and scalp staining the green grass red. The fingers on his hands raw. Nails black and broken where, dragged, he had tried to clutch the ground in frantic desperation. Anxious fingers fastened upon his brother's wrist, where the pulse still throbbed a feeble beat.

He eased the clothes from round Richard's throat, uttering aloud a prayer for his life while he straightened the still form. A shout, a figure on top of the surrounding bank. A horseman leapt down and the boy Pearce galloped to where Martin knelt.

"Go! Tell my father Richard is sorely hurt."

His pony swung about, rowelled spurs raked red the flanks as Pearce took off to head the field of huntsmen. Gently Martin placed his pillowed jerkin beneath his brother's head; he knelt by his side, holding the torn hand, willing him to live.

They gathered about him as Jenkyn surveyed the scene and gave his orders: "Thomas, go search in that far byre for bier on which he may be carried, see if there is a cart or waggon. Sir John, yonder manor may help us in our plight, we will take him there."

In the ancient building hand tools lay, cobweb covered, awaiting the call of spring. Above, lying across the truss, wee bundles of woven hazel to pen the lambing ewes. Swiftly Tom chose the stoutest and ran with it to where the huntsmen

173

were clustered in concern around their fallen comrade. Carefully they laid him upon the lattice to follow the narrow lane where Sir John had gone before.

A high wall of stone part-hid a handsome house. They made their way through double wrought iron gates down a flag-stoned path to where Hawkyns waited in the open doorway. He stood aside that they might enter, to meet the commanding presence of the mistress of the house. She was dressed in black, relieved only by embroidery of semi-precious stones. An erect white ruff framed the mass of auburn hair that crowned a face of aristocratic mien. The bearers stopped before her. She looked upon their burden, lifted and felt his limp wrist. Paused. And raised his eyelid to peer beneath.

"Pray follow me," she led through rich-carpeted room, and beckoned them to follow up a broad, carved oak staircase, where from the landing led a wide passage to a chamber beyond. She drew back the curtain that surrounded a massive bed.

"Sebastian," she addressed an aged manservant who throughout had maintained his presence by her side, "pull back the covers. Gentlemen, lay the poor soul, gently now, to rest upon the bed."

She leant across to place slim fingers upon his forehead. "He is sorely hurt but in my care will surely mend. Now, pray tell me sir, who are you and who is my injured guest?"

"I am Jenkyn Keigwin of Mousehole, my lady," giving a slight bow, "and this my friend, Sir John Hawkyns. It is my son, Richard, who is injured. Today we have been hunting of the stag."

"Well, Master Keigwin and Sir John, I am Anne Vivyan, mistress of this house and my servants will attend to your needs. I and my niece will examine the extent of your son's hurt. Never fear, Jenkyn Keigwin," as she noted the surprise upon his face, "we womenfolk have nursed gentlemen before."

She smiled at his discomfiture. "Sebastian will arrange for some ale and light repast if you will follow him. Then Sebastian, send Mistress Elizabeth to me. Tell the servants to attend the needs of the horses."

She turned her back upon her guests to look, once more,

174

pensive upon the motionless figure. A young girl, Elizabeth, shortly arrived with pitchers of steaming, aromatic water and cloths of soft linen that she set beside the bed.

Richard stirred. His body an aching mass, his eyes barely open, he squinted through long lashes to the canopy above. Where the devil was he? God's truth, his bones. Had he been racked? He did not know that colour, nor that pattern. He turned his head sideways. Pain shot through him. He flinched and closed his eyes. What in Heaven's name had happened? He disciplined his mind through the haze of a memory confused. Think. They had hunted. Where? They had found at Landithy. Where did they draw? They had found below Trengwainton tarn. His eyes flickered open to stare wide-eyed. Slowly he recalled the hunt. The freedom of the open fields. The pace, the horse banking the granite hedges at the canter. Up, dwell a second, and down — kick on for the next. Show Martin how to pilot across the country! He tried a smile at the thought of their contest. A race, a match between the brothers. All was blurred. He must remember. He tried to raise himself upon his elbow, to fall back once more and into the soft black arms of unconscious peace.

In the shallowing waters of the river's bend, brown reeds grew in regimented profusion, tufted heads swaying gently in the breeze. Upon the bank, rusty, spear-shaped leaves of goat-willow still clung to green-twisted limbs. There, where chill waters ran to his belly, the stag stood, deep hidden where none might see. Motionless save for the flare of nostrils sensing, testing the afternoon air for scent of hound or horse — or man! But of scent of danger there was none.

Alone with their charge, the women struggled to cut, to pull and release the clamp of harsh leather from his leg. Thence to breeches and hose.

"Your virtue must remain unsullied," Anne looked to her niece and with some play and a wry smile she cast a linen

175

sheet across their patient's loins.

"But, Aunt, sometime surely I must know what it is that makes him a man and me a woman?"

"That day will come soon enough."

"Not even a peep?"

"No! Not even a peep." Anne smiled as her niece gave mock pout of disappointment. Then to lift his head and shoulders upwards to be bathed. His scalp was gently washed, likewise the whole of him. Sensitive fingers probed his wounds and delicately examined the swelling of his leg, where intricate pattern of purple veins suffused the swollen ankle.

Lady Anne stood back that her niece might feel the injuries and thus learn, then made her judgement.

"His scalp is torn, yet will heal. But of his skull I am unsure. It may well be cracked. We must show great care. There are bruises and cuts in plenty, they too will heal quickly for he is fit and strong. We must, however, guard against any form of infection. 'Tis his leg that is of grave concern. The muscles and the tendons are stretched and twisted and will be painful. There is no doubt that bone too is broken, but until the swelling is reduced, none can be sure how serious it may be." She smiled at her ward, "But dear niece, he will mend in our care, and you shall learn some secrets of your forefathers. Now, watch over him, and stoke the fire. Do keep him warm whilst I inform the gentlemen below."

They rose as she entered the room. "Sir John, Jenkyn Keigwin. I trust you have dined well?"

They nodded and Sir John started to proffer his thanks but she dismissed them with a smile and downward wave of her hand. She turned to Keigwin: "Your son, sir, is sorely hurt but will mend. Except his leg will need utmost skill and patience for him not to become lame or crippled. Fortune has blessed me with a knowledge of the healing arts and I am versed in the remedies and potions that nature has provided for our use. Those employed by our forefathers." She looked with unusual intensity into Keigwin's eyes. "With God's help, your son will mend in my care. He must not be moved. I have looked closely at his wounds and thus I speak. Entrust him to me."

"My Lady Anne, pray what may I say?" For once Keigwin was at a loss for words. "Your wisdom is renowned. We are indeed fortunate that the injury happened where you, my lady, were so close at hand. I do indeed entrust him to your care and pray to God that your medicines may repair his battered body."

"Gentlemen, come see him when so ever you please." She turned to Sebastian, "See these gentlemen to their horses."

Richard began to stir, his eyes flickered open to gaze bemused at two strange women at his bedside. "In God's name, where am I?" He tried to turn his body the better to see them only to utter a yelp of pain that he could not suppress, as his shattered leg advised him of his injury. Anne spoke to him in soft assuring tones and told him of the day's events: the hunt and the fall; of his father's concern and of her knowledge of the wonders of the wild herbs that God had planted for the needs of Man. Sebastian entered the room with lighted candles set in silver sticks. These he placed upon a nearby cupboard and at his mistress's behest, made good the fire and left.

"Now, Elizabeth, place your arm carefully about him and lift his trunk, for, Richard, I wish you to drink of this potion of herbs that I have prepared to ease your pain and to help you to sleep." He did as he was bid and sipped the brew. Elizabeth's strong arms eased him gently back upon his pillow. As they tended his wounds Lady Anne told him of the history and the nature of the plants with which she was treating him, that he too might have confidence in their healing powers and also to distract him from his pain and suffering.

"This is a concoction I made, the recipe of which my mother gave to me, as did her mother before her and so from generation to generation. 'Tis called by the Celtic name of vervain. We gather it upon the hillsides about, as did the Druid priesthood of our forefathers. Merlin the magician was given to using this, the wizard's herb, when making his spells and magical potions. Perhaps they had learned of

177

its mysteries from the Greeks and Romans whom they had fought." She continued to bathe his wounds with clean pieces of soft fabric which Elizabeth passed to her.

"When the Druids dressed the wounds of those smitten in war with the leaves and juices of this herb, their heroes were believed to have become inviolate and therefore immortal. But of that enough." She looked at him, her eyes questioning, "Does that soothe the pain?"

"Aye my lady, indeed it does."

"Then so it did for our Saviour. For it grew upon the hill of Calvary. There it was gathered to staunch the wounds of Christ Jesus. Thus I prefer to name it 'the Holy Herb'. Let us pray its gifts will heal your wounds, as it did His and those of your war-like forefathers. I believe it will. But of immortality — well of that I cannot be so certain." She looked up from her task to smile into his eyes. "We shall have to wait and see." She smiled. "Now shall we attend to your leg? We must pull the sheets aside. Hold the candle above, Elizabeth, that I may better see." Again her finger-tips caressed the smooth, swollen skin that concealed the damage beneath. Satisfied at last with the examination. "Elizabeth, replace the candlestick and please to pass the compress." Upon the bed she placed the dish that held the potion. "Now, Master Richard, this may be hurtful. There-fore clench my niece's hand when you can no longer bear the pain. Elizabeth, hold that of Richard whilst I place the dressing upon the injury. This is a compress of the root of knit-bone, sometimes called the comfrey, that grows by the streams edge, or where 'tis damp amongst the woodland shade. Elizabeth has newly-gathered this to grate the root into a paste." Carefully she poulticed the injured limb which she then covered with bruised, dark green leaves of that same plant. " 'Twill soothe and then will heal." Tenderly she wound a bandage of linen to hold the dressing in its place. Done and nearly knotted, she sideways cast a downward glance to see and to smile. Richard had relaxed his grip upon his nurse's hand, but still he held her fingers with his own. Her niece too was gently smiling, unwittingly, upon her patient.

*　　*　　*　　*

Dusk had settled as Jacob and the boy Pearce led the pack and the following clatter of huntsmen into the yard at Landithy. Taciturn as ever, Jacob would not delay for victuals for himself. His own hunger would play but second place to the welfare of horse and hound. He would take them to their own stable and kennel, where they would rest in straw and upon the benches that were home.

News of the fall had reached the ladies of the household and the nature of Richard's injuries had not diminished in the telling. Thus it was with relief that they heard the true details of his accident, awful as it might be, and with thanksgiving that he was being cared for by a lady so skilled in the healing arts.

Dinner over, the ladies retired to needlework and to music, leaving the menfolk to relax with wine and with cards after the exertions of the day.

"Gentlemen," John Hawkyns carefully looked at the hand he held before throwing a card upon the table, "I thank you for your courtesy and your hospitality, sir," nodding to Nicholas. "I must therefore repay you in some kind, although," he continued in rueful voice, playfully rubbing his rear, "by God's truth, I may have to take to my bed tomorrow, since my arse may be less amused by the punishment it has received this day, and my crotch would have me believe I am gelded. Same as that aged nag of thine! Thomas, you will doubtless join me at sea with its dangers and mayhap its fortunes. You other gentlemen may feel you are much safer upon land. So you will be if you heed what I say."

His mood became serious as he addressed them in sombre voice. "The Queen will now wish to tease King Philip, to show that with our victory this small country of hers is as mighty as that of Spain." He paused to ensure that all were intently listening. "She will wish to strengthen her grip upon her country and her throne. To rout out those vipers that could threaten her. There is many a loyal Roman that will be taken for trial for treason, to be burnt or racked; mark my words. Therefore do I beseech you, as so you live and value your family, speak well of your sovereign. Do not associate with any of the papist breed lest you be tainted." He looked at Jenkyn then to Nicholas, "Let not your church

179

celebrate Mass in the manner of Rome lest it be thought you too are of that kind. Distance yourselves as far as ye may, but not so far as to become as Calvin's flock. Keep to the middle of the track. Be watchful, be wary and be seen to praise our Queen. Now have I said enough." He looked downwards at his cards. "Let us resume our play, for I fancy the hand I have."

Jenkyn looked toward Nicholas for support. "I speak for my daughter's husband and myself. We know your words are spoken with good intent and for our benefit. We will indeed be careful and, Sir John, we shall faithfully follow your sound advice.

Nicholas nodded. "Indeed, I shall advise Ralph Harbarte, our parish priest. As you rightly know, Sir John, in these parts we do indeed have many who pay tribute to the Bishop of Rome, but they offer no enmity towards our Queen. There are those of Spanish blood that would not take up arms against us and are loyal, wishing only to continue their worship in their own fashion. We must ensure they are encouraged to do so in some other parish."

Returned to the yard of The Mermaid, Teek and Becky unsaddled their mounts and turned them into their stalls, where fresh hay and water awaited them.

"I have been away too long and must go down to the harbour to see all is well on the *Golden Hind*." The seaman looked upwards to the clouds above and shook his head. "The sea is flat at this moment but the wind is swinging easterly and I am feared for her as she presently lies." He reached his hand to squeeze hers. "I shall be back within a couple of hours to sup with you."

"Nay, Teek, do not return for my sake, for I have other duties to which I must attend."

"Pray, what duties?" his voice was surprised, "surely only business of the inn?"

"What calls me I cannot say, for I shall be away awhile. But all in good time you shall know."

"Becky, for Christ's sake . . . ."

"Ssh." She placed her finger on his lips. "Don't fret,

dear Teek. No need for jealousy, but 'tis a secret that shall shortly be revealed. Be you patient now!" she chided.

Chapter Eleven

Jenkyn knew Thomasine was fretting. He had done his utmost to assure her that Richard was in the most caring and capable of hands but his words would not convince. Only the evidence of her own eyes and ears would suffice, "For what, Jenkyn, if his leg be shattered or badly broken? He will be a cripple for life. Supported by a crutch as some poor beggar! What maid would want such for a husband? Only some plain or barren Jane, ill-favoured to breed more sons for the line of Keigwin!"

To Thomasine for a son so physical, a son so active, to become a cripple would be a double blow. Thus did she torment herself until at her insistence Jenkyn put quill to parchment to write to Lady Anne acquainting her with the proposal that Thomasine, in the company of her daughter Elizabeth Flemyng, wished to visit Trewinnard to see such progress as Richard was making. The boy Pearce was summoned and entrusted with the letter for delivery.

Jenkyn hoped that the few days delay that his procrastinations and protestations had bought, would have allowed some of Richard's uglier wounds to have healed, and he would be less disfigured for his mother's gaze. Pies and cheeses were prepared, those that were his favourite. Fruits and delicacies that Lady Anne might not possess were packed in panniers, together with rare spices and wines, to which few but Keigwin would have access. Gifts to her ladyship.

With an armed Jacob as escort, Thomasine sat side saddle upon her favourite palfrey as they departed early in the morning to break their journey at Landithy, to lunch with Elizabeth, thence in company, to resume the journey east-

182

ward.

Lady Anne greeted her visitors with informality that put them at ease. Up the great staircase she led, pausing upon wide, oak boarded landing, where she raised her hand and finger for silence. From the bedchamber beyond came the tinkling ripple of girlish laughter and the deeper tones of Richard in rebuke of his nurse.

"What! I saw you — put it back at once. Those are not the rules by which gentlemen play! By Jupiter! — I would call a man out for less!"

The laughter continued. "But pray sir, are you so damaged that you take me for a gentleman, sir? Most that I know seem to recognise a lady when they see one. And those gentlemen allow a lady a little licence when playing cards!"

"Licence be damned. Had we been playing for sovereigns, you'd have had my shirt off my back by now I vow. And me a poor patient who is sick and helpless in your witch's care!"

The laughter continued afresh as Lady Anne coughed, and ushered her guests into the bedchamber. Confronting his mother, seated beside a blazing fire, was Richard, one leg outstretched upon a stool. Upon a low table a deck of cards. A young lady rose from her seat, a blush adding further compliment to feature and form of exquisite beauty. Elizabeth bobbed a curtsey and Thomasine extended her hand.

Lady Anne introduced the visitors.

"Our patient's mother and sister have come to see how he fares. Mistress Keigwin, Elizabeth Flemyng . . . my niece, Elizabeth Carlyon."

Elizabeth smiled a welcome and went forward to kiss her brother's cheek whilst Thomasine engaged Lady Anne in earnest conversation as to Richard's wounds, and the medication with which she treated them.

"And so, you laggard," Elizabeth addressed her brother, "whilst dear Mama thought you sick and ailing, we find you in luxury's lap playing trump with a beautiful maid. Aye, and one such as can trounce you, or so would seem by the cards before her! We have travelled tirelessly to be at your side, sir. Shame upon you," she teased. "You are naught but a malingerer."

" 'Tis not so, in honesty, Mistress Flemyng," Elizabeth rushed to his defence. "Richard, hitch upon the nightshirt and show your sister your broken limb." She turned. "In truth your brother has been sick, but only now does he commence his recovery. A debt due to the skill of my aunt who is versed in the healing arts."

Elizabeth reached for her namesake's hand. "He is my brother that I truly love, and I do but jest."

Richard raised the hem of the woollen shirt to below his left knee. There they looked upon a leather gaiter, laced with leather thong.

"This is my own device that I have used to mend the bones of animals. Lambs and the like, when they have suffered similarly," Lady Anne informed them. "But in the case of Richard, the gaiter holds in place a compress of healing herbs and into its leather sides are stitched wooden splints of ash to hold the bone in its firm position. This he must wear for several weeks, until the potions have worked their cure and the bone is properly knit."

Thomasine smiled at Richard and reached to squeeze his hand as she bent to inspect the simple device, that she might herself both learn and better report to Keigwin upon the remarkable skills of Lady Anne.

"Some would say that my aunt is a witch with magical powers, when in truth she is a healing angel who puts to use the herbs and the powers that God has granted her."

"Do you also learn these arts?" Thomasine gently inquired.

"Indeed I do, for it would be foolish to have access to the knowledge of our Druid forebears, yet not to use it for those who are distressed. Rather akin, would it not be, to the parable of the talents?"

"Indeed it would and I believe you may be blessed with a wisdom beyond your years," Thomasine honestly replied. She rose to kiss her son upon his forehead and look into his eyes with a mother's concern.

"Lady Anne, thank you with all my heart for that which you and your niece do for my son. I now know that he is in skilled and loving hands."

"Come ladies," said the mistress of the house. "I am now embarrassed and in truth 'tis time we retired to let our patient rest. Richard, I shall send Sebastian with your broth and the potion for you to take. Until the morning," she smiled with undisguised affection. Had Sir Edward not been killed, might not she too have had a son such as Richard? Perhaps yet he might become part of her small family, for she could sense the bond that was unwittingly growing between the two young people. Would that tender plant one day blossom into love? Who can tell what fate may have in store, except those blessed with the gift of prophecy. Yet she would aid that for which she knew Elizabeth wished deep down within her heart.

She placed her arm around Thomasine's shoulder. " 'Til the morning, Richard, sleep you well."

Whilst others had returned to their homes, Sir John and his lady continued to enjoy the company of the Flemyng household.

The girls had done much to restore the spirits of Lady Katherine as they eagerly awaited the presentation of their brother's mystery play that was soon to be performed. Little had they seen of John, who was absent for long periods, striving for perfection in performance and presentation. Writing and rewriting, criticising and rehearsing the actors. The making of scenery, of costumes and masks, to be carried by those who by movement and gesture would simulate that which the story outlined. The rocks. The sea. The voyages.

Becky's nimble fingers cut and stitched the costumes.

Oblivious to all else, John was lost in a world of yester-year. Where God rewarded the humble and meek and the unrepentant evil-doer was damned for eternity.

The soft rains of the previous night had now cleared from the west. Gutters were flushed, the narrow streets and alleyways cleansed. Dressed in Sunday attire, the folk of Mousehole walked the hill to the church at Paul. To stop on occasion to converse, or to turn and admire the sea-wards view, a pause to regain their breath from the steep ascent. By placard and by word of mouth it was widely broadcast that there was to be a performance of a mystery play which John Flemyng, Doctor of Divinity of Oxford,

185

and from Madron, was to present for their pleasure and education. It was said that strolling players and musicians had been hired, and many a local personage pressed to display their talents.

The Keigwin family pews were filled and Jenkyn Keigwin noted with care all those that were present. For not to attend was to offend the Squire on the occasion of his grandson's presentation.

The nave and the side aisles were thronged: the men anxious to glimpse sight of Sir John, newly-knighted hero of the Armada; the ladies to observe the latest taste in the fashion of Plymouth and therefore London and hence the Court itself.

A hush within the crowded church, as from the north transept the gowned figure of the young cleric stepped forward upon raised platform to address the people in the language of England and of Cornwall. He was, he said, both actor and chorus. With blank verse he would link and describe the scenes that all might comprehend the unfolding of the play.

By oratory and by gesture John led his audience back to the days of the sixth century. There he introduced Perphius, a Celtic chieftain of South Wales, who had a son named Paul Aurelian. He told how it was the wish of Paul to attend monastery school upon the island of Ynys Pyr. There to be tutored by Saint Illtuyd, the wisest of all Britons. Perphius was pleased to grant the wish of his son, and there, the young Paul sat at the feet of this Holy Man until he had learned all that his master might teach to him.

In dumb show the scene was portrayed to all assembled within the church.

"At sixteen years of age, Paul left his tutor to build a chapel and simple cell in which to lead a life of prayer and piety, until such time as he himself might be raised to the priesthood."

By use of simple property, the scene was changed again to create the magnificence of Castle Dore, the seat of King Mark of Cornwall, to whose attendance Paul Aurelian had been summoned.

"To the west of his country, the King proclaimed, the

populace had adopted the teachings of the evil Morgan —
a Celtic monk who had taught his followers to deny the
importance of God and the concept of original sin. Patiently,
Paul converted the heretics and restored their faith in the one
Almighty God. He inspired these people to build a place in
which to worship."

Step by step the play revealed that the church in which
they were presently gathered was that founded by Paul
Aurelian nearly one thousand years before. It began to dawn
upon the congregation that their own history was before
them, explained in a manner they could comprehend, for was
it not their people who had been the heathens who had
turned their faces away from God?

"Such was the affection and esteem in which the young
Paul was held that the forebears of those gathered wished
him to become their bishop. Yet he could not do so, for
such was his humility he would accept neither rank nor
office."

The audience watched an angel arise to beckon Paul, and
point for him to travel across the water to where the land of
Brittany awaited.

"Together with twelve of his disciples, from the pilgrims'
port of Mousehole, he embarked to travel thence, as he was
destined so to do."

John Flemyng, both Paul Aurelian and narrator, captured
the congregation by his art as he transported his listeners to
where, upon the eve of his leaving, Paul visited his sister and
other nuns of her calling, who lived a life of solitude and
penance where now is Newlyn. As he spoke, from behind
the pillar of the south transept, palms together in symbolic
prayer, stepped the robed figure of Sitofalla his sister.

"By the sea shore of Gwavas Lake they wished to build
a convent. Yet the site they chose was too confined. At
low water Paul and Sitofalla marked the retreated line of
sea with two rows of rocks. Side by side upon the shore
they knelt, to raise their faces heavenward in prayer."

A gasp from the congregation as the cowl that covered
Sitofalla's head slipped backward and the mask held before
could not hide the handsome countenance of Pearce, the
boy. However, as John described the two at prayer the

187

face behind the mask was soon forgotten as the canvas that portrayed the sea receded and the people who were rocks stood erect to become pillars, and the pillars a wall that held at bay the water as it returned upon the flood.

"By a miracle dry land had been created in answer to their prayer, there was the convent built."

The words of the narrator now took them to the isle of Ushant, off the ragged coast of Brittany, where Paul settled with his followers, to build simple cells of rock and turf in which to live and pray.

Yet once more, the congregation witnessed the angel beckoning Paul Aurelian to cross the wild water to live upon the mainland. With manner and with word did the youthful John give very likeness to the ageing of the Celtic wise man, as he portrayed his gifts of prophecy and the many miracles he wrought whilst living a life of devotion and simplicity, loved by all his spirit touched.

In the final act holy men were guided into a reluctant acceptance of the Bishopric of Leon, where Paul lived to a venerable age.

Thus did John Flemyng write and act the play of miracle and of mystery in a form to which all might relate, portraying the life of a high born Celtic holy man, who had linked the three countries of his race, near one thousand years before. The portrayal of his deeds had reached out to touch them all, an example of piety and wisdom everlasting. For was not Ynys Pyr the Holy Island of Caldey? Was not their church, his church? And upon the coast of Brittany, was not the town of Pol de Leon the place where he once lived?

None might escape the message of the play. The meek shall inherit the earth.

Dinner at the Manor at Mousehole was unusually solemn, even the bluff and worldly-wise Sir John was in a humble mood and retired earlier than his wont after only a brief game of cards.

In the high meadows above Mousehole where the springs rise to fall and turn the mill wheel far below, Becky removed her bonnet from her head, to toss free her hair to stream at the

188

whim of a playful breeze.

"Teek."

He looked at her with a start, into the eyes the wind had filled with tears, guilty that his mind was upon the sea below.

"Teek," she squeezed his hand, " 'tis time we told the vicar we wish to wed."

"Aye, my love." He looked to where the thrashing sea was covering the little island, dousing the chapel in a torrent of white spray.

Again she squeezed his hand. He turned to face her. Never had he seen her more beautiful than on this wild blustering day.

"The barque must first be put in safe anchorage, then Christmas over, we'll be wed directly. I'll talk with your father, for with him I must consult. Your father . . . "

"No, dear Teek, we cannot delay, for don't you see, you yourself are soon to become a father."

"Becky," he held both her hands, to gaze hard into her eyes, "you be certain, sure?"

She took away a hand and patted her belly. " 'Tis a warm and comforting feeling, Teek. For I wish to be the mother of your children." She looked up at him, the wind pink of her cheeks concealed her blushes but could not hide the glow of pride. He held her tightly to him.

"When you are at sea, I shall never be alone, for I shall always have a part of you with me. Dear, my dear Teek," she whispered.

The visitors' stay was near its close. The days were short and the gales of early winter were gathering in strength. Heavy breakers crashed, thundering against the harbour wall, throwing spray high into the air to fall as rainbow mist over the house of Keigwin.

The *Golden Hind* rocked and snagged at her anchorage. Thomas must take her to safe harbour at Falmouth. There to lie in the lee of St. Anthony's Head, safe from storm. The batteries of the twin sentinels of Pendennis and St. Mawes would guard her haven.

It was the last evening for the guests at Landithy. Flemyng

ladies and household servants excelled themselves, preparing a feast Sir John declared, "fit for the Queen of England!"

With sonnets by candlelight sweetly sung, the ladies entertained their menfolk, to be greeted by much applause and laughter. Nicholas Flemyng, at the head of table, tapped for silence, to rise and speak in handsome terms of his guests and their attributes. Finally and with a flourish, he doffed his cap and bowed to Sir John and Lady Katherine and bid his family rise to drink a bumper health to their visitors.

Sir John was not to be outdone and in similar and jocular vein, acknowledged his host's compliments and praised the unstinted hospitality of all that had contributed to their pleasure.

"Would that I could spend more time in this land of the west, this haven of culture and christianity, of wise and fearless men; and ladies of captivating charm." He bowed. "In future Lady Katherine and myself will come by sea. Not that we wish to be better informed as to the dangers of your wild coast, but rather that we may be less informed as to the torment to be derived from a saddle placed upon some poor and undernourished horse whose every step is agony to its rider! Indeed, I would rather suffer the extremities of the Inquisition than to trust my buttocks once again to one of Nicholas Flemyng's wooden-headed nags, particularly when rising to the trot!" Midst such laughter he rubbed that portion of his anatomy most aggrieved by his equestrian exploits.

The ladies at last retired to leave the men to their own devices. Pipes were lit and liberal quantities of wine were drunk, as the younger men besought Sir John to recount to them more of his past adventures.

Little persuading was needed. Hawkyns, now relaxed and in fine fettle, spoke of his exploits on the west coast of Africa. His bargaining with friendly Portuguese settlers. He enthralled his listeners with descriptions of strange animals, and even stranger peoples. Men and women naked, save a small covering for their privities, of warlike and of peaceable peoples. Thence to the Indies, where he had taken his human cargo to trade with Spanish colonists, where Indians carried sheaves of arrows tipped with a poison so fierce it would cause a man to die in seconds, where prized womenfolk supported voluptuous breasts with cups of beaten gold.

Of their treachery — and of their treasure he recounted at length. He told too of pearl fishers who would dive to great depths, unaided, to grovel and gather the large oysters that concealed the greatest pearls: to risk all for but a mere trinket in return. He spoke of lands that grew exotic fruits and spices; of seas clear and blue where swam weird and wonderful fishes. Spellbound they listened. John the priest, Thomas the soldier, plying their guest with questions to which he gave full answer. Did these unclothed heathen know of God? What did they worship? How were the Spanish ports fortified? What numbers of fighting men did they possess? Each answer gave rise to further question.

" 'Tis enough," he said at long last. "Time for my bed-chamber. Tom, do not fear, for you will also have adventure and the wealth that becomes the brave. And for you, John, why there are many heathen, black, red, aye and yellow, so I hear tell, who have never heard of our God and whose souls are waiting for you to claim them in His name. There is much work for the both of ye. As consequence of our Queen, and of our victory, we are entering into a new and golden age. Sir Francis and myself receive intelligence from my Lord Walsingham and upon such do we oft-times act. Indeed I have appeared before my Lord Burghley regarding some knowledge he had of my deeds. As consequence do I know the value of a good intelligencer. You, Jenkyn, have many strands that lead to the centre of your web, each a line of information, some you may pass to Godolphin and he to Walsingham. But that smaller fry by which you and Thomas may benefit, methinks you keep close moored, that the *Golden Hind* may strike alone."

He smiled at Keigwin. "Little fish are sweet are they not?" He thumped the table before him. "But, only in company, and that well organised and victualled, can one obtain the prize that gives the greater reward to us; and a deeper sword thrust into the guts of Spain!"

"So, Thomas and the *Golden Hind* will join with Hawkyns and so deprive old Jenkyn of his just rewards," Keigwin nodded, as to himself. "Poor Keigwin will surely starve." He looked about the room with an air of hurt at which his fellows smiled for well they knew his wiles. "Ah deary me, so be it, for if needs must I will find some other adventurer with whom to share my intelligence."

"Nay, sir, nay," protested Hawkyns, "we need your intelligence to advise us direct. You have your spies ready placed, your Breton fishermen, your French and Jewish merchants. There's many a Spaniard or Portuguee will sell you news of which galleons go best laden, and whence they voyage. Sir, provide the information and you will not lack for gold. I, John Hawkyns, put my word on't; aye, and that of Sir Francis too! Do I not speak with truth Thomas?"

Keigwin smiled in quiet satisfaction as Hawkyns clasped his outstretched hand to clinch the bargain.

" . . . and I may use my merchants' skills to dispose of that which you take?"

"No, not always, Jenkyn Keigwin, for then you will doubly gain by virtue of your merchant's profit."

"Not so, Sir John, for I will render you proper inventory and fair account of my dealing, that you may be satisfied in your trust. Without trust no man may do business."

Hawkyns paused before replying.

"So be it, Jenkyn. For here in West Cornwall's port of Mousehole, Keigwin is King." He doffed his hat in mock homage and then spoke in earnest.

"I acknowledge that you have the wherewithal to hold our prizes in secret. To dispose of them by land or sea be it fishing boat or pack pony."

Keigwin sucked his pipe in nodded agreement.

Visitors gone, Sunday saw Jenkyn Keigwin cabined in his pew, head sunk low upon his breast. He scowled at Thomasine as she removed her elbow from his ribs.

"I'll be damned as a heathen," he whispered, "if the sermons don't grow longer and the pews harder by the Sunday. Did not John Tremearne lapse into English on occasion? Latin is God's language and the parson should address his flock so, or else in Cornish!"

English was to invite disunity. For some could comprehend

192

it. But many could not, thus would be divided the educated from the illiterate, and the travelled from those confined in Cornwall. Cornish was their mother tongue, and thus they should be addressed. He would speak with the vicar.

White beard again sank into white ruff. Eyes opened, blinked, as he listened anew.

Banns of marriage. Teek Cornall, Rebecca Trewhella . . . "know cause or just impediment why these two persons should not . . ."

"I'll wager there's no impediment that they've discovered!" He smiled a wicked smile at the thought of them in act of discovering! "Healthy young man, fine strapping wench. Fit to breed a dozen such as they!"

His smile softened as he looked upon his dear Thomasine. Once they had been of those same years and had attended together to hear their own banns read. It seemed such an age ago! He must remind Thomasine to place another cushion in the pew.

The sun shone with a strength that belied Christmas was but a month away. At the sign of The Mermaid laughter echoed around the granite courtyard as maids plaited ribbons into Becky's hair. Silk that matched the blue of her shining eyes. Her dress was of cream silk, adorned with golden trinkets that once had been her mother's, a crown of wild woven flowers they placed to rest upon her brow.

Trewhella's eyes tear-filled with pride and with sadness. Would he could have shared the magic sweetness of this moment with his own dear Tamsyn. Would she had been spared to witness this day by his side. He looked up to where the sky was blue and prayed that she might look down upon the girl child she had borne him, now grown to womanhood in her very likeness; on this, her wedding day. He filled with wine the silver bride bowl to be carried before his daughter, it was tied with gay ribbons and sweet smelling rosemary.

In escort was a hobby-horse that, gaily caparisoned, plunged and reared as John Pearce wove his mirthful way amongst the throng, accompanied by tawny-coated musicians hired to prance and dance behind, leading a troop of village

j

maidens, garlanded about with herbs and flowers, gathered that morning in the dew of the winter's day. They carried bride cakes of saffron to offer as they made their way laughing and singing. They passed from the courtyard, beneath the archway, and into the street beyond, to wend their path in spritely procession through those that had gathered to watch.

Once within the house of God the mood was changed as in solemn ceremony Vicar Tremearne joined them together in holy matrimony before their friends and fellow parishioners; who bore witness, as bride and groom confirmed the vows that each had made the other within the ancient Baptistry.

"Now are you bound as man and wife both in the sight of God, and in the knowledge of your peers. An honourable estate ordained for the procreation of children, the avoidance of fornication and temptation, and for the help and comfort of each for the other," intoned Tremearne. As eyes looked each on the other, they smiled in guilty secret.

"Wives, submit yourselves unto your own husbands . . . let it not be that outward adorning of plaiting the hair, and of the wearing of gold, or of putting on of apparel . . . For after this manner in the old time the holy women also, who trusted in God adorned themselves; being in subjection unto their own husbands; even as Sarah obeyed Abraham, calling him Lord . . ."

Keigwin nodded his approval, he must remind Thomasine of those strictures and give emphasis to her subjection to him, as was God's will.

Side by side, at ground-devouring canter, uncle and nephew hacked across the peaty moorland tracks that led towards the home of Lady Anne Vivyan. Martin was consumed with curiosity for news of his brother's welfare, and more so for sight of his fair nurse. Tom, equally inquisitive, offered to accompany his uncle.

"Since I trust him not to escape the wiles of such delicious creatures as you have described, Grandmother. For by Heaven," he looked aghast, "versed as they are in the mysteries of herbs and potions, mayhap they'll drop some love philtre in his ale!"

194

"Pray, Thomas . . . " Thomasine began to protest.

"Take no notice, Mother," Martin laughed, "the coxcomb does but jest in jealousy. Come, nephew, on our way."

And so, early in the morning, they left the little harbour to arrive by noon at the Manor. Riding into the stableyard they handed their reins into the gnarled hands of an elderly groom. No sooner so, than the ever-curious Sebastian appeared to enquire what visitors had arrived, and as to their business.

"Present the compliments of Martin Keigwin and Thomas Flemyng to your mistress. Say we have no wish to intrude, but have taken advantage of the clement weather to enquire as to the progress of my brother, Richard Keigwin."

"Aye, good sirs," a half bow, "that I will do directly." He winked a bright and knowing eye with an undue familiarity, the privilege of aged retainers. "Mayhap you would firstly wish to witness for yourselves Master Richard's well-being?" It was both question and suggestion. "If so, pray to follow me." He hustled to where a low wooden door was set in the yard wall, and beckoned them to follow.

Lifting the latch slowly, he quietly pulled the door ajar, and peered cautiously into the sun-drenched garden beyond. Pointing across kempt lawn to where bloomed a rose garden.

Thomas followed Martin forward over the threshold, closing the door behind him with firm deliberation that Sebastian might not intrude upon their intimacy.

Before them was a vision that they never thought to witness. Their kinsman, dressed in silken shirt with breeches and hose, his left calf encased in a leathern gaiter and beneath his armpit a wooden crutch, held, in his other hand, a trug filled with an array of winter roses. Before him, clad in bonnet and frock of a country style that could not disguise the quality of fabric and of cut, was a maiden of rare beauty whose perfection of figure was ill-concealed as she reached upward to pluck stems of flowering jasmine that climbed unruly to cover a rustic arbour. She turned to her companion who held the basket to her as she sweetly smiled her thank you.

Uncle and nephew looked at each other, amazed.

"May the Lord strike me dumb," Martin whispered. "Never did I think to see Richard Keigwin a-gathering flowers!"

"Aye, Martin. What chance has a simple seaman, away from the ocean and safe anchorage, when confronted by beauty and witchcraft thus combined? Aye uncle, I am beginning to learn the wiles of women." He gave a dramatic sigh. "I fear all is lost. He has slipped his anchor and doubtless will soon drift, helpless to beach upon the rock strewn shores of matrimony!"

In loud voice Martin proclaimed, "Stop Richard! Hold fast! whilst Tom and I take in the scene, that thus we may report."

"Martin, Tom!" Richard started. "Elizabeth, 'tis my brother and nephew come to visit."

He placed the basket upon the turf and hopped to greet them with fond embrace.

"I present Elizabeth Carlyon, my brother Martin Keigwin."

Elizabeth bobbed a curtsey, as her visitor bowed and doffed his cap in majestic sweep, Tom to follow suit with an even more extravagant gesture and broad grin, " . . . and Thomas Flemyng my nephew."

"Ever your servant, M'lady."

There was so much to amuse and so many stories. As Elizabeth listened to the tales, she painted a mental picture of the family, the relations and servants, to feel almost part of the all-embracing house of Keigwin. How she would relish that which she had never had: cousins and uncles, sisters and aunts to comfort and support in times of need.

They bade their farewells as dawn was breaking. Overhead curlews uttered their wild and haunting cry to fly to their feeding grounds in the estuary beyond and follow the retreating tide. Lady Anne watched them mount. "Convey my warm felicitations to your parents. Tell them Richard will soon be fully healed. For now he must exercise the weakened muscles lest they become cramped and wasted. This I will teach him. Pray tell your mother he will not be crippled and that when the time is due, we shall be sad to see him depart. Be that not so, Elizabeth?"

"Indeed it is, dear aunt."

"But we shall use Richard's mishap to advantage. For we have forged a friendship. One that I know will endure."

Her ladyship raised her hand in farewell and the horsemen

responded with a flourish of their hats as they turned and spurred away.

Elizabeth slipped her hand into that of her patient and watched the departing figures.

In mean lodgings Richard Burley sat, overlooking the harbour at Ferrol. Much of what could be salvaged of Spanish pride lay at anchor, to await the shipwright's skills. The messenger now left, he closed the door behind him and turned the letter over and over in his fingers. His hand reached to his waist and slid the dagger from a bejewelled scabbard. He peered at the ornate seal as he slid the blade beneath the wax to prize and lift. It was written in open Spanish and without cipher. An invitation to Paris, there to attend upon Don Bernardino de Mendoza, spymaster to King Philip.

Chapter Twelve

It was April, 1595. Jenkyn watched the men as they laboured upon the new house. He ached. Oh how his bones did ache. His knees, his shoulders, his back, his hips, everywhere. The damp weather suited him not at all. Thomasine gave him but little sympathy. Elizabeth had said to take a daily dose of that vile concoction proffered by Lady Anne. Thomasine insisted that he drink it, but the taste was abhorrent. Women, nagging women. Still Elizabeth had nursed Richard to health and strength and now was wedded to him and by all that was holy Thomasine believed in these potions and extractions. Perhaps he would try it yet again: anything was better than this pain which didn't help his temper over much. He lifted the glass to his lips, grimacing as he did so.

Temper, there was a time to keep it and a time to lose it, he reflected, but if one lost it when it should be well reefed, then it could lose a deal. The deal, that was what kept you young and alert, better than any potion. Pitting your wits: the prospect of buying right and selling right, knowing the market and what it could stand. The art of leaving a little profit for the next man, for him to come again. Deals built on trust, and trust built on years of fair trading. His integrity sailed before him, that was the secret of his success.

Thomasine felt it was time for him to move aside. As she reminded him, he was no longer a spring chicken: maybe so, however he was still cock of this particular dunghill! Perhaps he should meet her half way. Richard was no fool, able to speak both French and Spanish, a smidgen of Hebrew too when called upon, learnt from old Fernandes. Perhaps he should now factor for him. Travel aboard the merchant ships

198

to look for new markets, fresh opportunities for import not confined to wines and hides.

Meanwhile, the old cock would be much engaged in the prizes that Drake and Hawkyns shipped secretly to his warehouse: that should be enough to engage him fully, and reward him greatly. Jenkyn Keigwin counted his blessings Martin was a good sailor and much respected by the menfolk. He would oversee the fishing, the pressing and the salting of the pilchards, whilst helping at home. Thus would he provide due inheritance for the children and the grand-children. He smiled, grandchildren, Tom was more youngest son than grandchild. Now if any man could survive and prosper it was he. Jenkyn chuckled, Tom was possessed of the cheek of the devil himself.

He will go far, praise God, if he survives his adventures. 'Tis difficult to place an old head on young shoulders. Had he not been the same at Tom's age? He turned the medicine phial in his hand. He should learn some of the guile and caution of Hawkyns, but tempered with more honesty than Hawkyns. Of the others with whom Tom mixed, Cumberland was brave, but also foolhardy. 'Twas said the Queen did much favour him, for he had a silver tongue, and wore her glove upon his hat to flatter her. A good man in a fight, the champion of the tiltyard, but he was rash, many a treasure ship he cut out, only to lose what he had so dearly bought. Thomas should give the Earl a wide berth.

Hawkyns was given to greed, yet he had let it be known that in Mousehole there was a gentleman of Cornwall that a privateer or merchant venturer might truly trust to safely handle goods. Thus at this first landfall of England could they take on fresh water, revictual and unload their cargo in the greater safety of a landward journey, in return for Keigwin gold or pledge. With only short delay they could return for further foray against ship or shore of Spain, or else continue to Plymouth or to London, with no one the wiser that a portion of the booty had been off-loaded at Mousehole. The benefits Keigwin gained by purchase or commission did more than balance the earnings of the privateer as Hawkyns had foretold.

Thomas was now captain of the *Charles*. A Queen's ship

on duty to patrol in company with the *Moon* about the southern coast of Ireland. For that poor and troubled land would sell corn to France, that they themselves might feed. Since the Armada the Queen had remained obsessed with the prospect of Catholic invasion from Spain via Ireland, a country easy to inflame by printed pamphlet and tract.

Carefree and devil-may-care Tom might seem, but scratch the surface and a hurt beneath was hidden. Jane, his child-bride, she whom Tom had first loved, herself with child, was lost to them. The memory of her dying. Her son at sea, Elizabeth had fought bravely to save wife and child.

With a shake of his head he tossed the memory from his mind and turned instead to the future. The house for Richard next to the Manor would soon be complete. He missed the seaward view, but they were now sheltered from the cold and easterly wind. That would ease his aching bones: and he had enjoyed his season's hunting. They had eaten venison in plenty and given much to the needy of the parish. The pack was benefitting from the out-cross of some years before. Merlin had proven a fine stallion hound, and fathered many a worthy litter. Jacob was beginning to show his age, but so indeed he was entitled. How well he related to John Pearce. Perhaps the son he had never had. To him, but no one else, would he impart his country lore, the wisdom of generations that he had so jealously guarded. He had even overheard John Pearce voicing opinion from which hounds to breed and cross, and watched Jacob nod approval!

He watched the figure cross the yard beneath the window: Teek going to oversee the labourers on the house. Teek had proved a god-send. With money put aside and now a wife and family he had sought consent of his captain to spend his time ashore. Tom had been reluctant to give it at first, yet did so on condition that Teek remain in the employ of Keigwin. Teek knew men and he knew the sea. He had the ability to command and retain respect and he could organise: thus he enabled Richard and Martin to travel and to trade for greater reward, a benefit to the Keigwin fortunes, thanks be to God.

The sound of laughter returned his thoughts into the

house. Thomasine too was content. Once more anxiously awaiting the birth of another grandchild. Hence they must hasten the building of the house for Richard and Elizabeth, for there was not long for her to go.

Thomasine, his strength and support, not always easily pleased by the servants of the household, but how she and Becky did so agree. A pleasing and handsome wench was Teek's wife, with three strong children of her own, Thomasine had in mind that she wet nurse future Keigwin offspring.

Aches and pains forgot, Jenkyn Keigwin knelt to praise his maker and thank Him for his bounty.

Would that every voyage across the great bay be so swift and sure. Safe within his doublet, Burley could feel next his skin the sealed orders of the King. He had come from Court by post to Santander and there boarded the waiting pinnace; she was part of the squadron recently entrusted to the command of Don Carlos De Amelrola. Thence to southern Brittany and the safe harbour of Blavet, where still the King of Spain maintained a slender foothold.

At his sovereign's behest he had conversed with Don Diego Brochero de Anaya and Don Pedro de Zaubiaur. Together they had been as one, and proposed that the galleys at Blavet should be put to purposeful use, to test the defences of England and to ravage English shores. Intelligencers reported to Mendoza that Drake and Hawkyns were fitting out a fleet at Plymouth, soon to sail for the further pillage of Porto Rico. Therefore King Philip had commanded Don Diego to hand his command to de Amelrola and speed to the passage as General of six sail and four of pinnace to join with others at Lisbon, there to follow and to thwart the fleet of Drake and Hawkyns.

Meanwhile the Englishman would accompany Don Carlos upon the raid. Whilst Drake's ships were out of commission refitting and revictualling, the Squadron of Blavet would strike, exacting revenge, landing spies and Jesuits and retrieving the booty, stolen from the treasure houses of Pernambuco.

The wind on her quarter, a bone in her teeth, onward the pinnace sped to leave the Isle de Groix to windward, take in her sail and enter the harbour by the southern passage. Rounding the haven's entrance, Burley was greeted by the imposing presence of four great three-masted galleys. Without protection of a guardian fortress they lay in staggered line astern, that seawards their ordnance might bear. To the fore, the *Nuestra Senora de Begona*, from whose top fluttered the flag of their commander. The pinnace passed her bow, to proffer proper salutation. The incoming tide stemmed the seaward-going waters of the twin rivers confluence, whose greater expanse blessed the helmsman with added steerage room within those shallow waters, safe there to drop anchor in line abreast of her sister.

In the aft cabin he inspected both his appearance and attire. Alongside came the skiff to transport him to the flagship, there to receive the formal greeting of Don Carlos.

The commander, with utmost courtesy, in vain concealed his anxiety for sight of the orders from his sovereign. He ushered his guest to the luxury of his stern cabin, and with interest and concern enquired as to his well-being and the condition of his travels from Madrid. At last, civilities concluded, the royal document in his hands, he introduced to Richard Burley a servant who would accompany him to his cabin and invited the captain to dine with him presently; for first he must digest his sovereign's orders.

Thursday, and Solomon Fernandes would be paying his weekly visit. Whilst the Keigwin wealth might be mounting, the spice of life had surely withered. With Tom so much away, there were no adventures of the privateer to heed. More than ever did Jenkyn look forward to his old friend's coming, to the banter and news of trade whilst drinking wine; to dine amidst amusing conversation and afterwards, continue with their game of chess.

There was financial gain as well as social pleasure. Ofttimes the weight of trade required larger purse than even Keigwin owned. Thus a syndicate was formed, a partnership of trust, by which all did benefit.

More and more did ships returning from their mission

stop off to revictual at Mousehole and avail themselves of the Keigwin reputation for hospitality and fair trade: so more and more he bought their booty or sold their goods on terms of fair commission.

He ushered his friend to a seat by the sea-coal fire. "What news, Solomon?"

"There is but little of note. Except . . . "

"Except what?"

"There is news I hear from Santander . . . yet it may be false."

"False be damned if it be intelligence from the tribe of Israel it is bound to be exact!"

"It is indeed from a merchant of my race who does say to beware."

"Beware of what?"

"That he cannot say, except that Richard Burley has recently left Santander on a pinnace of Blavet, where lurk the slave galleys of Spain."

"Indeed I have heard that such a fleet still lingers there. Could there be evil afoot, Solomon Fernandes?"

" 'Tis thus I am afeared, Master Keigwin. There is a ship in my employ that does sometimes trade with Le Conquet. Thereto she is now sailing. I have told her captain to make diligent enquiry and return with haste. Thus may we verify without alarm, and so inform Godolphin or no."

"You think as me, old friend?"

"And pray, Jenkyn, what may that be?"

"That with Drake and Hawkyns preparing their fleet to treasure hunt for the Queen at Plymouth, many of our men have there been pressed, and ordnance requisitioned." He sipped his wine in meditation. "This is the underbelly of Cornwall, it is easy to strike without the Western Squadron for protection. Betwixt Mousehole and Marazion we do not have even steep cliffs for our defence."

"I fear you assume rightly, Jenkyn, for I believe as you, and thus I am concerned."

"You will keep me acquainted when your ship returns?"

"Assuredly."

"Then let us talk of pleasanter matters. I have recently had news of better things. That Lancaster has joined with some Hollanders and with Captain Venner, has taken and held Pernambuco in Brazil." In confidential tones, "It is said the place is a veritable treasure store."

Fernandes opened his eyes wide. "That is news indeed and if it be true, then there is much advantage to us?"

Yes my friend. Richard has been informed by good intelligence intended for my ears. Do you recall that in September last, three good ships, the *Consent*, now, whilst I think, the *Consent*, yes," he ticked his fingers, "the *Saloman* and the *Virgin* did take on fresh water here?"

"Maybe perhaps, but I cannot justly recall."

"Well, James Lancaster is commander of the trio and is to be trusted. My good friend, Alderman John Watts of London City has commissioned the enterprise. He has long since told me that he will require his voyagers to victual here before returning to Blackwall, that a portion of their prize should be off-loaded to travel overland. He says this is to prevent loss by pirate or by storm, but in reality it is so that his peers do not know his true wealth and prosperity."

"Then know you well, Jenkyn, that your good friend, Solomon Fernandes, will put his shekels with your silver if you so bid. And should that prove short, then there are others of my race upon whom I may lean." He smiled a smile of genuine affection, that few, but very few, had witnessed. For rarely did he bare his soul to other men, fearful they might take advantage. As was the nature of his kind.

Frustration and delay. Nothing but delay. Quill pen in hand, Drake sat within his cabin calculating the cost of the expedition. He too wished to enrich his country and replenish the coffers of the Queen, just as she had commanded. But why, oh why the parsimony? What cause to be so mercenary? How could he equip a fleet of twenty-seven sail on such miserly allowance? Too many of the ships were weary with usage. Indeed many would think them unseaworthy for such a voyage. They were ill-equipped and riddled by the gribble that so plagued the southern harbours. The tiny holes of the toledo worm that pierced the planking was all that could be seen upon the surface. Yet snug within their wooden boards they fattened as they fed, often to the size of a man's finger, as they gnawed their way below the water-line. There were devices that might be used to mend. Yet the cost, always the cost. And the delay!

In November the royal orders had been given and here it was June! Many a ship now lay careened safe within the Hamoaze, below high water's mark, that shipwright and carpenter might attend, to cut and to splice and follow the advice of Hawkyns and heed his strictures. Thin planks of elm, for sheathing, plastered with pitch hot from the cauldron, to be coated thick with hair, then nailed in place. He could trust Hawkyns. It was good to have a man one could trust as Vice Admiral. Hawkyns, a wily rogue, was his cousin and long time friend. He had used his guile to purloin and requisition cannon and ordnance, powder and ball taken from the countryside about.

Sir Nicholas Clifford too, was tried and tested. Friendships forged in battle's flame. His the command of the soldiery aboard and upon the shores. Men fit, trained and experienced in the use of arms. Men of the West Country who had rallied to their leaders that they too might profit. If Drake was going venturing they were going too! His smile turned to frown. He knew of their trust. Yet he was concerned. Delays, such delays. Now surely would the spies of Spain know of his intent. Surprise was the secret of all his past success. Twice armed is he whose blow is just, perhaps so, yet thrice armed is he who has surprise within his armoury!

The servant was commanded to replenish their goblets, then De Amelrola waved dismissal. With the door firmly closed, the Spaniard lent forward in conspiratorial manner.

"At a time of our choosing, when favoured by wind and tide and our soldiery rehearsed, the squadron is commanded to sail forth and ravage the coast of England." He had hoped his words would be of some great surprise but Burley was already privy to King Philip's wishes, lacking only the detail. Don Carlos continued, "A raid of reprisal for the deeds of Drake, who even now our spies inform us, is fitting out for further expedition. We are required to attack where England

205

is most vulnerable, the country of Curnow that forms her western tip. Ill protected save by forbidding cliffs. Know you of it Captain Burley?"

"Indeed and very well, but pray to continue Don Carlos."

"There is a great bay, named Mount's Bay."

"I know it well."

"To its west upon its southern lip, there lies the port of Mousehole. Here and to the place named Marazion, the granite battlements are softened and much of the land lies low and thus can soldiers more readily be landed." He jabbed his finger at the renegade. " 'Tis we shall exact a measure of revenge. Speed and surprise, Captain Burley. Speed and surprise! I am ordered to command the squadron at sea, whilst to you falls the honour of commanding our soldiers."

"That will be my privilege." He stroked his moustache with manicured finger. "His Majesty must have known of my wish to be avenged upon those that live within that town — but that is yet another story. I digress. Forgive me."

"I can see you have an appetite for this foray." The Spaniard chortled. "That was a pertinent comment that lends greater credence to the intelligence gathered by our sovereign."

"This de Zaubiaur would know."

"Ah! How well he picks the cast that the play may be perfection!

Burley nodded his agreement.

"Then, Burley, that is our intent. Yet there is more."

"Pray what can that be?"

"Our further duty once arrived, to land priests and other English of our faith that they may give heart to those that oppose the Protestant rule. Be guided in all matters of our faith by the chaplain of our fleet, Friar Domingo. It is his desire that with God's help we will wreak havoc amongst those who practise heresy."

"This venture grows more worthy!"

"You know of a Cornishman named Keigwin?"

"The merchant of Mousehole? 'Tis upon him I seek revenge!"

"Then you know that English privateers oft-times use his

quay, his warehouse and his pack ponies to deposit and thence distribute the prizes that they have stolen?"

"No, that I did not, Don De Amelrola, no indeed I did not," in thoughtful tones.

"Of such doings our intelligence does assure us. The English have raided Pernambuco. There is likelihood they may use Keigwin to factor for them and store the booty within his warehouses. We must await further news from our spies."

The following day a lone man walked the beach, picked a pebble from the shore, weighed it in his hand and skimmed it far into the shimmer of the blue unruffled sea. A black-backed gull dipped its wicked head into the water to preen in the shallows. Richard Burley grinned. Underneath fine feathers, each had the instinct of the predator. He hurled another stone towards the bird, causing it to flap upwards with screech of anger. He half bowed in mock salute, for he was a happy man. Soon, but very soon, after seven long years of waiting, God was to give him his reward. He would kill not two but three birds with one stone. He aimed again at the gull that had settled along the strand.

His advice was heeded. Mendoza had sent message that two English navigators with knowledge of Cornwall's coast would accompany the mission. They were on their way in a fishing boat of Don Zaubiaur's fleet, with intelligence lately gathered. It had been an English helmsman who brought Burley back safely to Santander when all seemed lost around Ireland's alien coast. In the wild seas of western Cornwall one must have helmsmen who knew of every rock and shoal. Someone familiar with that shore to say where best to land, and with knowledge of inland terrain where the enemy might safely lodge. By avoiding or dominating such a place, might the venturer achieve full reward.

The soldiery were fretting for the fray as hounds in the slips, straining to be unleashed upon an unsuspecting prey.

The Friar spent most time in prayer and discussion of religious doctrine with those exiled English priests and converts now awaiting safe return. Brave men all, to dare the

207

dangers that confronted them, prepared to risk horrible death in the cause of Rome. Determined to hold Mass and propagate their faith, and to dispense dissent against the Protestant rule that it might be overthrown. The gall within the mighty oak. The maggot planted in the ripe red apple.

Idly from the stern-castle he watched the fishing boat sail into the harbour and circle, head to wind to settle alongside the flagship. Two passengers clambered the steep walls to come aboard.

Evening prayers over, dusk began to fall, De Amelrola requested Burley to attend within his cabin. He tapped upon the door that was opened by the commander. Seated upon a stool within, the black-hooded figure of the Friar of St. Dominic, Domingo Martinez. Chin cupped in hand, eyes half closed, yet Burley knew that they would miss nothing. His bow of courtesy was acknowledged by wan and distant smile. Within his mind Burley made note to court the priest, for here was a man not without influence and power, far better a friend than enemy. There was always tomorrow against which to guard.

Two strangers rose to greet him. One burly and black-bearded, with a half bow he proffered his hand.

"I am Thomas Nicholls of Newhaven."

Fine rapier thought Burley, fine clothes, yet not worn with the ease of a gentleman.

"Captain Richard Burley, in the service of King Philip. We have met before, Master Nicholls." He bowed and turned to the other, in a seaman's attire, from whose open blouse glinted a medallion that hung from a leather thong about his neck. Burley raised his eyebrows in polite enquiry and reached to look closely upon the token: a replica of Christ crucified.

"I too have such as this. Did you also sail aboard the Armada?"

"No sir, I had no such privilege. For I was forced to fight in England's fleet. This reminder of my faith was taken from a brave soldier of Spain, whose need for such had long since gone. He toyed with the emblem in awkward silence, as Burley's eyes were drawn to the seaman's little finger that boasted a ring of gold where, in encrusted setting, was bedded a large black pearl of rare magnificence. He reached for the hand to inspect the jewel, to question the seaman with his eyes. But no hint of response did he receive.

Lest his authority began to slip, De Amelrola sought to command the discussion.

"Gentlemen," he drew their attention, "I am under sealed orders from our Majesty, who has entrusted me to lead my squadron of galleys in an expedition against the shores of England. Captain Burley, who has soldiered in many a campaign," Burley half bowed to acknowledge, "is entrusted by the King to command the foot soldiers in an attack against our enemy. You have been chosen, Nicholls, on the advice of Don Pedro de Zaubiaur, since you are a navigator who knows the waters off the coast of France and are fluent in the Spanish tongue. You are well trusted, for long have you served the Duke of Guise against the Protestant cause."

De Amelrola looked toward the impassive figure of the Friar. A hint of a nod was the response. Then to continue. "Nankervis," the seaman drew himself upright, "you are to join with us for your knowledge of the coast of Cornwall. Later, when my commanders have made their plans, Captain Burley will brief you as to the part you will play. For now, we wish to know more of you, and why you wish to serve the cause of Rome. Thomas Nicholls, you shall speak first."

Pink tongue wetted lips half hidden in the dense forest of the black beard. The Englishman told of his service for the Duke. Of the tracts he took to Ireland, fresh from the press of Father Parsons. Of his landing of the Jesuits, of his discovery by Flemyng and his capture, the loss of his ship and its cargo and of his determination to avenge himself. Yet Burley he could not recall.

"I was travelling in the guise of a pilgrim . . . "

"Now, what of you?" The squadron commander pointed to Nankervis, who made answer in a falter of Spanish.

"Sir, it would seem that Captain Nicholls and me have been on opposing sides. As indeed sir, has Captain Burley and me. Yet what was opposite is now outweighed by a bond we have in common."

He told of his exploits upon the *Golden Hind* in the taking of the *Hope of Newhaven*, and of the part the pinnace played in the action against the Armada. His voice rose as he gained in confidence and his eyes blazed with a zealous fire.

"We are of one faith," he ticked upon his fingers. "We have desire to see that faith restored within our homeland. And, sir, what more we have common? To avenge ourselves upon the house of Keigwin who ill-accused me. My body is now made good but within my soul there lies a deeper wound. A hurt left to fester for seven long years, and will only be healed by a bloody revenge."

De Amelrola looked to the stern-faced Friar. "Methinks Mendoza and de Zaubiaur have chosen our navigators well." He returned his look upon the seaman. "Tell us more Master Nankervis."

"I have said enough. But such little knowledge and skill as I possess are thine to command, should it assist to give God's vengeance upon the Mousehole that I hate, and the family that therein rule."

"You know Mousehole well?"

"As well as I know my own face."

'Know you also that coast that lies between the Cape of Cornwall and that they call The Lizard?" he queried.

"Likewise, Master. For I am of Pensans and have sailed those waters all my life, as my father and grandfather did before."

Prodded, prompted and encouraged, the two vied to disgorge all that they knew of the bay of the Mount, the tides and the shoals, where the wind luffed around a headland's crag. Of the people and where they prayed and in what form. The shape and height of hilltop, the concealing depth of a wooded coombe. Where advantage lay, what field of fire did it command, from where would they first sight assistance to the enemy? From where would they suppose Drake, or Godolphin's militias, to appear? At last they drained the dregs of all that Nicholls and Nankervis might impart.

All was noted and recorded, to be compared with intelligence revealed from fishermen of St. Keverne, who had been captured by a shallop of Blavet from under English noses when within the Bay of Falmouth. They too knew the vagaries of the tide from off the Lizard, and what ships Drake had within his locker at Falmouth and beyond, and how to round that dangerous point into the Mount's wide bay.

"Now all the cards are dealt. Together we shall determine how best they should be played."

De Amelrola turned to kneel before the Friar, Burley by his side; clumsily the seamen followed, for they also sought a priest's blessing upon their deeds.

Chapter Thirteen

Side by side commander and captain pored over the charts spread before them. Pensive, each conscious of his responsibility. Upon their shoulders fell the task to salvage Spanish pride.

North-west they traced the wild jagged coast of Brittany. Thence due north, across the water from Ushant to Cornwall's western tip, to study the coast of that untamed land.

"Don Carlos. To you falls the duty to land our soldiery safe upon those shores, once there to deposit the priests and the converts?"

"Indeed, Captain Burley, yet more besides."

"To that I will come. Mine is the taking and the holding of the land whilst the Friar Domingo will scourge such heresy as he may find. I will also on his orders, raze and punish such heathen town or village as we may hold?"

"That is so."

"Yet to you Don Carlos, falls the major task. For it is yours to ensure the harmony of our actions. The time of each event. The landing is dictated by tide, weather and terrain. Thus we must consider every factor. Darkness and daylight, concealing mist of morning or sunshine's clarity. As a consequence I wish to fashion a much larger chart, that we may see more clearly what each function should be and where it should take place."

"What do you propose, Captain Burley?"

"With your consent, I will fashion a Cornwall in the sand. The part that lies betwixt the Cape and that they call the Lizard," he warmed to his theme, "not only coastline and rock but hill and combe in careful detail. Thus we may

212

interpret how the land lies. Then for you and me to discuss and debate the form our action should best take from the intelligence we have gained. Once done, to show our captains and commanders our plan and form of attack. This wild country must be no stranger to them when they go ashore. Also may we determine how to defend that which we take, and where the flotilla is best left at anchor."

Thin lips split brown face, a flash of white teeth. "Excellent my friend, excellent." He placed his hand upon the Englishman's shoulder. "Take Nicholls and Nankervis. Build your mould of Cornwall in the sand."

Fashioned with aid of chart and memory, under Burley's critical eye Nankervis completed his task. From Cape Cornwall to the Lizard's Point the dampened sand was sculpted. In careful form and detail of Mount's Bay. Each landmark, each church was shown so that whilst at sea the outlined stump of tower might be identified. From Sennen thence to St. Buryan and to Paul. Seaward, and below, the island of St. Clement, guardian of the haven port of Mousehole.

"Now to call to council Don Leon Dezpeleta and Gaspar de Perea, since they must be included in our planning. Doubtless they will wish to make some valid contribution."

The flag of Spain was run up on the shrouds in summons for the captains to attend a conference aboard the *Nuestra Senora Begona*. Courtesies exchanged, they joined with Burley and the Friar in the stateroom where charts of Brittany and Cornwall were laid upon the table top. Burley resigned himself to the silence of diplomacy that those of Spain might freely converse without comment from an Englishman.

Don Carlos De Amerola outlined how they might best implement the orders of their King.

"I require you to gather upon the shore complete with subaltern and serjeant major that Captain Burley may reveal his model of Cornwall that you may better envisage the task that awaits you. Now gentlemen do I beseech Friar Domingo to give to us his blessing."

He stood upon the hillside's slope, hand shielding his straining eyes from glare as he peered into the westering sun.

A solitary figure, whose white dress and black, pointed hood proclaimed him to be a friar. A Black Friar, one bound by vows of chastity and obedience to the order of St. Dominic: a zealous order that preached the Catholic faith to heathen and to heretic. Strict unrelenting guardians of the doctrines of Rome, it was they who presided over rack and Auto da Fe: who proudly bore the flag of the Inquisition. Friar Domingo Martinez, senior chaplain, he who was responsible for needs spiritual of soldier and of slave within the squadron. By those powers so vested in him, in truth real master of the galleys and implacable enemy of the Protestant cause.

With melancholy satisfaction he watched, as helmet and burnished breastplate reflected the afternoon rays. Pikemen and arquebusiers in ant-like procession were drilled to follow the commands of bugle or the silver whistles of the officers. The arms of Burley, constantly pointing and directing, the bellow of his voice praising, chastising in soldier's Spanish.

The robed figure nodded approval at the discipline instilled by the Englishman as they practised their landing from the galleys that lay beyond the white rollers breaking upon the shallowing shore. Clifftop gained, the ground secure from threat of enemy, with block and tackle artillerymen swung the pieces to the heights, to be carried inland to command a field of fire upon the ground below. Long did they practise and rehearse the rocky landing upon a low cliff-top that Nankervis claimed was likened to the granite steps off which stood Merlin's Rock — the unseen southern sentry of Mousehole harbour, out of view of Newlyn and Penzance.

De Amelrola ordered flags to be raised that gave a signal to all officers a council was again commanded. Boats were lowered away as his officers scrambled up the low waist of the flagship. Upon the raised aft deck their commander made his address:

"Friar Domingo Martinez and His Majesty's Captain, Richard Burley, have witnessed and approved your practice that soon you will effect upon the soil of England. By the Grace of God, to you, gentlemen, falls the honour, and the privilege, to avenge your brothers, killed by English heretics on land and upon the seas. Our Gracious Majesty has

214

commanded us to sail, with God's help, against that country and her heathen Queen. Now we are joined by English pilots of our faith to guide us through the dangerous waters that we may land with safety upon those alien shores. English priests of the faith will be landed there, that they may relate the might of the Bishop of Rome and his servant, King Philip. There they will convert the heretic and provide support and comfort to those who have suffered for their faith under foul Elizabeth's rule. That our ventures may receive God's blessing we will journey in accord with advice of our Padre and at a time he deems propitious to our cause. We are God's hand of retribution!"

His arm outstretched to quell the cheers, the officers of Spain knelt to receive benison from the tall, hooded figure whose presence gave them aweful fear of the power and might of their unforgiving, unforgetting God.

Her bows dipped into the trough to rise and roll on the following crest as through her scuppers she tossed away the white foam. On patrol. The *Charles* and the *Moon*; ships of the Queen off Ireland's coast. For three years Flemyng had been her captain. There was no doubt his exploits had found him favour, but there were days he longed for challenge and independence, to tread the deck of his own privateer: and face the glorious uncertainty of not knowing what each day would bring. The thrill of the hunt, the chase, whether on land or sea.

However, patrol they must, for from Ireland's sheltered eastern coast could come a Catholic invasion of England; here now was England's greatest threat. O'Neil was fretting, the son of the bastard, now Earl of Tyrone, blessed with wealth and a hatred of oppressive England, and the clans were rallying to him. Minstrels, fostered and fomented by Spanish intrigue, wandered the land to sing their lays and rouse the rebels to his cause. Spanish fishing boats landed covert message, tracts or Agnus Dei. Irish ships carried corn to France that onward went to a hungry Spain. Flemyng's duty was to detect, then deprive the enemy; to isolate the Catholics of Ireland whom Elizabeth maintained in unjust depression, so fearful was she for her kingdom.

Thomas ached for the danger and comradeship of battle. Drake and Hawkyns were preparing; much of England's fleet was a-venturing abroad or preparing to do so, leaving their homeland ill-protected.

Godolphin had built his castle upon the St. Mary's isle, thus the Scillies were now guarded. Falmouth had two castles to guard her entrance. Yet in the great bay of his own home there was but one miserly battery for defence. He missed, oh how he missed his family and his friends.

"Oh should it please You, God, give me relief from boredom that I may better serve both You and England."

"By all that is holy, what is it?"

Irritated at the interruption Keigwin looked up from the ledger in which written in careful script was noted all detail of his trade. In the doorway she bobbed, aware of his annoyance.

"Please you, sir, Teek Cornall gave me a message. Three great ships are off Lamorna and look uncommon like those of Alderman Watts."

"Is that so?"

She smiled a knowing smile at his mood change and bobbed again before departing.

"Not so hasty, Mary." He rose to peer seaward into the sun's bright rays that streamed through the window. He turned towards her.

"Tell Teek to go to the wharf where I will shortly join him. See too, that Master Martin and Master Richard are also present. Tell your Mistress that mayhap we have company and ask her to join me."

With nod of dismissal he turned once more to peer southwards past Penzer Point where, in full sail, the stately bulk of the *Consent* hove into view.

Thomasine came to his side. "Mary said we may have company?"

"Aye, 'tis so," he pointed seawards to where, in line astern, the three merchantmen sailed towards the harbour. "Will you please look to my appearance, Thomasine, and

216

afterwards thine own."

She smiled at the husband she adored. "Now turn towards me that I may see. Why, Jenkyn, your beard is straggled and needs the comb. Your cap too is awry. Why are you so excited at the advent of three ships?"

"Excited? Never!"

She smiled a fond and knowing smile, as she attended her husband's dress.

"But 'tis the *Consent* and with her the *Virgin* and the *Saloman*. You recall them? They are the fleet of John Watts that now return with James Lancaster their Admiral. We had intelligence of their coming from Captain Venner who sailed ahead. God was provident, so 'twould seem, and they have much booty. Tomorrow they will revictual and take aboard sweet water. Whilst I, my flower, will be entrusted with the treasure." He wagged a joking finger. "Tonight we celebrate their safe return and invite their captains ashore and afford them every comfort." He smiled and rubbed his hands in gleeful anticipation at the prospect of profit and the stories of adventure that would be recounted as the wine was circled about the table.

Belt and rapier now buckled around expansive waist, Thomasine fussed and fastened the cape about his shoulders. Anxious for her man, as any hen her favoured chick. For had he not position to maintain and influence to preserve? Position and influence, and above all trust. These were the keys to profitable trade. The impression they first gained of him, awaiting on the quayside, would be one that might have bearing upon a deal waiting to be struck.

At dinner where Elizabeth had joined them, little was said as the three captains devoured their delicacies with noisome relish.

"Mistress Keigwin, there may be finer boards in England off which to dine, but if there be so then I, James Lancaster, have yet to discover them!" He leant back in his oak chair, smiling at Thomasine who beamed in return her pleasure.

"Master Lancaster, may I tempt you to a little more of my codlin tart?"

217

k

"Indeed you may, but just a morsel, in God's truth I have never had better, but my belly will burst should I have much more of your dainties. How do you say Edmund?" He looked toward Barker of the *Saloman*, engaged with busy napkin wiping rich cream from his beard.

The threesome, with John Audely of the *Virgin*, had developed a friendship borne of trust during the ten long months of their voyage.

"I have a real problem James."

"Pray tell me on't."

" 'Tis to determine which does merit the greater compliment, the apple tart or the steak pie."

"Master Audely," smiled Thomasine, I did conceive you might have had a sufficiency of fish whilst in the Indies, and perhaps our Cornish fare of home grown beef and fruits would be best suited to your palate."

"By all that is holy you have judged well, Mistress Keigwin. Our compliments, eh gentlemen?"

They doffed their hats in united, laughing salutation.

"Now we embarrass you. Yet," turning towards his host, "never have I known such wines, such choice, such delicacy of flavour. Many a fine drink have I savoured yet your cellar does uncommonly compliment the fare." He raised his glass of Burgundy and quaffed in lip-smacking appreciation.

"Captain Lancaster, we have important business to discuss."

The captain nodded as Jenkyn's words changed his mood from joviality to solemnity.

"But I suggest that is a matter to which we can later return, for we are agog to learn of your adventures and can scarce forbear to hear the telling of 'em." He paused. "Are they fit for our ladies also to hear?"

"Aye, there is nothing amiss saving some small element of death, but little of real hardship, thanks be to God!"

"Then shall we light our pipes, gentlemen? Martin will you fetch the tobacco and Richard replenish the glasses. Shall we retire to the withdrawing room?"

He rose to usher the ladies and their guests to the greater comfort of the adjoining room.

Pipes lighted, glasses filled, James Lancaster began his

218

story.

"As you will doubtless recall, it was in October last, the year of our Lord fifteen hundred and ninety-four that we left Blackwall to sail for Pernambuco. You will remember that we anchored here awhile to take on fresh water and victuals."

Keigwin nodded his agreement and puffed upon his silver stem.

"It was a syndicate of the City of London that provisioned our ships and well provided they were too!" He partook of his wine. "Do you know, ladies, that so prepared were we as to carry aboard a galley frigate in pieces, that our carpenters might set together for her use in the shallow waters. But of that anon. After, what, but fifty leagues of Mousehole, a great tempest came upon us. I on the *Consent* was lost, as were the *Saloman* and the *Virgin*."

" 'Tis so," adjoined Barker, "for well founded as we were, there was a time when I was tempted to run the *Saloman* for France, but dare not turn her nose from the wind lest she be overwhelmed whilst so doing. Such was the violence of the storm. Thus we held her into the wind under bare poles and 'twas God's will that we survived."

Lancaster continued, "The last we saw of you was when your spars were lost and some said your main mast spent. Yet in the gloom of the dusk 'twas impossible to be certain and assistance would be in vain, lest we too should founder. 'Twas each for himself." He drew his pipe in recollection. "When the storm abated, we took the *Virgin* onwards to Tenerife."

"And that is where," interrupted John Audely, "the *Virgin* and the *Consent* were reunited."

"But only after the *Consent* had had some sport."

"Aye, we took a ship fully laden with Spanish wine."

Lancaster sipped his wine, " 'Twas dawn and off shore we ran, a breeze on our quarter, sailing merrily. Before us, we sighted a merchantman, she lay so low in the water we judged her to be well laden." He pointed with his pipe to Richard and Martin. "At Tenerife the Spanish merchantmen deposit their cargo from the Indies as form of staging post, to revictual and make speedy return thereto. The island is easy to discover, you can see her lofty peak from one hundred miles away. But I digress. There she was, becalmed, in the lee of those high cliffs, close inshore where there was no wind to aid her passage, towed by her own longboat, making for safe harbour. She must have thought us one of her own kind, and we saw no reason to enlighten her. 'Steady my beauties' I cried 'take her not too close' — lest we also lost the wind. We lowered our longboat as if to render aid. Our men were well armed and warming for a fight. We rowed toward the Spaniard; of a sudden their longboat, realising what we were about, cut their cable and sought to save themselves by flight. 'A shilling a man if you catch her!' Our men rowed with a fury and caught and boarded them and took their ship as well! Ah! She was well laden too! Eighty tons of Canary wine she carried, Jenkyn Keigwin, but none so good as this!" He held his empty glass aloft for Richard to replenish.

"We lingered awhile and the very next day was similar occurrence. One brave young fellow of our own did have his arm taken away by their gunnery. Never fear, Mistress Elizabeth, for I am informed you are dexterous in the use of medicine: so neat and so clean was the wound that he survived, thanks be to God, and escaped infection."

"Yes," it was the turn of Barker, "it was here at Tenerife that we found the *Consent* gloating in her glory, eh James?"

"Gloating? Never Edmund! But pleased we were to see you, never fear. Yet ever anxious as to the fate of the *Saloman*, for your men would have it that she had been forced to repair homeward to make good her damaged mast."

"That was but false conjecture, our own carpenters made good the damage," Audely corrected. "And so we sailed, as was agreed, on course for Pernambuco, not knowing whither were gone the *Consent* and the *Virgin*. Yet ever hopeful that God would spare them and direct them to where we lay. You can imagine our joy when at Cabo Blanco we sighted the topsails we knew."

"Yet, Mistress Keigwin," Edward Barker puffed out his chest in jest, "in truth we could well have spared them. For by time of their arrival we too had had a tidy frolic and taken a mere twenty-four sail of Spain and Portugal! Some but fishermen I would grant you, but no bad hand to hold. For 'twas by these captures that we learned of the great East Indiaman, a carrack of Spain, that had been cast upon an uncharted shoal, and all her goods transported to the warehouses of Arecife, which is part of the lower town, that lies safe within the shelter of a guardian reef."

James Lancaster again took up the story: "In truth it was a joyous occasion and we thanked God for the safety of each other. Was it not so, John?"

"Aye," continued Audely, "not only were we pleased to discover Edmund and the *Saloman* were safe arrived, but our sailors too were overjoyed. The dancing on deck, Mistress Keigwin, and the joyful singing in that hot, steamy evening were such as one will never recapture, nor in truth forget. God had answered all our prayers. Then we set sail for Maio some one hundred and twenty or more miles to the sou' sou' west of Pernambuco, where we gained intelligence of further plunder. There, safe within the arm of the reef that shelters the port, we set about the piecing together of the galley frigate that I mentioned afore. Whilst working on her a sharp eyed look-out gave a warning cry 'Four large ships of sail'. Firstly we thought of further plunder, that these were Spanish carracks laden with booty! But lo and behold, damn-me if it weren't Captain Venner with a fleet on similar enterprise to our own. Together we joined our forces. Three weeks our carpenters laboured in those unhealthy climes until the galley was complete. Fourteen sweeps aside and mast and sail. I agreed with Venner that as consequence of what my ships had achieved already, any further spoils would be divided as to one quarter to him and the remainder to ourselves. Thus reinforced we sailed once more for Pernambuco. The harbour of that port is also guarded by a reef where within lies sheltered water, the port is made of an island with a narrow causeway linking to the mainland. There are forts that guard the entrance, at which lay three great Hollanders come to trade. Should they choose to side with Spain, they would frustrate all our endeavours." He paused to sip his wine.

"Please continue, Captain Lancaster, for I am sure the

ladies find your account most fascinating, is it not so Thomasine?"

"Not just the ladies, Father," interjected Richard. "Martin and I would give much to partake of adventure such as this."

"Aye indeed, 'tis great seamanship that is required to navigate such a voyage!"

Lancaster coughed and resumed his tale.

"We gave notice of our intent by challenging the forts with shot from demi-culverin at a range of two thousand paces, and they replied, but to neither side was damage done. Our concern was to display to the Dutchmen our determination so that they should not hamper our intent, yet plans were prepared to board and fire them should it be of need. From ship to ship our General went, rallying to arms those that would serve with him, with promise of a bounty for their bravery. Armed with bow and musket, pike or bill they gathered in the boats we had captured, for our ships could not enter the harbour until the fortress had been taken and their ordnance spiked." Lancaster looked around the table.

"But do I bore you?"

"No, no, we are fascinated by your tales of places and peoples. I, for one, will never thus far venture, and shall only see them through your eyes," answered Jenkyn.

"So be it. At noontide the Governor sent a Portuguese to parley with me as to the nature of our trade. I told him we had knowledge of the East Indiaman, that her goods were ashore, and were to be ours for the taking! Upon his return he rallied the townsmen until they numbered over six hundred strong, they mustered about the fort. But we were determined not to be denied. 'Twas not until the afternoon that the tide favoured us, by which time, the Hollanders who were riding in the harbour's mouth, seeing our warlike preparations, laid down hawsers and wound them each one out of our way that we might have a clear passage. Then, with the tide on our heels, the wind in our sails, backs bravely bent over the sweeps, we ran our boats through the harbour entrance to make direct for the fort."

"Aye, James, above the sound of surf came the roar of those rascally seamen from the *Saloman*. Such fearsome yells

222

as would drive the Devil from his kennel."

"Aye, Edmund, with such as they at your side, you take no notice of fear. So we fired the saker as she ran, from point blank range of seventeen score paces, followed by dice shot from the murderers that hailed into Spaniard and Portuguese."

"A word, Squire Keigwin, 'tis my turn to speak a word," John Audley interrupted. "If I do not tell he will not say himself. Tell me, James Lancaster, what other orders did you give your commanders?"

No reply as James sucked and sipped, in alternate fashion.

"What might they have been?" Keigwin curiously enquired.

" 'Twas nothing, Jenkyn," said Lancaster.

"Nothing but undaunted bravery. For you ordered them to run their boats hard against the shore, that they be holed. Why, it was you yourself broke the back of the galley as she beached."

" 'Twas so as to ensure my soldiers could not retire, that there was no escape and but one way to go. Forward!" He thumped the table with his fist.

"So that was the manner in which we took the Port of Pernambuco," Barker continued, "but you yourself led the charge, though outnumbered — and outgunned!" He paused in recollection of the scene. "Yes, yet such was the ferocity that Spaniard and Portuguee ran before your onslaught and forsook their ordnance leaving their defences intact for our use! Many an adventure did follow. For such was the value of their goods in store that they attacked us with all at their command. Twice they attacked us with fire-ships and sent native swimmers to cut our cables as we rode, that we might drift aground in those strong tides. But we guessed their intent and were prepared."

"We stayed there some three weeks."

"Aye," Barker laughed to himself, "and took a Portuguee with negroes and women aboard whom we set loose. But the menfolk we kept, for we had no mules or oxen to pull the carts we captured, thus we retained their services to load our ships with their merchandise."

"Pray, what booty do you have?"

"Why," Lancaster replied, "some has gone ahead with Captain Venner, but we have an assortment more valuable than gold!" He sucked his pipe and leant back to tick upon his fingers: "Brazil wood, to extract the dye; calico cloth and sugar, then there is in particular: pepper, cinnamon, cloves, mace and nutmegs, and much more besides! We are laden to the gunwales! I vow, Mistress Elizabeth, if you were to twitch your pretty nose you could smell the spice from here!"

Elizabeth raised her head and wrinkled her nose. "Indeed, Captain Lancaster, I do believe I can!"

"This we must see, Martin."

"Aye, Father. If it should please you, Captain Lancaster, gentlemen, may we come aboard tomorrow?"

"The sooner the better, Martin Keigwin, for I am anxious now to be on our way with fresh water and victuals and agreement with yourself, Squire, for the sale of much booty. Shall we say nine of the clock, Master Keigwin?"

" 'Twill do well, Captain Lancaster, for the tide will be making, and you can bring the *Consent* into harbour should it please you."

Pleasantries concluded, Lancaster and his colleagues departed to rejoin their ships gently riding at anchor in the warmth of the afternoon sun.

Jenkyn was excited.

"My sons, to the study, come, we must confer."

They left Thomasine and Elizabeth, and followed their father to the privacy of his counting house.

"This would seem to be the most valuable yet of all the prizes we have held."

"Aye, and as consequence will offer most reward."

"Only if the purchase price allows for a fair profit — otherwise it could render our greatest loss," retorted the Squire. "Lancaster is not a man with whom to trifle, but as long as we are fair and reasonable." He dwelt awhile. "Now to decide to purchase, or to sell on terms of commission?"

"Father."

"Yes, Martin?"

"To buy all would be foolhardy, all our eggs in one basket. I propose we purchase that part of the spices and cloth which is the sailors' share. They will take less for promise of immediate gold. We know what is the market for such goods, and 'tis easy to transport. Timber and such like is better to unload where they dock at Blackwall. Agreed?"

"Aye, my son, 'tis correct. If we can give coin straightaway we deal with greater authority and the better the price we can obtain. Remember the art of the transaction is in the purchase. If one buys at a price that is prudent the selling becomes child's play. Yet still we have need of further partner. This is the subject of a syndicate. Do you agree that we include Solomon Fernandes?"

"Yes Father," Richard replied. "He is a true friend and a syndicate lessens the risk. Then he will come to you when the boot is on the other foot. He also keeps a still tongue, and whilst others proffer friendship, I fear they are eaten by jealousy and envy, and oft-times have de Zaubiaur as a paymaster."

"And Nicholas Flemyng?"

"But, naturally, he is family!"

Keigwin looked questioningly at Martin.

"I agree with Richard, Father."

He nodded. "Richard, ensure the storage is ready, and tell Teek Cornall such as he may need to know. Martin, send John Pearce to Fernandes. Let him hasten, give the Jew my compliments and that I have need to see him at light of tomorrow morn for purpose of trade. My old friend will realise the import of the message. We can speak for Nicholas."

Beneath his hooded lids the black eyes looked at his friend from a face bereft of expression. Head bowed, chin resting upon his pointed fingertips. Fernandes was contemplating.

"We must needs dispose of goods at soonest. Not only, Jenkyn, for quick reimbursement of our outlay, but Lancaster's expedition has dealt a further blow to Spanish pride and pocket." He shook his head in sorrow. "Jenkyn Keigwin, I say this to no one else but to you. Whispered words of envy fly swiftly on the wings of jealousy. The spies of Spain will soon be informed of our dealings, and where the booty is held."

"I too am uneasy and have strange feelings of foreboding that trouble me greatly and can only be shared with thee, old friend," Keigwin replied. "We lack for proof and dare not trouble others whom we love."

Gathered in Don De Amelrola's cabin to take wine and to confer, were the Friar, Burley and Captain Don Dezpeleta.

"Why do we delay our departure Padre? It is now June, the weather is clement, we are prepared and fully victualled and our soldiers impatient and fretting?" He looked about for support to his question. The Friar gently shook his head as he looked into Burley's eyes, a rare smile easing the corners of his thin lips. He placed a slim hand upon the captain's shoulder.

"We wait further intelligence."

"Of what, pray, Father?"

"As you have been told, we have news that in the Americas for many weeks a fleet of English and of Hollander has pillaged our Portuguese possessions. We still await news of their return. Many a fishing boat of Brittany is a spy for de Zaubiaur acting upon that merchant's orders. They fish off Cornwall's coast and will hasten home with intelligence, should there be the prospect of a greater catch — the return of the fleet and the whereabouts of that which it has stolen. It is our belief that at Mousehole they will take on fresh water and will trade much of their goods with a certain merchant there by name of Jenkyn Keigwin." He swung his open palm from Burley's shoulder to hold clenched fist before him, gradually opening his fingers to peer closely within as if a mosquito was caught there. " 'Tis there we will surprise and smite them to retake that which is ours."

"Thank you, Father. Now I know the total intent I too can bide my time."

"Not for long, good Captain Burley, as your Admiral will confirm. Soon, very soon, all the pieces will be in play. Then our Roman bishop shall be ready to take revenge upon the English Queen."

Chapter Fourteen

He eased himself in the saddle and swung his leg over the quarters of the sweat soaked bay, dismounted with reins in hand, he leant back upon his hips to stretch his aching muscles. With the promise of an ample reward he had ridden long and hard to cross Brittany to deliver the important missive with which de Zaubiaur's agent had entrusted him. The booty the English had captured from Pernambuco was on its way to Cornwall. Fishing boats had made sightings of the great ships, and duly reported to their master.

The rising sun peeped over the horizon into the harbour. The high masts of the galleys cast long shadows across the unruffled silver water. The twenty-sixth day of July, fifteen hundred and ninety-five. Before the altars the chaplains completed their devotions with blessing sought from Saint Anne, mother of the blessed Virgin Mary and most holy of saints, for today was her feast day. A fortuitous day for the departure of the flotilla. A day of significance to the soldiery that would augur well for a crusade against their heretic enemies.

Gently the lapping tide lifted the ships upon their moorings, as it greeted the outgoing waters of the twin rivers. Red-legged waders fed upon the pebbled shore, to dart from incoming wavelets, to advance and retreat in short, sharp bursts of stuttering steps. Above the lagoon, migrating terns, swallows of the sea, heads cast ever downwards, hovered then plunged for seaborne fry. Where westerly wind kissed granite headland, spiralling gulls rose and fell in the sensual embrace of the updraught. Nature was at ease with the world.

Envious eyes in shaven heads looked hungrily at the freedom of the birds, would that they could enjoy such liberty. Chafed ankles chained to iron staples shuffled upon the boarded deck.

Groaning windlass weighed the anchors from their sandy bed. Flags and pennants flew from the mastheads. At the beat of the drum, scarred brown backs bent forward upon their narrow bench. The sweeps dipped in unison beneath the water's surface. Whips cracked and backs straightened as wooden blades pulled the galleys under way.

In line astern Carlos De Amelrola led his command as he followed the orders of his King. Westwards they went, through the harbour's narrow entrance, steering a course betwixt the Ile de Groix and the Pointe du Talut. Upon the starboard beam the low outline of the Iles de Glenans hove into view.

Sails were raised, each bloody cross proclaiming whom they served. Oars were shipped and the slaves were rested, that their energies might be reserved for future days, as the course was altered to a northerly track, for the westerly wind to urge them upon their way.

All day they sailed wafted 'neath the azure sky, escorted by small shoals of tunny dashing and flashing through the shallow wavetops. Once past the rock-strewn seas off the Point de Penmarch, they turned to bear inshore, to shelter in the lee of a headland, where Nicholls knew of a safe anchorage. There they lay, to rest away the night, cradled in the unruffled swell.

A contented smile upon his face, Lancaster was seated in the Keigwin counting house, drawing upon his pipe as Jenkyn and Solomon pored over the inventory he had recorded when the ships were laden on the harbourside of Pernambuco.

"Ye Gods, Master Lancaster, but there be wondrous great riches you have taken. The King of Spain will be sore indeed his country is so deprived by your brave deeds."

"Aye Keigwin, when news of the venture reaches Spain there will be many seeking vengeance."

Solomon Fernandes straightened from his task.

"Methinks such intelligence could already be in his possession, for the journey from Brazil to Fuenterrabia is shorter
than to Cornwall. You may be certain that they would have
alerted their homeland with all haste. News travels fast, but
bad news travels fastest."

" 'Tis so, Solomon, and we were at Pernambuco for some
three weeks. There, a messenger could have slipped away
when we were newly landed. Consequently I am anxious to
conclude our deal and discharge my goods. Too often have I
seen the wine of success dashed from the lips before it could
be savoured. Do you recall some six years since, Cumberland's
great prize? The Indiaman, richly laden with gold and silver,
that foundered yonder in the bay?"

"I do indeed, James, for I saw her go down," he looked
gravely at his guest, "lost with all her crew."

"Master Lancaster."

James looked across to where Solomon spoke, the papers
ruffled between his nervous hands.

"We also have intelligence that a squadron of Spain's
galleys remain in harbour at Blavet. Our defences here are
weakened in support of Drake's planned expedition," the
Jew lamented. "I am fearful what they might achieve should
they venture to these unprotected shores."

"And rightly, Master Fernandes. But shall we now to
business, for the sooner 'tis complete and the cargo within
your warehouse the better shall I be pleased and on my
way to Blackwall!"

Punt and long-boat jostled for position alongside the
merchantman, plying endless procession between ships and
wharf, urged by mix of threat and promise from Teek
Cornall's impatient tongue as he supervised the stacking
within the warehouse; whilst Jenkyn Keigwin trusted no one
but himself to mark the inventory.

Within the stockyard ponies were tethered, Jacob and
John Pearce adjusted the balance of the panniers and
tightened girths with care. A saddle-sore or gall would be a
useless hindrance in the long hard journey that awaited them.
Martin had ridden on, so that a fresh relay of ponies might
be awaiting them at the next stage of their journey. Men,
trusted and armed, were called to escort the trains, lest

robber bands waylay them upon the wild and lonely moors they must traverse. All for safe and speedy exodus, that these rich commodities might be transferred to merchants and persons of rank who sought the merchandise they had to offer. To such as these Richard was destined, with lists provided by his father and Solomon Fernandes.

At last all that was purchased or commissioned was ashore, guarded within the warehouses that lined the wharf of Mousehole. Sentries were posted by Teek who placed himself as master of the watch. Silver was paid and bills of exchange written by Solomon, with promise of payment by the banker. Careful account was kept by Lancaster and Keigwin, proof if needs be, to others, of the fair deal struck.

It had taken days to unload, to record and to stack. Such a hubbub about the wharf. The wafting of aromatic smells and the winding trains of pack ponies along the pilgrims' path proclaimed to all the wealth and nature of the goods. A secret that no longer could be maintained.

Above the great beak of the battering prow, he leant upon the gunwale, lost in thoughts of what might be.

"Master Nicholls."

He turned, as Nankervis joined him on the crowded forecastle.

"You saw the port we passed by this morning? The arm of a quay wall, and the fishing boats sheltered within?"

"Before we rounded the high headland? 'Tis a place called Plezmarg."

"Aye, that was the one; what did you notice?"

Nicholls looked at him awhile and shook his head.

"I'll tell you. 'Twas uncommon like Mousehole."

"Maybe so."

"Tell your master, 'tis so! The crags and cliffs softened. The wall is of same nature. Even the cottages not unalike!"

"Well, what of it?"

" 'Tis held by those that favour Spain."

"So?"

"So we need fresh victuals, for there are many of us and little room for stowage."

"That is true."

"Well man, a trial."

"A trial?"

"A trial against an enemy! 'Twill raise the soldiers' spirits and give them further practice."

"By God, Nankervis, 'tis true!" He half turned to face the Cornishman and grabbed him by his forearms.

"I will speak with Captain Burley and acquaint him with your thoughts."

Nankervis smiled and turned to leave the Englishman. It would be presented as the idea of Nicholls, but then Nankervis sought no credit for himself, only relief from the canker that burned within his very bowels.

The flag was raised high into the shrouds. A solitary shot was fired. A council of captains was called upon the *Capitana*, the flagship.

They gathered to hear De Amelrola give the orders for the morrow, and chuckled in appreciation of his commands; Burley was called to fill the detail, and Friar Domingo nodded his benign approval.

In the dawning light the peeping sun turned a black sea to molten silver beneath the rising mist that skimmed the restless surface. In slack water, with little wind either to help or to hinder, anchors were raised as stealthily the squadron went about, to return on the track of the previous day.

The folk of the fishing village awoke at daybreak to see the four great galleys, sweeps outstretched, paddling into their harbour. To come to rest, facing inland, their ordnance threatening net-loft and cottage, fishing boat and warehouse of the fishermen who gathered in anguish and in awe upon the quayside. Silver whistles blew their orders as launch and longboat were lowered. Files of soldiers, the peaked steel of helmets and burnished breastplates gleaming in the sun's slanting rays, clasped pike and arquebus and prepared to disembark. Intent upon attack.

From amongst the flock of fishing boats, a wooden punt came forth. Sculled toward the *Nuestra Senora de Begona*. Those she bore, shouting as they came. They were words of Latin, of prayer, that reached the aft-castle so high above. Three brave men, deputised to talk, perhaps to plead, on

231

behalf of their town.

Midst stares and jibes from curious Spanish soldiery they climbed aboard the flagship to be escorted to De Amelrola's daunting presence, to be greeted with the gracious courtesy that serves to further enhance the authority of a man when in a position of total power.

"Gentlemen, some wine? We are called in here for refreshment and victuals that we shall purchase," he paused as his smile did little to mask the threat, "always provided we consider the sum you demand is reasonable."

In gawky silence they sipped their wine and nodded.

"That being so my friend and paymaster, Don Sambujero will treat with you."

A nod of dismissal as a servant relieved the trio of wine that they had hardly sipped. They turned to go.

"Now act with haste, gentlemen, we and the tide have but little time to dwell."

The food was swiftly purchased for a pittance and taken aboard the galleys that held little space for victuals and fresh water.

"That was good practice Burley, was it not so Don Domingo?"

"Aye, it will keep the men in good heart. See how quickly cowed were the fierce Bretons at the hint of a threat! Thus it will be at Mousehole!"

The morrow was the 28th July. With little breeze to aid them, the flotilla crossed the calm waters of the Baie d'Audierne, skirting the forbidding headland of the Pointe du Raz, as the Ile de Sein slid past to larboard.

Pacing the floor of his Plymouth home, Sir Francis impatiently awaited the visit of his generals. Again he went to the window to peer into the street. Another letter from his Queen both demanding and entreating him to hasten with his mission.

Outside was a bustling throng, sailors and soldiers, merchants and townsfolk. He looked across to the harbour wall and westward to the Hamoaze. The skeletons of undressed masts and rigging of his fleet stood stark against the evening sun. Little boats bustling busily, toing and froing provisioning the ships, as ducklings to their mother's cluck. Merchantmen, lading to depart for shores unknown or newly-come to discharge their cargo.

In Lowsand Bay too, were great ships anchored. Awaiting his orders, to accompany him to his destiny. From around Penlee Point came the billowing sails of a fat merchantman that gave him notion of flouncing matrons. He smiled at the reminder, for never did the sight of this port of all England fail to stir his imagination or speed the flutter of his heart. He turned away, to reach for and light his pipe, to pace the room, impatient for the coming of Hawkyns and of Clifford.

A knock, the servant relieving them of sword and cape as he showed them to Drake's room, to be seated and relaxed with pipe and with wine.

"Now, tell me John," he pointed his pipe stem at Hawkyns, "how fare the vessels in your charge? What further progress need we to make afore we can set sail?"

"The sheathing is now complete and ordnance set in place."

"Then to ballast and to trim 'em?"

"Aye, Sir Francis. Most are in ballast already, the remainder," he shrugged his shoulders, "two weeks maybe? Yes, Admiral, two weeks will suffice."

"Make it ten days, John Hawkyns, and I would it were but two."

The Devon burr of his boyhood added emphasis to his concern. "Then time to victual. Time for the captains and their men to accustom to their craft. Old seadogs they may be, but still they need to grow wise to the ways of their ships. Time, time, time. A commodity of which we have very little to spare!" He hissed between his teeth and shook his head.

"Now, as to you Sir Nicholas and your soldier boys, how are they a-faring?"

"Admiral, we have chosen the finest of the soldiery the west can offer. They have their arms and their armour, and are now well rehearsed in the use."

"Aye and so, by God they should be. They have had both time and money a-plenty to prepare, whilst all delay has been with the ships and garnering of ordnance."

233

He turned to Hawkyns. "Tomorrow, John, we shall inspect together. Ensure your captains are made aware. Such ships as you say are prepared we shall visit as you direct. We meet at nine of the clock in my cabin. From stem to stern of every ship, with each man at his post, mark you. Then again on the morrow until all is done and all outstanding works are noted and made record. I find it tedious gentlemen, but there is so much yet undone. Having the fleet seaworthy is but the half. Stores and ordnance for so many requires much forethought, especially when we are treated with such parsimony and have such a meagre purse in which to delve!" Drake paused, before continuing with feeling. "In confidence, we and our men do deserve better. There remain a thousand and one things to consider." Then, louder, "Ah! John, but that we could go a-plundering once more as once we used!" He sighed a mournful sigh.

"Aye Sir Francis, one well-found ship, and but a hundred men! And no one to answer to! Save ourselves and our God."

"You are now some three and sixty summers, and still a'venturing when 'tis a young man's sport. But our Queen has commanded us and therefore must we go. Daily does she require news of our progress." Drake turned to Nicholas Clifford. "How fare your men with pike and sword?"

"They diligently rehearse, Sir Francis, and will be worthy of you on their day of reckoning."

"So be it Sir Nick, keep 'em well drilled and disciplined in use of pistol and of arquebus, for by all account we may have to make a proper fight on't."

With door and window open wide in the warmth of the summer evening, from within The Mermaid spilled the sound of jollity that spread across the harbour front. After long months without taste of English ale or sight of English maid, the men of Lancaster's fleet were now released ashore. Silver in their pockets, huff-cap in their bellies; they cheeked and cheered the serving wenches that plied Trewhella's ale.

Outside were sweetmeat stalls and pie-men; as they vied with the landlord's fare, so did the seamen vie, in the

234

extravagance of the stories they told.

There were tales of exotic islands on which naked maidens thrived; of unicorns of the sea, with long and twisted horn, of great whales that spouted water to the heavens. And gold! Spanish gold, and spices rare and precious.

Relieved of his duty, Teek was seated in his favourite chair, pipe clenched in teeth, ale jug clenched in fist. He listened with quiet enjoyment and guffaw of disbelief to the rich tales the ale unlocked. He rose to stretch himself, determined the men of Mousehole would not be outshone, he hailed a burly figure in the corner. "Pentreath, come you here."

Red stocking cap on head, black patch over one eye, came he who steered the privateer. The big man with elbow and gentle shove made passage through the throng.

"Tell these seamen of the wondrous sights we too have witnessed, and of how this inn became so named."

In accent broad and of a commanding presence, the one-eyed man spoke that all might hear. It was the turn of Lancaster's men to gather round to listen, as the seaman told his story:

"When I was but a lad, in the autumn as I recall, we had weeks of terrible storms and seas, the like of which I hope never again to see; bred of easterly gales that swept unhindered into the bay. The family was hungry. Mousehole was hungry, and me the eldest of six starving children. No fish could be landed, for no one dared to brave the temper of that raging sea." He drank deep to drain his jar, looking toward Teek, who gave him but hint of a wink, as he replenished the empty vessel.

"Thank ye. It was the middle of the day. When suddenly the wind was stilled. As if commanded from above." He raised his one eye heavenwards to continue in dramatic tones. "The water was calmed, the colour of pewter beneath charcoal skies that still spewed down soft rain. The silence was eerie, even the gulls stopped their scream and the surf ceased its roar." He paused to shake his head in fearful remembrance. "I recall that day so well. 'Come boy,' said Fayther to me, 'today you be a man! Let us to the punt!' Outside the harbour we went, into that still, silent sea. Into

235

the bay we rowed a solitary boat, alone, to shoot our nets. First shot we hit a shoal. Pilchards by the million. Never seen fish like it! 'Twas all we might do to haul in our laden nets. How we heaved and struggled, tipping that jumping, silver harvest into the safety of the boat. But manage we did, to turn about, ready to come to harbour before the foul weather could return." He licked the froth from off his upper lip, and lowered his head, shaking it in recollection. "Suddenly the stillness of that day was shattered. The roar of one, lone, long lingering clap of thunder. Then scream of gulls as higher and higher they towered above the island, to wheel and circle, 'twas like a snow storm beneath that black sky. Unseen from shore or chapel, a shaft of sunlight blazed to tear apart the clouds," his raised voice lowered as his audience leant forward to hear, "and shine its shaft upon our boat. Where the rainbow ended its coloured arch, we saw her, as she lay in all her loveliness."

He finished his ale with a deep swig and wiped his mouth upon his homespun sleeve and waited. His jar replenished by eager hands, he continued with his story.

"Aye," he nodded his head at the recollection, "her scales reflected the seven colours in all their beauty, as a mackerel, fresh from the sea, and girt great tail withall!"

"What was it? What was it?" they cried.

"What was she," he emphasised, "with wondrous eyes of blue, blue as a clear sky on a summer's morn, her smooth skin cream white as milk newly squeezed. Long tresses of fine spun gold, that could not hide her bountiful breasts. For big as pumpkins were they — yet finely shaped." He outlined her form with his hands. "Why, a mermaid she be! A beauteous mermaid!"

He finished the ale and stood the pot upside down upon his head.

"What next? What next?" they urged.

No answer, till once more the jug was filled.

"Why, I threw her a fish, she dived from her rock and came up alongside with it, caught between her pearly white teeth. Then she tossed it in the air and swallowed it whole — as a seal might do — I held my hands to her, which she quickly grasped in slender fingers, and I pulled her up and

236

aboard." He drank another draught, there was silence as all waited to hear what was to happen.

"Many a long minute we talked. For she revealed that in the great storm she had become confused and separated from her father and mother. A maid of merely four score summers, she was lost from her home beneath the sea — the land of Lyonesse."

"What then?" Wide-eyed they asked.

"Why, Fayther grew impatient and jealous of our friendship. He told her which way she should follow, picked her up and threw her back into the sea from whence she came."

"For shame, for shame."

" 'Tis so," he supped again, his audience in suspense. "Said she were a poor specimen. Not complete. Not good enough to keep."

"Why, why?"

"She had no button on her belly! No sign of dimple or blemish, but smooth as buttermilk!"

From the fringe of the throng an elegant traveller called to the story-teller:

"Foolish fellow, a mermaid is reckoned part fish, part mortal. Since fish lay eggs, her mother had no cord. Hence she no navel!"

" 'Tis true," they cried, "what say you now?"

"God forgive such ignorant fishermen as we! You are right, sir! Had we but thought o' that we would have had her to this day. For I was smitten. Ah! I was smitten! For these many years have I loved that maid-of-the-sea. True to her have I been." He shook his head in sorrow. "In consequence never have I married, a virgin same as her I be." He took a ragged kerchief and blew his nose and wiped a tear from his eye, as his jar once more was filled.

The small boy who had pushed to his side, listening to the story, reached up his hand to tug upon his sleeve and spill some ale.

"What be you at young Matt?"

"Fayther, Mam says to come home soon for Dorothy will not sleep until you tell her a story."

"Right me robin. I've now supped ale enough. Let us on

our way."

He drained his jar in a mighty draught, a broad wink
at Teek as Becky's bottom received accustomed slap. His
head thrown back in deep roar of laughter in which all did
join, as his tousled son led him homeward through the
open door, anxious to hear one more of his father's fisherman's tales.

Blessed relief. Time to return to harbour for fresh water and
victuals. The *Moon* would maintain the patrol. North-west
beneath the towering headland of Old Head of Kinsale.

Flemyng ordered the helmsman to take her to larboard. On
broad reach, to drop anchor outside the harbour's entrance
to await the aid of the flooding tide that would waft them
upon their way up the river estuary, there to tie up alongside
the harbour wall.

Sails furled, deck gear made orderly, warps checked, orders
given; and then time to relax for today he would dine at the
invitation of Joseph Barrye, kinsman of his grandmother; and
a gentleman of that turbulent land.

A servant awaited him with spare nag upon the quayside
that he might make his way to the Manor where they lived.

It was no wonder his grandparents felt at ease at Madron.
For was not the landscape and structure of cottage or manor
so similar to that of their native Munster? Feuding and
rebellion had forced them to leave for greener pastures that
would pay better reward to labour, and prudent business.
The Celtic cross, circles of standing stones and quoit gave
evidence of a common ancestry that could not be denied.

"Mistress Barrye," Thomas finished his meal and wiped his
mouth upon his napkin, "I have been deprived at sea these
last days, and as consequence appreciate fine food the more.
Your table does indeed provide a banquet of rare quality.
I drink your health." He raised his goblet to his hostess and
sipped with relish the Madeira wine. Pipes were produced
and a hovering servant passed the tobacco in a chased box
of silver.

The three now seated, his host cleared his throat to speak
with lowered voice.

"Now, Tom, we were sorely saddened to learn of the tragedy in your life. The loss of one so young, and with child . . . " he stopped, wondering how best to continue and mournfully shook his head.

"Thank you, sir, for your thoughts. 'Tis true, I lost not only one, alas, but two. Yet I was fortunate, for though our happiness was brief, sorrow cannot extinguish the memory of our joyful days together. Few can have known such love as that we shared."

Each sunk into awkward silence until, with a slap of his knee, Barrye rose, "I make a poor host, drink up Tom. Let us banish maudlin thoughts. What news do you possess of our family and of Cornwall, for in God's truth it is many a year since they left these shores, yet often we recall the happy days of our youth together here in Munster. Is it not so Eileen?"

The lady of the house nodded. Her husband continued.

"How is my cousin Catherine? She is now of great age. Still she lives?"

"Indeed sir, my grandmother is well and recounts the happy days of your youth together." He blew a cloud of smoke towards the ring of candles that hung from the high ceiling. "She rules us all with a rod of iron, and has a rare determination of her own. And yet," he thought awhile, "she harbours a fiendish form of merriment that tricks and teases."

"Thus she was as a child I recall. But what of other matters? What news have you of Spain and the Papacy? What mischief is there now afoot?"

"There is little I can add to that already known to you. Spanish boats still fish these waters. Doubtless some render other services of a less peaceful cause, but 'tis difficult to obtain proof. I suspect, as others may, that Spain has received a bloody nose and now has lost her will to gain Brittany for her own. In consequence it may be her intent to invade England with the aid of the Irish chieftains. This is our fear. For Brittany has but few harbours and the winds that beat upon that coast would contain their ungainly galleons, to offer England little threat. But on Ireland's eastern coast are harbours, and readily would the westerlies waft an Armada across these narrow, sheltered seas to land their soldiery upon our English shores."

"Those thoughts are also in our minds."

"I have had other news that is of slight concern."

"Pray what may that be?"

Tom paused awhile before replying. "There remains in southern Brittany a squadron of Spanish galleys. 'Tis my belief, and one my father shares, that they could pose a threat to my home. Mousehole lies unprotected by the English fleet as a consequence of our captains' adventuring abroad." He drew upon his pipe. "This must be known to Spain also, for indeed Mendoza and de Zaubiaur possess marvellous good intelligence."

"Thomas, I am of Irish blood and know but little of ships or Spain's intrigue. May I ask a question?"

"Why, Mistress Barrye, that you may. I trust I may have the wit to make fair answer."

"What nature of ship, I prithee, is a galley?"

Thomas thoughtfully tamped the bowl and sucked the tobacco to glow and give time to mull an apt reply.

"Mistress Barrye, the galley is like the blue shark that haunts the waters of the Mediterranean ocean; oft he comes to your southern coast or ventures to our Cornish seas, but he dislikes the chill of more northern waters: long and slender yet muscular and powerful." He paused to sip and savour his wine before continuing. "I recall many a time when off the Isles of Scilly, aboard the *Golden Hind* when boredom was upon us, we would while our time dropping a line over our stern, baited with headless mackerel pinned on an iron hook."

"What then? It seems I must learn something of the sea. Being of the country I know little but of animals and flowers."

"We would watch and wait. The flash of blue black, a sickle fin. A half roll and show of a white underbelly, then great gaping jaws beneath a protruding snout, that chopped upon its prey," his hands clapped together in emphasis, "never to release."

"How exciting, did you eat him too?"

"Rarely, for unless one is needy, there are other fishes to be preferred."

240

"But what of the galley?" Eileen pursued.

"As the blue shark has over the millenium perfected him-elf to be the perfect hunter of the sea, so has the galley leveloped in those same warmer waters, aye, since before the birth of Christ!"

There was a silence.

"Doubtless Master Barrye your study contains works of he scholars of ancient Greece who would confirm?"

" 'Tis so, Thomas, but continue with your simile."

"The galley, as the shark, has been perfected in the seas of the Mediterranean and adopted and developed for war by he craftsmen and shipwrights of Venice. Lean and slender is the shark, like that fearsome fish, it is armed to the fore. She has the snout of the shark in the battering ram of a projecting prow. To the fore are her mass of fighting men, that when her enemy is rammed, will grapple to board and overwhelm by weight of numbers — for each ship musters some four hundred men. Beneath the prow her teeth, pieces of ordnance with a further cannon that may only fire straight to the fore, firmly mounted upon her coursier."

"Coursier, pray what is a coursier?"

"The centred gangway of the galley, that bridges the fore-deck and the aft. Here the boatswains parade, to wield their whips upon the backs of the hapless heathen slaves. Some six chained to each great sweep, that pulls them through the sea."

"A sweep?"

"It is the oar, mistress, laid out in banks, perhaps twenty-seven a side. Thus does the galley pursue her prey. For, like the blue shark, she depends for much on her speed of attack. She is faster than the fastest ship of sail and has no depen-dence upon wind or tide as other ships of sail are forced to do."

"And who are these slaves?"

"Oft-times Moors, infidels taken in battle. Sometimes criminals who pay penance by period of servitude. Or heretics. Sometimes of England, those who do not or will not follow the edict of the Prince of Rome but worship their God in another form."

"Are there other ways to compare Thomas?"

"Aye, Master Barrye, when one thinks on't. For the sails

241

too are like a leg o' mutton, as is the fin of the shark."

"Is the wine to your liking, Thomas?"

"That it certainly is."

His host replenished his glass and that of Mistress Eileen.

"As the blue shark has no liking for the colder waters, so the galley. For in the waist she is close to the water, as her sweeps have to be set low to bite into the seas. Her oarsmen, oft from much warmer climes, suffer sorely in our cold and damp, and the roughness of our oceans can cause them to ship water. Furthermore there is lack of space for provisions or for water. Therefore she can only be used on those expeditions that are of a short duration."

"What a terrible thing it is that mortal men are chained and thus treated."

"Ah! The Spaniard would have it, Mistress, that the heretic and the heathen so manacled will, by their suffering, be purged of the evils of heresy and, by their confession and the prayers of the priests aboard, will obtain the reward of everlasting life! Thus they would contend the slaves are blessed indeed!"

"Do you believe the galleys could launch such an attack on Cornwall?"

"Surely it may be possible, but praise God, 'tis hoped that our wild cold seas will be our saviour from such evil."

"May it please God you are right. For you should know the nature of our enemy, you have encountered him in battle."

"I have had my share of him. The more times we have met, the less I know."

"You fought against the Armada?"

"Indeed."

"Doubtless to serve with some of our finest sailors?"

"From whom I have learned much."

"Drake and Raleigh — and Frobisher?"

"That dog-rough pirate? A rare character!"

"What of another Cornishman — Grenvylle. A brave, brave man!"

"Aye, Master Barrye, I have adventured with him."

"What kind of man was he?"

"A man of rare temper!"

"Temper?"

"When a mood was upon him he possessed a rage so vile — why he would chew his glass in anger when provoked, so his mouth ran with his own blood!"

He looked thoughtfully at his own glass of red wine as if in recollection of the scene. "Brave or foolhardy, I know not which."

"You knew him well?"

Tom looked up into the eyes of his host and spoke bluntly: "Well enough; I saw him die."

"You were at Flores?"

"Aye, Master Barrye, Captain of the *Dolphin*, of my Lord Howard's fleet."

"You have witnessed much action for one of such youth."

"I have witnessed much bravery and some cowardice, be it Spaniard or Englishman. I have seen many young men killed or maimed in the cause of their faith." He gave a rare and melancholy sigh. "A curse on all priests. Surely Christ did not save us to slaughter each other in the sulphur of a smoking gun deck? I have drunk too well of your very fine wine and now I am melancholy and make poor company. Forgive me."

He rose, to thank his hosts, to bid farewell and return to his command.

Chapter Fifteen

Along the quay walked two men, one in puffed doublet of rich scarlet and matching hose, the other in jerkin and cloth breeches. Jenkyn Keigwin and Teek Cornall were about their rounds. The Squire paused to look upon the peace of the bay, his servant by his side.

Up on the cliff top the huer stood, bush in hand to direct by whistle and by gesture the boats that fished below to where the water's surface rippled from shoal of the pilchard.

"With Master Martin and Richard away trading, 'tis for you, Cornall, to safeguard the fishing. Ensure the catch is properly counted and costed before I am called upon to pay. Tomorrow we will discuss size of catch, whether to pickle or press. You will receive a bonus, according to our profit."

"Thank you, Squire." He grinned his gratitude.

" 'Tis only your deserts, for there are few we trust as thee. But never let me down!" He turned to gaze hard into Teek's eyes.

"Never, Master, never will I do so, that will I swear before God."

"So be it." Keigwin looked up at the puffs of white cloud that dappled the heavens. " 'Tis set calm for awhile, there will be pilchard in abundance."

They went their way together, backs toward the bay, up the shallow hill to turn into the stockyard where, from within a byre came a soothing sound – the hiss, hiss of milk as the maid squeezed the creaming stream from the soft pink teats of the house cows.

Amid the scratching hens and crowing cockerels was the murmur of voices as Jacob confided his country wisdom into the eager ear of John Pearce. The son he never had. They were returning from their labour in the meadows to tend the whelping bitches and the puppies that could boast old Merlin as their grandsire.

In the Manor House, Thomasine watched the restless Elizabeth with an understanding smile.

"The baby will come when due and not before."

"But I feel ill at ease and so full of fidget."

"It is always so. The waiting is the worst part on't. 'Twill be a little while yet." She paused in her stitching. "Do not fret so, my dear, Richard will not be gone for so very much longer."

Elizabeth turned to her mother-in-law.

"Mistress Thomasine, the house is near complete and will be by the time of Richard's return. Whilst I am still able, would it displease you greatly if I was to visit my aunt for a day or two? There are items that belong to me that were once my parents' which I wish to collect. Then, upon my return, Richard and I will make our nest. It will take me out of myself awhile, for when the baby is born I will be unable to venture far."

"Of course, my dear soul. John Pearce can be spared for the farm is now between seasons. He can ride ahead to acquaint Lady Anne of your coming. Jacob shall accompany you. You shall break your journey at Madron, your sister-in-law and Nicholas would welcome you the night. Lady Anne will be pleased at the company."

"Thank you."

She bent to kiss the rose red cheek and Thomasine smiled.

"But do not linger over long, for I too love you dearly as a daughter, and will miss your company in this house of men!"

Through the rough waters Nicholls and the Breton pilot steered, giving wide berth to the hidden rocks whose lurking menace lay off every towering point. Rounding the Pointe du Van, thence east and so to starboard into the gaping maw of the Baie de Douarnenez. The westerly wind astern, clewed up sails unreefed, oars shipped, they sailed upon the turning tide, that weary slaves might rest.

In the clear blue, unruffled waters of the summer's day Nankervis stood upon the prow deck with others of England, anxious once more to be upon their homeland's shores. The high grey cliffs etched in the sunshine's glare were constant reminders of his Cornish childhood.

"How fare your countrymen aboard, Captain Burley?" De Amelrola stood beside him.

"Cramped within their quarters, but 'tis no matter, their hearts are lifted by thoughts of home and . . ." towards the black-robed figure, " . . . the dissertations of Friar Domingo."

"They may be few in number but they are great in heart."

"In my country, Don Carlos, we say 'from little acorns, mighty oak trees grow'."

"With God's help we shall plant these acorns."

"Mighty will they grow until the will of Rome is restored to England!"

Defiantly the banner fluttered above the battery seated upon the guardian castle of Pouldavid. Long had the garrison withstood the French siege and held the harbour they had fortified, that one day an Armada of Spain might lie within the haven, prepared for an attack on foreign shores. However hopes long nurtured were now fading into a dream of what might have been. Forgotten and forsaken by their motherland, still they held out. Short of rations and munitions, but with plentiful store of pride. An outpost of Spain in an alien land.

The disbelieving sentry looked again into the dazzle of the twinkling sea. Four great galleys, lateen sails resplendent with the rich red cross of Malta. Atop from main and foremast, streamed gay flags and banners, emblems of his country. He blew his whistle to call out the guard, that they too might witness the approach of the galleys and alert their fellows to the coming of aid and fearsome friends.

Orders were whistled and shouted at sea, sails clewed in readiness to furl, sweeps thrust outwards to dig into the rippling azure of the water. The galleys made their entrance. Flags dipped and raised as courtesies were exchanged.

The gathering crowd upon the harbourside roared their

246

welcome, cries of blessing shouted for King and country. Above the stone steps officers gathered about their commander, impatient for news of their countrymen, for knowledge of the outside world.

The ships settled at their anchorage. The skiff was summoned and the garrison commander escorted to the presence of De Amelrola. There to be given the biscuit brought from Blavet. Food for the hungry garrison. Powder too was needed for the siege had near exhausted all they held in store, but little could be spared. Of the twenty quintals requested, only a fifth was granted, for none could foretell what demands there might be upon the galley's guns. Thus it was that, early on the morn of the thirtieth of July, they bade farewell to their beleaguered countrymen to put to sea once more.

Within the inn at Crewkernewell. Richard impatiently awaited the coming of the packhorse train that must surely now be due. Once more he went outside, worried that they might not come. Some way along the track he walked, to breast the rise and scan westwards.

God be praised! They came! With merchandise and news. An endless procession of ponies, heavy-laden, that would return without a burden but with fresh orders that Richard had now negotiated. Rife rumour exaggerated the details of the spoils and booty which further enhanced its worth as to Exeter it made its way. His mission had bettered every expectation. Spices were the fashion. Never before had such demand been witnessed for pepper and for cloves, cinnamon and mace. Merchant and noblemen vied each with the other with purse wide opened for purchase.

Richard dared not return across the barren moors alone, prey to every cut-throat and vagabond gang within that untamed country, for some had paid in gold and silver for an extra discount, whilst others used bills of exchange made in Fernandes' name. Few would wish to ambush upon the outward way, for little could they achieve with those pungent flavourings; but the jingling song of a pocket full of silver. That sung a different tune.

The weary winding train of laden ponies flanked by men

of trust, armed and wary against attack, continued along the ancient Icknield Way to the welcome of the hostelry.

Richard strode to meet his dust-begrimed and saddle-sore brother. Martin dismounted and the two embraced in fond affection. Ponies, checked within the stableyard, were relieved of their loads and turned out to graze in the flush of green meadow. Booty was stored in poste house, stable and barn, and guards posted to keep watch.

"This one trade alone will ensure our future for many years to come, if the profit is wisely used, eh Martin?"

" 'Twill bring a sparkle to our father's eye and a new bonnet for Mother's head. What is more, I'll be damned if it doesn't bring even a smile to the dry face of old Fernandes. That is a sight that I surely wish to witness!"

Joyfully they ate of the finest fare the hostelry could offer and gurgled down the landlord's double ale. Early to bed they trod the oaken staircase, that they might early rise and set forth to Exeter.

North-west they rowed, beaked prow into the wind as they departed from the sheltered waters. The steady beat of the drum. Oars rose and fell in monotonous rhythm, headland after rugged headland passed, until the Pointe de St. Mathieu was reached, and west to the Isle of Ushant, where once had taught a certain Celtic saint named Paul.

From there they continued through slavering fangs of rotting rock that lay in wait, with anxious appetite, for those who knew not the nature of the rip tide that raced through those foaming waters. Thence to Le Conquet, far western Breton port; harbour for a fishing fleet. Here, with the aid of a westerly upon their beam, the ships of Mousehole oft-times plied their trade; laden with oil or fish on the outward journey, to return with wine. And Le Conquet's ships went to Mousehole, bound by the bond of language and of trade.

Above steep cliffs thronged many men of Brittany, to watch the galleys in procession in the waters below, standards held high and strong-armed. They roared a fierce shout of defiance. A challenge to De Amelrola to test his men ashore. How dearly he wished to accept the thrown gauntlet! But time was his enemy, and he dared not be deflected from his task, lest what they sought should be lost. There was always tomorrow. There would be another day, another time, to settle the score. It would not be forgot, but safely stowed within the locker of his memory.

Despite the mutter of the men they rowed a further league or more to the shelter of a headland's lee. There to relax without the weight of Atlanta's rolling seas, to await the easing of the wind.

With slaves rested, they sallied forth in calm seas. Northward to the open water. Here was no shelter should a gale torment, but neither were there hidden rocks to fear. English exiles knelt before the altar, blessed by the sombre Friar. Prayers were said for the success of this, their voyage of retribution. A murmur ran, for now it could be said, that when land was next espied it would be the rugged coast of Cornwall. Burley was well pleased.

The yardsmen shouted and pointed aft where into the dawning light the captain's eye should peer. The little craft of Le Conquet could only guess what the strangers' presence might foretell, but threat of danger bid them alter course to run before the wind. Drumbeat quickened, whips cracked upon a laggard's back. The identity of the flotilla was soon undoubted. The little boat could only hope and pray.

Within the hour the flagship bore down upon her quarry and fired a commanding shot for her to heave to. Her crew, ordered on board, scrambled to the galley's deck, to be greeted by the curious eyes of those assembled there.

From high above her, the captives looked down upon their precious boat, their livelihood, their only link with home and those they loved. On the orders of De Amelrola, they watched, eyes filled with pain, as planks were stove and she was left to drift astern to bob a curtsey of farewell, as bows sank to settle beneath the ragged waves that closed above her masthead. The cargo of wine destined for English throats was locked forever in her holds.

Prodded by escorting pikes, the Breton seamen lurched through the cabin door, where sat the daunting figure of Friar Domingo. The import of his garb they knew. A Dominican. Conscience of the Catholic faith. Guardian of the

Inquisition. He rose to transfix with penetrating stare those unfortunates who, incoherent in their stress, babbled in a dialect that none could comprehend. An interpreter was summoned to unravel, to challenge, and to question the garbled gabble of the panicked men.

The Friar listened, attentive to all they might impart, to further brief the translator as to the answers that he sought. He learned that a ship of England had been sent to Le Conquet for intelligence of their mission, knowing that the flotilla had departed from Blavet. Upon hearing that the galleys had ventured thus far north, they had gone about in haste to report on that which they had discovered.

The Friar watched his words translated, slender fingers toying with his rosary. A change of pitch, of emphasis, to his keen ear could tell him much despite his ignorance of their tongue, for was he not well practised in the art of listening?

Yes, they traded with the town of Mousehole and knew her people well, and yes, the fleet of Drake was still safe-locked within the harbour.

"What of the true religion? What manner of service is there held in Mousehole?"

"Spoken in God's own language," came the reply.

"Latin?"

Head cocked, his ear to catch a sign of hesitation, of fear, of heresy.

"They say yes, saving sometimes maybe in Cornish."

"English?"

The reply an ardent 'Never' that crossed the boundaries of tongue.

"And of the ritual? The liturgy? The celebration of Mass?"

With little left to lose, and but his life to keep, the seaman shrugged his response.

" 'Tis only hearsay."

Arms now folded, hands thrust deep within opposing cuffs, intent eyes flicked from question to answer.

"Yes . . . " The Friar waited expectantly as the fisherman sought the affirmation of his fellows.

"It is said that at the Church of St. Pol de Leon, no longer do they conform to the ways of Rome."

"Upon whose orders?" Quietly came the unthreatening question.

"They are uncertain, Father, but little is allowed to happen without the authority of the Squire."

"And the name of this man?"

"Keigwin."

"Keigwin," repeated the Friar, "Keigwin . . . " he rolled the name around his tongue. "A name I shall remember."

"The white hound in the Cornish."

"White hound? Then mayhap has come the time when this hound himself is hunted!"

Their purpose complete, the prisoners were escorted from the cabin.

Tall and gaunt the robed figure rose, his back turned upon them, his eyes ablaze with hate. Crucifix held in his hands before him, he sank to his knees and made his solemn vow to God, then summoned Burley to his presence.

" 'Tis as I promised, Keigwin."

Jenkyn had never before seen Solomon in such a state of fluster. The perspiration poured in rivulets down his sallow cheeks. Whilst the day was warm, it was not so hot as to cause such lather upon master or on mule.

"Teek," he called, "shut this creature in the stable yonder, whilst I tend to my friend."

He turned towards the Jewish banker and placed stout arm around the narrow shoulders.

"By Jove, Solomon old friend, you and your mule do vie as to which is in the greater sweat!"

"I have ridden fast, Jenkyn, that we might together ponder what I have to tell."

"Let us to my study that you may refresh yourself and we may discourse undisturbed."

Seated upon an oak chair, goblet of ale untouched within his grasp, Solomon continued in agitated tones.

" 'Tis as I promised, Jenkyn, I would tell you when my craft returned. Upon this morning's tide she came, but without a cargo. That will cost me dearly." He shook his head in sorrow.

251

"Calm yourself, Solomon, sip your ale and tell me all."

"The galleys have left their harbour, crammed with soldiery and, 'tis said, they carry Englishmen aboard. They steal their way along the coast of Brittany no doubt in readiness to attack us, for they must know that we are at their mercy!"

"Of this we have no certainty. They could be relieving one of their few garrisons along the Brittany coast. Or perhaps to launch a punishment raid upon a Breton port? I would doubt," spoke the Squire with authority, "that with those craft they would dare cross those open seas twixt us and Brittany."

"Think you so?"

"Why yes indeed, in God's truth I do. But nevertheless we should use caution." He paused to think and sip his drink. To question. Should he tell? "I too have some small concern," he raised his pot to drink deep. "A ship of mine laden with pilchard should by now have returned with hogsheads of wine from a merchant of Le Conquet."

"Overdue?"

"But a short while. Yet still, 'tis July and the seas not yet unfriendly. I am a mite disturbed lest she be lost."

"What shall we do?"

"Nothing 'cept wait, and keep our eyes and ears well tuned lest any note of warning should escape our notice. Our fishing boats must be our sentries. We must alert but not alarm their captains. Let Godolphin know our fears, but in absence of intelligence there is little we can do. Let us think of brighter things!"

"Aye, Jenkyn, for now I am much relieved that you know as much as I, and in some small measure my worst thoughts are thereby calmed. Pray tell me, have you news of the pack trains and our treasure?" He rubbed his hands and made an attempt to smile. "Is there something for which we can be grateful?"

"There is little Keigwin silver left in Mousehole for a Spaniard to steal, for all that I have rides on the backs of a team of ponies, or with paper promises within the satchels of my sons, and yours too, Solomon my friend. Reports I have received tell we shall make a fair profit on our

252

venture."

"Fair? How much is fair?"

"Keep calm, good news might bring on the ague, for you are so dismal."

"Not I, just cautious and concerned, but what of the trade, Jenkyn? The trade, pray tell me."

"I have received word, yet to be confirmed, that they have had greater success than either you or I could dream."

"Tell me more!"

"If you stop washing your hands with glee, old miser that you are, I will do so."

"Miser? Never. Careful man of trade perhaps — but tell me, Jenkyn, tell me please."

"At Exeter Richard was well received. Teek has only recently returned with an empty train and news. The last of the pack ponies has gone some three days since with an escort that will return with Richard, who has some gold and many bills of exchange, and is due any day."

"Perhaps part of the gold should be left with those whom we may trust?"

"That too was my thought, Solomon. 'Tis left in Richard's judgement. But I did advise that upon his return one third should be left in the care of Lady Anne, should she so wish, and another third with my son-in-law at Landithy — leastways 'til we sleep a little safer in our beds."

" 'Tis good thinking."

Later, as Teek legged the slight figure safe into the saddle, the two friends made their farewell.

"God be with you, Solomon, until your next market day visit," said Keigwin. "Now you have made yet another fortune, keep a button on your purse, for I vow I shall skin you at cards and relieve you of that weight of silver that carries so much worry!"

"Me? Another fortune? Aye aye aye . . . " Solomon cast his eyes heavenwards as he slowly shook his head from side to side. "I am but a humble merchant striving to make a meagre, honest living, whilst those about me impose upon my lack of wit and take advantage of my stupidity."

"Ah, old friend, I have yet in trade to meet the man who can gain advantage of Solomon Fernandes. You rascally, conniving old rogue!"

A slim hand was held out to be grasped by Keigwin's paw. "Guard yourself well, Jenkyn Keigwin, for if any ill should befall upon thee or thine . . . " his words trailed in emotion.

"Aye, and you too my very good and trusted friend. Fear not for me and may our God go with you."

Solomon gave the mule a squeeze of his thin shanks and then a kick. A slap of his cane upon its quarters, encouragement for the reluctant beast to return to Marazion.

"Until next Thursday market!" he called behind him.

"Keigwin turned upon his heel with Teek in close company.

"The Le Conquet ship is overdue, Master."

"Yes, 'tis often the way of it. Those Bretons have no sense of time."

Teek nodded as if in agreement, yet he was not convinced, for he had heard Fernandes speak his fears.

Thomasine had not been married two score years and more without she knew her man. The prospect of such trade should have brought him a fine humour, yet too often of late was he lost in melancholy reverie. She knew he missed his sons and the adventures of the privateer, yet there was more to tell. All in good time, he would confide as he always had.

Keigwin, who had never long kept secrets from his wife, could not decide whether to voice his fears. Together they sat in the drawing-room. Too rare were the occasions when they could be alone and at ease in one another's company. Always the pleasant intrusion of family or friends, or the call of merchant or factor in the ever demanding pursuit of trade.

The tapestry was growing as stitch by stitch the nimble fingers dived and darted to complete the picture that they told, whilst Jenkyn did his utmost to relax with pipe and text. He stirred upon his chair, she knew by instinct that this was the moment she had been awaiting.

"Dear wife, I loathe for us to be parted yet, whilst Elizabeth is with Lady Anne, and our sons have yet to return, I would commend that you stay awhile at our daughter's home, seize a break from your busy household duties! Take advantage of their absence."

Thomasine looked up from her work and watched as he

drew upon his pipe.

"After all," he continued, "soon our sons will be home and, God willing, Elizabeth presenting us with yet another grandchild. You will be in much demand and should rest whilst you may."

"Perhaps, Jenkyn, but what of you?" Now she would learn what preoccupied him so.

"You have tutored the servants well in our ways." A compliment she knew, to lower her defence. "They will tend my needs right worthily."

"But what of hospitality toward our guests? Then there are the poor of the village. With so many of our able men abroad, they will need my assistance, as do those poor lepers. Without our aid they would surely starve. No, Jenkyn, I will stay here with you. Maybe we may both visit Landithy, Plymouth, even Exeter, when our sons are returned and the baby is safe arrived."

"I would prefer you to go now, Thomasine." His tone was firmer.

"Jenkyn, you have a burden upon your mind that you must surely tell." She placed the needlework firmly on her lap and lifted her head to listen.

He sighed a deep sigh. "So be it, my Tommy, you know me too well my love. I cannot disguise my feelings from your perceiving eye." His face softened, he sighed his love.

"Dear Jenkyn, tell me all, together let us share your burden and both be the better for it."

Into the dusk they talked by candlelight. Yet still one confidence Jenkyn held close. Tethered. The prophecy which he had first learned when but a child at his grandfather's knee.

The power of the sweeps drove the squadron upon her northern way and ever closer to the shores of England. By mid-morning the wind had shifted to blow from the south-west. Now the weary slaves could be rested from their labours and partake of their daily diet of vinegar and biscuit. Sails were hoisted as the canvas filled in the freshening breeze. The seas rose at the bidding of the strengthening wind to

255

speed them on their course. Landfall would be made too soon, the coast of Cornwall would be upon them in darkness, and in danger.

The galleys hove to awhile, to wait upon their commander's orders, to weather the waters as best they might. The soldiery aboard had no stomach for the sea as the ships rolled and pitched to the unremitting motion of the chops of the Channel. Burley laboured to lift their flagging spirits, for should they be asked to endure their sickness for too long, weakened beyond recall, they would be unfit to land and fight ashore.

Upon the high aft-deck he approached a knot of English braving the wildness of the weather.

"A good evening, gentlemen."

"Good evening, to you, Captain Burley."

"You seem in remarkable spirits, Master Loe, despite the temper of the sea. Ah! But soon you will regain your freedom!"

" 'Tis so, I have been promised, God be praised. But 'tis also the yarns that Nankervis tells."

"What nature of story is this?"

"Why, he tells of a strange prophecy — begging his pardon, no one but a Cornishman could believe such a tale, 'tis but mad invention."

"Not so!" The Cornishman's hand flew to his dagger.

"Steady, Nankervis." Burley laid a restraining hand.

"Upon my honour, 'tis true."

"What honour? 'Tis cheap from what I heard tell!"
Nankervis struggled.

"Steady!" Burley held him tight. "Silence, Loe. Tell me, Nankervis," commanded Burley, "what is this prophecy?"

" 'Ewra teyre a war Merlyn, Ara lesky Pawle, Pensans ha Newlyn.' "

The Englishmen laughed aloud at the strange language, Burley too smiled. Nankervis would have slain with his glare.

"Translate into a tongue we may all understand." Burley pulled upon his beard as he listened to a warning of fire and death. "This is true, Nankervis? Destruction is prophesied?"

"Before God, I swear it."

His colleagues ceased smiling. Nankervis stared unflinchingly before Burley's thoughtful gaze.

"Gentlemen, pray excuse us. Nankervis, accompany me to my cabin."

Across the rolling deck they staggered until, seated within the tiny cabin, Burley faced the seaman.

"Tell me more — who else would know of this prophecy?"

"Why, Captain Burley, those such as I have heard it told many a time. It is one of the prophesies accorded to the Wizard Merlyn, sir. That's why I sculpted the rock upon the sand. 'Tis where we are destined to land."

"Friar Domingo must learn of this."

His story once more told, Nankervis closed the door behind him, puzzled as to what Burley and the Spanish friar might make of the fragment of Cornish folklore.

"We are of one mind, Captain Burley?"

"Indeed so I suspect." The tale had captured the interest of the priest, just as Burley had anticipated. "Father, where we are headed is a wild land. There are many who hold to the old ways. Their Christian beliefs are but shallow and hide their deep fear of mystery and magic."

"Then we shall carry out the work of God in accord with a pagan prophecy, and thus strike greater fear into the hearts of those Cornish heretics."

"And to burn the church?" enquired Burley.

"Has not Drake burned our churches?" He paused. "We have learned that no longer is Mass celebrated in the church of Pol de Leon. It is a place where heretics worship false idols! If you lack courage . . . "

Burley shuffled upon his seat. "Never doubt my courage, Friar."

"Then your faith?"

"Nor my faith neither."

"So be it. But better it were a soldier of Spain." He thought awhile. "Ramirez de Arellano. He is a fine soldier and imbued with the enthusiasm of youth in the cause of God's work. Yes, to him shall fall the honour."

The Spaniard stood and laid his wand upon the head of the seated Burley. His eyes softened. "Should it please you, Captain, before the deed is done I shall require proof of our

257

suspicions." He paced the cramped cabin. "I shall instruct Don Carlos De Amelrola."

The flagship raised her sails, her stern lantern lit as a signal to be followed as the squadron pursued its course, ploughing onward through the waves to ease the sickening roll.

The brothers had ridden hard upon their homeward way, along the travellers' track that wound its devious route between tarn and tor across the bleak harsh beauty of the lonely rock-strewn moor. At last, peering above the low hill crest, the beckoning grey form of the inn's stark shape. The weary traveller's haven.

The yard of rough-hewn stone was wind-sheltered by the open hovel that faced eastward. Reins to the surly ostler and Richard glanced within to ascertain the nags were well rewarded for their labour, advising the servant to choose between kick or coin as recompense, dependent upon the welfare of their horses. For they must be kept sound with three more days of hard riding left before Mousehole would be reached.

Into the comfort of the inn, away from their father's watchful eye. If the company was in good humour and of their kind, they would make merry that summer's evening, for what benefit to them if they could not enjoy the fruits of their labours, and celebrate the success of the mission as some small share of their reward?

In the early hours of the following morning a figure writhed upon the bed. Martin was sinking slowly, then faster and faster still, plunging headlong round and round within the whirlpool that giddily sucked him downwards into the darkening abyss. Was this a form of Hell without the inferno's flames? He awoke with a start. Where in Heaven's name was he? From the rough pillow he raised his head as best he might to squint about the room.

In truckle bed close by lay the form of Richard. Why was he still clothed in the day's attire? Was he dead? He could not note him breathe and surely the pallor was as death. God forbid his brother dead! The body grunted. Blessed relief. To roll over to snort and snore once more, and then to subside as before.

Cyder — rough cyder. He would skewer that landlord!

"Try some of my special brew. Famed throughout the country."

Others there, frequent visitors to the inn, commoners too, sank their cyder in deep draughts. So he had followed their example. Commoners. Shepherds. Knew about sheep. Knew how to fleece! His mind began to recall. They had surely taken some of the wool off his back. How much had he lost? A month's wages for most men. Never play cards and drink. Never play cards and drink cyder, and with strangers, that's for sure. Especially with those that had drunk it with their mother's milk, and had done so ever since. By God, they must have heads as solid as cannon balls, and tin lined bellies too! By all that was holy, he was ill. Indeed, God's truth, he felt very ill. Onto the floor he swung his legs, still shod and in their hose; his ringing, senseless head held still between his hands. If he could only die!

Cyder, delicious cyder, stuff for lads and ladies. "Hardly a drink suited to quench the thirst of a man," he had said.

"Not my cyder," the landlord had retorted. "Coloured with the aid of beet. Fortified by hunks of rotting meat, hook held through the cask's bunghole 'til all was eaten away. Gone. To give it body." His host had said.

Could he please have a new body? The one he had was fit for nothing now. To where did the meat disappear? Eaten by the acid of the cyder. So that was what was happening to his innards. His brains as well. He winced as he staggered toward the pitcher and leant his head above the basin to trickle cold water upon his crown. Armed with chill water, he went to awaken his brother that he might share the anguish.

The rising sun pinkly shone through the sea mist of the early morning. Sails now reefed, English navigators gave orders to Spanish helmsmen. Ahead, the blurred outline took shape and form to become one grey mass of land. Closer, where in the strengthening sun the veil was slowly lifted, oars rose and fell in time with the sombre message of the drum. Light and shadow etched cliff and crag, capped by the sharpening

259

colours of moor and meadow.

Burley peered with sleep-swept eyes, moistened with emotion. Nankervis too, squinted through the haze, guiding the galleys past landmarks he had known since boyhood. The sturdy stump of a church tower, St. Beriens, honoured lady of Ireland, standing in gaunt outline against the pale backdrop of the sky. Safely seaward past the dreaded Bucks. Cleft valley of Lamorna. The frowning face of Carn Du slid by to larboard. He pointed to the white blaze, the cave of the horse-in-the-stable, off which he had first lifted his father's crab-filled withy creels. Penzer Point, towards the guardian isle of Mousehole, now clearly to be seen.

Emotion to apprehension amongst all aboard. Could it be that Drake had been alerted to their coming? Anxious eyes looked east into the sun, from whence his fleet would first appear. But the haze of the morning still hid the Lizard's Head.

Chapter Sixteen

The second day of August 1595. Beside the bed they knelt, in same manner as since the first day they were wed, their morning ritual. Jenkyn and Thomasine were at their prayers.

Below, the customary clatter, and interruption of shrill laughter as Becky told Mary a tale of the tavern, the more shocking, the more they giggled in mock horror.

Thomasine opened the window wider, to breathe in the morning air and the rich, sweet smell of baking bread that arose from the ovens beneath. Shortly she would be robed and in the kitchens herself, to give her servants their duties for the day. Granite floors to be besomed and strewn with fresh rushes. A visit to the pantry, thence to the dairy. Brawns and jellies newly made, capons to be roasted on the spit. Vegetables and fruits to gather, a knowing eye to be cast on hams pickling in their shallow, leaded trough, oozing the salt and sugar with which they had been rubbed, later to be wrapped in muslin and hung in rows from the iron hooks that studded the ceiling's joists. Milk newly-drawn, awaiting to settle, to be skimmed of cream for butter. A parade of cheeses in rows, maturing on cold slabs. Home brewed ale of varying degree, for guest or servant. Food there was a-plenty, and Thomasine prided herself on the excellence of her kitchen, and the repast it provided.

This was her domain. The home whose every nook and cranny could testify her influence. Upon her shoulders the problem and the pleasure of providing victuals in abundance for family or visitor, who might arrive unannounced and in any number. For this was a merchant's house. Hers to look to and anticipate the needs of others. To flat-iron the creases

261

that crinkle the fabric of family life. But transcending all, her love and protection of her husband, to arm him for the fray of business, to prepare for him, to plan for him: and never to betray. The wife it is that shapes the destiny and the fortune of the family. With the subtlety to point the direction that reflects her desires, that her husband may unwittingly lead her there. Her devotion went unsung, but the knowledge of her influence and the success it reaped for those she loved was, for Thomasine, reward in plenty.

Since dawn's first light Teek had been at his duty in the harbour. Looking to his master's interests whilst awaiting the arrival of the brothers. Ensuring that on their return they would be pleased with his endeavours. The last of the fleet of fishing boats had left on the ebb, for in the now calm waters of the bay were abundant shoals of pilchards, oil bloated.

Teek waited in the yard for the Squire to appear. To touch red stocking cap in respect and greeting on arrival of his master.

Square black velvet cap upon his head, frocked short-sleeved jerkin and fine hose his attire, Jenkyn glanced down. Pink tongue was licking his hand. The muzzle of a hound gone grey with age, nudged him in welcome and for titbit. Keigwin bent to pull the frayed lop ears and look deep into the red-hawed eyes.

"Ah, Merlin we are both of us no longer young, yet we have had our pleasures. Now must we pay the price. Not so, Cornall?"

Teek smiled, at loss as how to reply.

"Come boy, let us see what the world is about." Lamely the old stallion hound followed at his master's heels, wear and wet weather pained the swollen joints of both.

How peaceful it all was, the familiar scents and sounds of the farmyard. Hens scratched and cockerel crowed upon the dung heap, horses stamped in the straw of their stalls, champing on their forage. The soft tender lowing of nursing cows as painfully their calves butted swollen udders in an eager plea for more rich milk. Squeals of gluttonous glee from the black spotted pigs as they thrust their snouts into the fattening feed of swill and skim that Jacob had tipped into their trough. Smells of the farm mingled with those of fish oil from the presses.

"We are heaven blessed, Teek, to live here as we do. For some this would be paradise on earth. Yet within me there is a feeling of foreboding that shows how old and stupid I become." He shook his head, yet still his brain would not discard that fearful prophecy that so troubled his mind.

In the damp of the morning John Pearce strode the narrow lane, to stop and peer over granite hedges where red cattle grazed, belly deep in the rich, flower-speckled, meadow grass. Come the heat of the day they would lie down at rest, to fatten as they chewed the cud. Were they ruminating, he pondered, upon the follies of mankind? For here was no Roman, no heretic, no Protestant. Each lived at peace with the other.

His duty done, all within his charge were well. He turned to follow the cliff-side way and return to the Manor.

The veiled curtain cloaked the water that ebbed upon the shore. He cocked his head to the sonorous sound of the drum. What in Heaven's name was that? He stopped, to peer seawards through tunnelled hands.

Pennants streamed from the bare mastheads that prodded through the mist's white layer. The boom, boom of a drum. Beating in relentless rhythm that slaves might row in unison. Galleys. Boom, boom. Spain's vengeance was upon them! Boom, Boom! He ran for the home of his master as if the hounds of hell were in pursuit. As perhaps indeed they were.

They could not comprehend the warning cries that heralded his approach. With bursting lungs he ran the hill from Reginnis, to scatter the gander's noisome flock and enter the yard. He bent over, hands on knees to draw breath and gasp his warning:

"Galleys," chest heaved, "the galleys are upon us."

"Where, man, where?"

"Below Kemyel. Spanish galleys. Four. Flee, master! Flee! For God's sake, master."

"Jacob!" He came running to honk of geese and shout of Squire.

"Sir?"

"The Spanish are upon us. There are two nags; saddle both, quick. Teek, find your wife and children. They will accompany your mistress to Landithy."

He turned to the heaving herdsman.

"Go tell the town, John Pearce. Bid them run for safety and hide upon the hills. Arm yourselves, arm yourselves."

Suiting action to words he moved quickly to the house.

"Thomasine, Thomasine. Quick, wife, quick!"

"What is the alarm?" But within her she already knew. Somehow she knew.

"To Landithy with Becky. You must hasten!" He grabbed her by the wrist, half dragging, half running her to the yard.

Jacob held the horses by their bridles, as together they tightened the girths. Teek, a child held in crook of each arm, urged his Becky on.

"What are you about, Jenkyn? I cannot leave you."

"Do as you are bid." He shook her by the arms. "You have no choice. This is a job for men. My duty lies here. Yours is to our family. Save yourself. Alert Godolphin!"

She knew he spoke the truth and no argument could prevail.

"Go quickly with God. Go quickly."

She flung herself into his embrace to share a parting kiss, but a brief moment that told in second's fraction the certainty of the love that bound them. He broke her grasp and thrust her from him. His eyes clouded by tears he dared not shed, he bent to leg her surely into the saddle. Teek kissed his children. Keigwin took the young boy and lifted him astride the withers, that Thomasine might hold him safe and sure between the reins.

Becky bent down. Brown eyes held hers of brimming blue. Lips that once with moist passion had locked on his, now kissed him gently on dampened cheek, plump arms flung about his neck. She hugged him to her in an embrace that told her love.

"Farewell me handsome."

She smiled, "Until tomorrow." A tear squeezed beneath her lids as she winked a wink. A jaunty wink. A brave wink, as in sweet sadness of farewell she had done so many times before, that thus he might remember her. She too knew that perhaps for either, tomorrow might not come. Her daughter seated on the pommel, she kicked forward, her horse sent upon its way by slap of her husband's hand.

"Fast as you can ride," Keigwin called. "Tell all to make for the church or hills!" He turned. "Go get your sword, Teek, whilst I observe." He ran upstairs to the rear bedchamber that faced southwards. There, off the rock of Merlyn, the squadron of Blavet had come, to repay a debt long overdue. Within his head still hammered the ancient Cornish prophecy:

> 'Ewra teyre a war Merlyn
> Ara lesky Pawle Pensans ha Newlyn.'

Anchors were dropped. How knew they that good holding ground? Spies!

The thundering continued in his mind; the words continued to beat within his brain:

> 'There shall land upon the rock of Merlyn
> Those that would burn Paul's church
> Pensans and Newlyn.'

He was frightened, yet must show courage. He would he might flee like others but he could not forsake his duty. His was to lead.

Into the street Jacob joined him, armed with longbow and with arrows, an ancient sword upon his hip. They heard Teek calling to the people, adding weight to John Pearce's pleas. But of men they could rally but few. For the most part the men of Mousehole were gone to do Drake's bidding, or escorting Jenkyn's pack ponies, else fishing in the bay.

"What task for me?" from outside The Mermaid Trewhella called above the babel, the screams of women, the crying of children, as they ran with meagre belongings, seeking safety or sanctuary. "What of my daughter?" He pushed forward through the throng.

"On horse with children and her mistress to Landithy."

"Praise God!"

"Go light a beacon on Paul tower that Godolphin must see, then take sanctuary within."

" 'Twill be done!" He turned, drawn sword aloft, to disappear amongst the panic of the people. Up the lane that led to Paul.

Two parts of his duty done. His wife now sped to safety, the people alerted. Now to play out the final act. To delay,

m

delay the advance that the folk, his folk, might be safe until Godolphin came.

He closed the Manor's oaken door as Teek beside him shot home the iron bolts. Behind, the slam of doors. Jacob came into the hall, John Pearce close by.

"I have set free the stock and the hounds, master, lest they be ill used."

Keigwin nodded. "Now with God's aid, go! Save yourselves."

"What of thee?"

"I must stay."

"We shall never leave you, master," Jacob's gruff voice. "We are Keigwin men, Squire."

"Well said. John Pearce, lend me your shoulder." Teek was pulling a cupboard to wedge against the door.

Nothing the Squire could say could budge them from their will.

All that could be barricaded was now done. Keigwin tugged his cap from off his head, faced towards the east, to fall upon his knees and enjoined his men to follow him in prayer. White head sunk deep into soiled ruff.

"O God, thou art a strong tower of defence to all that flee unto Thee. O save us from the violence of the enemy. O Lord of hosts, fight for us, that we may glorify Thee."

He rose and replaced his cap. "With our Maker's help we may delay the Spaniards awhile, whilst our people flee to safety. Pray God Godolphin may know our plight. Now upstairs to scan the enemy. Jacob, you and John Pearce to my bedchamber. Guard the rear. Teek and I will to the drawing-room. You guard from Reginnis and we the harbour approach."

The old huntsman grinned to John Pearce, a fierce gap-toothed grin.

"Come, Jan," as he nodded him ahead. Clutched in his left hand his longbow of yew, goose-winged arrows in leather quiver slung across his back. John Pearce before, with sword and buckler, practised parry and thrust as he made his way to overlook the stableyard and the enemy flotilla that lay beyond.

Beneath high-vaulted ceiling Keigwin turned to Teek.

"Cornall."

"Sir?"

Softly he spoke to his servant. "By the Grace of God your children and our women may be safe and free. Aboard those galleys are traitors of whom you and I have knowledge. 'Tis their desire to exact vengeance upon us for our many mischiefs against them, and for our beliefs as well. Trust that we do not fall alive into their hands. Die dearly, Teek. Go bravely. For I fear that for you and me perhaps there is no tomorrow. Have no fear, my sons will safeguard your family and we shall be avenged. May God bless you." Then breast to breast each hugged the other, as only brave men may.

Eight of the morning. The mist was swiftly lifting to leave but a distant haze. The sun now shone in a cloudless sky. Blessed, addressed and exhorted by the chaplain, soldier and renegade had eaten of their ration and taken an issue of biscuit. Arquebusier and pikeman that numbered four hundred, paraded before their captains. The final inspection. Brown beard jutting forward above deep ruff. Rapier of Toledo steel upon his left hip. Breast and back plate finely wrought as became an officer of rank. Words of praise, sometimes correction, but to all Don De Amelrola gave encouragement. From the high prow Burley watched the coastline slide past to larboard, Nankervis at his side recalled the landmarks of his boyhood. The drumbeat slowed. Beneath his armour the Cornishman fingered the black pearl that hung about his neck. Upon a kerchief Burley wiped his palms, toyed with the hilt and eased his rapier within its scabbard, as was his wont when battle neared.

What if he be taken? The risen sun now burning up the morning mist, Burley squinted through the lingering haze. What was his fate? To be taken in chains and await the pleasure of Richard Topcliffe, torturer to the Queen? Imprisoned in the Tower? No mean event, for he was now of some consequence and would thus be treated. Condemned a traitor by his own screaming mouth as he was stretched and torn asunder on the rack. Sentenced. Thence to Tyburn.

267

Hanged and drawn as pleasure and example to the crowd. His head paraded upon a pike? Never! A shudder shook his frame. His lot was cast. He had ventured down this path before, his God had led him by the hand and kept him safe. The game was about to be played and winning was the only option. A victory for his God and King. He crossed himself, as panic passed, by faith restored.

Nankervis pointed where a scurrying figure ran the cliff path, on the way to Mousehole to alert the town folk of their coming. The slaves eased upon their oars. Off a blunt point, the sweeps were raised, where stark cliffs softened. The windlass rumbled, anchors lowered to splash and bite deep, to hold, where Nankervis had advised. A hundred and fifty paces out and sea-room in plenty. Shoreward, a black rock stood, dividing a narrow inlet, where steps of layered granite rose easily to the crumbling clifftop.

"Is that the rock of Merlyn?"

"Indeed, Captain Burley, it is so."

From high upon the aft-deck De Amelrola watched the sergeant major of the galleys order skiffs to be lowered away. The men, mustered in disciplined ranks, crossed themselves and formed in files to board the waiting boats. Toward Merlyn's Rock they rowed, past the green lichened mouth of the Mousehole, where fulmars circled their fledglings in guardian flight.

Bows nudged the granite gully between rock and shoreline, where waves now gently lapped. Larboard-side, dry foot Don Dezpeleta stepped ashore on sea-smoothed rocks, exhorting his men to follow swiftly, to hasten their clifftop scramble.

Starboard, Burley clambered upon the jagged rock. Barnacles tore his hose and bloodied were his knees. But he must enact his part as the Friar had proposed. Atop he knelt. His sword hilt held aloft in likeness of the Holy Cross upon which he made his promise.

Above the crumbling lip, Don Luis de Maeda waded through the tangle of bramble and bracken, his company followed in his wake. Hand raised, they halted at his command where narrow lane led to the town. A whistle's blast. De Arellano doubled to his side, Don Luis pointed to the track that joined opposite, to follow the contour of

268

the hill. The subaltern nodded his recognition and beckoned his men to follow, in single file. Sword at the carry, pikes at the trail, he led the left flank forward, close tucked into the hillside in the manner that he had practised at Blavet. He stopped where a rivulet crossed his path. He must not lose himself in this strange and foreign land. Where was he? North, a lush hill that would hide Newlyn and Pensans. Below to his right, the great sweep of the bay. Eyes raised east, there the gaunt outline of St. Michael's Mount where, through the haze, the brown sails of fishing boats made for Marazion, flotsam upon the silver surface of the sea. Beneath, the hermit's chapel, perched upon the black island of St. Clements, the harbour, then the little town that nestled at the foot of the hills that they now straddled. Were those the enemy? Those tiny fleeing figures?

The hills now safely in their hands a galley inshore inched to off-load falcon and falconet. The cannon were sited to command a field of fire that would embrace roof-top and narrow street close-huddled within their range.

Their gunners prepared to give a foretaste of hell to the heretics below. Burley watched two horses canter along the harbour's edge to make good their escape. Free to give witness of their coming.

Speed and surprise. This, and good intelligence, the key to success in their attack. Surprise now lost, speed must make amends. His runner came to his command. Order Don Luis de Maeda to press onward the left flank of De Arellano. The right flank would sweep forward down upon the town, in extended line, between shore and hill, lest more should flee the trap.

Don Gaspar de Perea commanded his men with caution toward the quayside Nicholls said he knew. His orders to capture that precious plunder stolen from Pernambuco that, according to intelligence, lay in Keigwin's care. By gesture and example Juan De Urbea urged his arquebusiers forward. Burdened by their muskets they fanned into a half circle to descend upon the town.

The cannon above were now ranging upon the houses. The thunder of powder and scream of ball crashed mercilessly down, adding further to the terror of those left and yet to flee.

Burley watched his forces. All were now in position, the trap could now be closed.

Scattered in wooded combe, or amongst the furze and bracken, mothers crouched, hiding their sobbing children until the danger was past. Others, old, infirm, or who wholly put their faith in God, sought sanctuary within His church. Safe, they believed, within the massive granite of her walls. Crammed together as cannon thundered from beyond; and ball of musket pitilessly pursued the people who fled. Was this to be the Armageddon? The last conflict? Would Good or Evil triumph? Upon their knees John Tremearne led his flock in prayer.

Laden with furze and faggot, Trewhella exhorted his folk to gather all that might both blaze and smoke from the beacon atop the tower. Bowed down by their burden, they panted up the hill to Paul.

Soon, Burley calculated, Arellano would strike the Pilgrims' Way that linked the church to town; the mosque where the heretics practised their beliefs, hid behind the hill the troops traversed.

The old man stood erect within the bedchamber, peering through the window upon the line of advancing soldiers, their muskets at the ready.

Every dog would have his day, and this was surely his. He was a man of the country and had never fired his bow in anger, only for the pot. Now he would use his skill to defend the land he loved. Iron tipped arrow chosen from the quiver. The longbow gripped in left hand of outstretched bracered arm, he leant his weight forward into the yew and slotted the string into the arrow notch. Gloved right hand drawn back, he sighted along the shaft, raised the bow a fraction, adjusted the aim and let fly. Before the arrow could find its mark, another plucked from the quiver, fired to follow a similar path.

A scream. The arquebusier spun about by the force of the strike, barbed head protruding through his shoulder. Clang of steel on steel another shaft glanced harmlessly off the helm of him beside. Exposed upon the open ground the soldiers knelt in such cover as they might find. Not knowing from whence their attacker had his vantage.

"Well aimed, Jacob," softly spoke John Pearce.

"Go lad, tell the Squire 'tis better he join with us."

Keigwin and Teek peered where Jacob pointed.

"We will go to the library and take position there." He ducked, armed with primed musket to run to the window of his sanctuary to await the raising of a curious head.

Sunlight struck the polished steel. A roar and the ball chipped splinters from the granite hedge close where the pikeman crouched. But flash and smoke had betrayed from whence the shot had come. From the high ground de Perea watched, his subaltern's advance halted by enemy fire. No need for unwarranted death with such overwhelming dominance. Yet he knew not how strong the foe might be in number and by weaponry. The defenders were buying time. Time in which to tell Drake of the flotilla's presence. time for Godolphin to marshal his men. He looked seaward toward where the flotilla lay, turned on their anchors by the flooding tide.

A runner was sent with report to Burley of where there was resistance.

The house of Keigwin! He ordered cannon to range upon the Mousehole Manor. Take care, lest shot fall short to land upon a friend. Nor must they overshoot and cause destruction of the treasure doubtless stored within the warehouses beyond.

An acknowledgement from the *Capitana*. Message received. Anchors raised, with measured drumbeat the squadron rowed between shore and island, to head around the harbour's guardian wall to face the quayside in menacing array as they had practised at Plezmarg. Projecting prows lined upon Manor and wharf that their cannon might blaze point blank.

Long barrels of arquebus laid on stone wall or cloven rest, upon the left flank in hills north-west of Mousehole to look

271

down upon the roof-tops. De Maeda ordered his men to fire at any man or movement seen. Figures too remote to be of flesh and blood. Not fellow beings, merely targets at which to aim and fire, perhaps to kill or maim. Too distant, too detached that close witness would cause remorse. Cover for de Arellano that he little needed as he ventured on toward the place of pagan worship as Friar Domingo had decreed.

Across the little stone-hedged meadows de Arellano lead, to slither down a bank on to a well worn road. The Pilgrims' Way.

What was that above the crackle of musket fire? A rattle of dislodged stones that fell behind him. Trewhella turned. Soldiers, muskets raised, called out in a foreign tongue. He could not understand the words but their intent was not mistook! He let fall the bundle he was carrying, as likewise did his fellows. His hand flew to the hilt of sword, then dropped to his side, to defy was but a pointless sacrifice. The Spanish subaltern led his soldiers toward the group, men and women, laden down with furze. De Arellano spoke but little English and Celtic not at all, but the point of a rapier spoke a common tongue. He had heard tell of England's beacons that roused her people at danger's onset. So this was what these craven creatures were now about!

The shooting had now ceased behind him. As ravening wolves Don de Maeda was now about to sweep his men down the slope of the steep hillside to torch the defenceless town.

The stout church doors remained unbarred lest more might want to enter. God was on the side of Spain! With press of pike and barrel of arquebus Trewhella and his team were herded amongst the kneeling throng. Sentries placed on guard at every entrance, whilst the soldiery within sought for evidence of heresy that they might report unto their priest. From the vestry came a cry. A shout of jubilation. A horse of wood and leather, painted and adorned. An obvious idol made for worship. Here was not a place of God, nor yet of heresy. It was a pagan temple. How the dour Domingo would glory in their find. Now in God's name would he, de Arellano expunge the evil, burn out the Devil. What honour to perform such deeds in His holy name.

With the threat of a massacre by Spanish musket Vicar

Tremearne lead his people into the churchyard, as Trewhella and his fellows heaped high a pile of furze and faggots against the wooden altar. Spanish hands quickly gathered all else that they might burn and with heathen vestments piled it high. Yet on top of all, they placed the horse god.

As Trewhella did as he was bid, he grasped to comprehend how the Spanish subaltern could be so besotted by the hobby horse John Pearce had fashioned with such care; that in its guise he might perform, to prance and prank on days of feast and festival?

The spark was struck. Encircled by soldiers, all looked in awe upon the white flames flying upwards from the furze into the faggots, to light upon the horse and thence the great timber trusses that spanned from wall to wall.

From the aft-deck of the flagship Friar Domingo clasped his hands in prayer. A plume of smoke was rising heavenwards, from where he knew the church of Paul to be. De Arellano had obtained proof that heresy was practised within its walls.

May the Devil take that Friar. The fire would alert half the kingdom. De Amelrola fumed upon the fore-deck, angered that the Friar could give God's commands to out-rank those of meagre men, to place in jeopardy their other tasks.

A skiff was summoned to cease its ferrying of fresh water from the Mousehole stream and carry orders to Captain Juan de Mercado for the *Peregrina* to take solitary station off the Point of Penlee. There they might best observe the low land, that linked Newlyn and Pensans, lest it be crossed by Godolphin and his men, alerted by the towering smoke.

273

Chapter Seventeen

Carefully Jenkyn Keigwin primed his matchlock to make ready once more to fire. But he could not take aim, for the arquebusiers' bullets peppered about the window where he stood.

"Follow me to the front."

Crouching, Teek and the Squire ran where they could overlook the street that led the short distance to the quay off which the galleys anchored. A flash above a jutting prow, black smoke, and cannon's roar. A thud as a ball struck the sturdy granite walls.

On hands and knees Teek peered through the window. A smell of smoke. The dull red glow of fire.

The Spaniards were in the town. As he watched, the south-west wind fanned the fury of the flames that fed and fattened upon the thatch of roofs dried to tinder by the summer's sun. Flames that leapt across each narrow alley to dance and crackle in fiendish glee amongst the roof-tops. Smouldering timbers crashed to the ground to send their pyre of spiralling sparks, smoke-laden into the sky above. The heat, another roar, another roof, another home destroyed. The same wind kept the flames away from the Manor.

The Spanish would wait awhile for him to come to them, driven to submit by cannon and by flame. Walls shuddered. Another ball had struck, but stout walls and favouring wind were Keigwin's protection.

Empty. The warehouses were empty. Gone was the plunder they had journeyed so far to take. Yet it had been here. Like a hound Juan de Urbea scented the air. Above the smell of oil and smoke and farmyard, there still lingered the pungent smell of spices.

Don Luis had fired the town. There was little left to salvage. Without the priceless plunder, their mission was incomplete. Except. Except Keigwin himself! The capture of Keigwin. To be paraded that all might see, later to be ransomed. He would report to Don Gaspar. He blew the signal to withdraw.

Another arrow notched. "Him with the whistle." John Pearce pointed. Jacob aimed.

The subaltern half turned to direct his men. An arrow tugged his sleeve.

"Blessed with the Devil's own luck," hissed John Pearce.

The Spaniard ducked and ran for shelter, to finger the rent in his doublet, to think and realise how close to death he had been. "This tear," he swore, "will be mended with a heathen life."

Falcon and falconet hurled their shot down upon the rooftops as Burley had directed. Now to rain upon the Manor, clearly seen against the pall of smoke, that hung low above what once had been a town. A place where business flourished, that had hustled and bustled with life, where now was only death.

Burley rejoiced as ball after ball struck home at his command. To him the power. The retribution. The servant of his God. Avenging angel in the guise of man.

As through ceiling and window the round shot came, Keigwin called his men to shelter beneath the stalwart staircase that would provide some further protection.

"Are we all prepared? Soon the cannonade will cease and they must take us by assault."

"As ready as ever shall be, master," answered Jacob. "But leastways there are some of Spain who weren't, not so, John Pearce?"

"Aye, Jacob and there'll be more besides, I pledge my oath."

He ran his finger down the blade of his naked sword.

Silence. Silence save for the crackling of the dying flames and the rumble as yet another roof fell in. Silence. The firing had ceased. Ominous. The waiting.

Gingerly they came forth and stretched their limbs.

Inaction. Time in which to fear and dread. Not knowing. Not knowing what fate held in store. Each dropped his head. Each to pray in his own fashion, to the Maker that dwelt within their minds.

Upon the hillside Don Leon Dezpeleta held a council of his captains.

"Do you think he remains within, Burley?"

"I have watched with care and seen no sign. They could not leave without our knowing."

"Burley speaks truly." Gaspar de Perea spoke. "De Urbea here has his doublet ripped by an arrow as proof, and there are dead men besides."

"All is quiet, could they not be killed by our bombardment?"

"Pray God 'tis not so; I have come too far and waited too long not to witness the death of Keigwin. The old fox is cunning and has gone to ground within his earth. He will not be bolted, so we must take him in his lair."

"Truly said, Burley. He cannot escape Juan?"

"He is surrounded," de Urbea replied.

"Then Burley will go with you. Take or slay the heretic, I care not which. Time enough is wasted. The tide will soon be on the ebb and we must away. The cannon are already forward. Take them for use at close range, then we shall embark upon the quay. Now hasten."

From the waist of the *Capitana*, Nankervis leant to peer into the clear green waters and drop a knotted lead to count the depth beneath the galley's keel. The tide was on the turn and before long they would be aground.

A cannon fired a single shot. The signal of recall for the waiting *Peregrina*, and Don Leon's men ashore.

Keigwin heard the cannon roar but once. " 'Tis a signal," he whispered. "Soon the tide will ebb and they must withdraw. Pray God we may yet be saved!"

Nicholas Flemyng drowsed over his papers. The Justice of the Peace and master of the estates of Landithy had dined well. The day was hot, the spices served with mutton made the meal; as consequence he had doubled his portion, ground cloves and peppercorns with nutmeg and cinnamon upon the custards. Now to slumber.

He looked up with a start, a hail from without, another urgent shout, through the sun-streaming window from the road beyond, horses stamping, bridles clinking.

"Flemyng! Are you about, sir?"

He ran to the door and down the path to meet Godolphin. "Sir Francis, greeting, sir."

"Arm yourself and mount up, Flemyng! Haste man, haste! Message has come from Marazion, Spaniards have landed at Mousehole. Four galleys and mayhap more besides." He pointed. "Look man, look. Smoke. Where is that?"

"Paul, Sir Francis."

"They have fired Paul church. The devil is afoot. Follow us. We make for Heamoor thence Pensans." He pulled his nag hard round by the head and rowelled the chestnut flanks to urge into a canter, followed by a motley group of men, some on horse with rapier, others a-foot with pike or long-bow.

Elizabeth, posy of fresh herbs in her hand, joined her husband.

"Our servants are old, Elizabeth, I leave them to fend for you. I must away. Noah, saddle up the bay."

"What of my parents? Dear God, please help them. You must hasten, dearest. Would our sons were by your side."

"Aye and your brothers too." He turned, hand held high in salute. Elizabeth stood at the garden gate to wave farewell. A picture he would hold dearly in his mind.

Rounding the church he cantered from her view. Now the stemmed tears were free to spring, helpless in their fear, angry in their frustration. She spoke aloud though none was there to listen.

"Why must men fight? Oh, might they but live in peace. War and threat of war. Always in obedience to God's call. Religion. What manner of God is this that men fight each with the other in His name? But surely they mistake God for mammon? Is it greed and envy in whose name they fight?" She must be simple, she must be stupid. She shook her head. For she did not comprehend. But what of Father and Mother? She was her father's daughter and knew him

277

best. Old he might be. Cornered he would fight as a lion to defend that which he loved: his family and his home. He would never be taken. He dared not be taken! But that Godolphin would be in time.

The smoke over Paul rose as the wings of a black angel. An angel of death. She turned into her garden, to fasten the gate and look across the sparkle of the bay that stretched before her gaze. Here, in her garden was a haven of peace within a troubled world.

Hoof beats from the west. Was it friend or foe?

"Mama!" She ran forward in greeting as the steaming nag entered the courtyard gate. She raised her arms to lift the children from the pommel and held the palfrey that her mother might dismount, then be enveloped within her thankful arms. "Becky, dear Becky, thank God, you too, and with your young besides."

She turned to her hovering, anxious maidservant. "Rowenna will bathe and feed the children for they must be sore and hungry. Noah! Forage and water for the horses."

Bent by age and by winter's damp he shuffled forward to take each horse.

"Come, Mother dear," she placed her arm about her mother's waist and ushered her into the cool shade of the hall. "I will bring you mead, it will restore you."

She returned with pewter goblet for each. In a calm voice that disguised her fears: "Now, tell me all."

Homeward bound they rode together, their spirits as full as their leathern satchels, stuffed with bills of exchange destined for Fernandes, for him to change for gold or use for other Keigwin trade.

"We turn here."

"Are you certain?"

"Naturally. Through St. Erth then westward over the hill beyond, and there lies the Manor, and a welcome that has escaped me for too many a day. I pray Elizabeth is well, for it will not be a long wait before I am a father and you have another nephew."

"Nephew? How confident you are it will be a son. Has

278

Lady Elizabeth worked her witchcraft?"

"Son or daughter, I care not so long as it be healthy. What dishes would you suppose they will serve at table? My belly believes my throat's been cut."

"Food, 'tis all you think on."

"Nonsense. I think also of my wife and my family to be. Elizabeth will be relieved to see us returned safe and well."

"Ho! Think you so, brother. Freedom regained is a precious jewel not lightly to be returned."

"What does that imply?"

"Surely Elizabeth has had her taste of liberty. What a relief not to fetch and carry as you demand, forever at your beck and call! A beauty such as she could easily find another as would treat her with respect."

"Nonsense, I dote on her as she dotes on me. And because each of us cares to do so. Huh! You've yet to find a maid as will endure your bachelor ways. Marriage is of give and take."

"Aye, she gives and you take!"

Unable to think of apt reply, Richard drove his heels into the sweat-streaked flanks, his nag broke from trot to canter that stemmed his brother's banter.

Shouting in the street, what was this noise? It was not the Thursday market, why the hubbub? Curious, Solomon Fernandes gingerly opened the door. Outside the clamour of excited voices, frightened voices. He cupped hand to ear. Galleys? Mousehole? He closed and bolted the door. From upstairs he looked across the bay. A ship off Penlee that even to his untutored eye seemed different in outline to any ship of England he had seen. Three more off Mousehole. These were the galleys of Blavet of which Keigwin had warned. Smoke. Smoke hanging low over Mousehole that half hid the village as it drifted east.

Thank God he was old and frail. No one could expect him to fight, for or against. But Keigwin, his friend, what of Keigwin? May their God preserve him. What of the bills? Those precious pieces of paper upon which depended his wealth and very being.

"Aye, aye, aye." He wrung his hands as he looked again

across the bay, and prayed that they had escaped the holocaust where once was Mousehole.

Silence, not a gull's cry to be heard. An eerie silence after the tumult of before. Tap, tap.

"What can that be?"

Tap, tap, louder.

" 'Tis at the window, master."

"Which, Teek?"

"Surely the westward window, that overlooks the side yard."

Tap tap, tap tap. A muffled call.

"Yeeou."

"Whatever 'tis is Cornish, master," from John Pearce.

Teek returned in crouching run. "Jacob, whilst I open the door a mite, be ready to fire."

Gingerly, Teek inched the door open. "Ye Gods, brother Ben!"

The ragged figure of the boy squeezed through the narrow opening, a wriggling terrier bitch clutched firmly in his arms, as Teek slammed the door and shot home the bolts.

Jacob returned his arrow as all looked upon the lad with questioning eyes.

"Where to Ben and what of Mam?"

"Mam is safe within the church as you had said so." Blue eyes wide open in innocence. Hair tousled, smoke grime half hid the freckles of his face.

"Why here?"

White teeth split the face in a smile. "I saw Mam safe, then I came back for Skilly, for awhile ago she whelped." In confirmation, from his undulating shirt, a pink nose peeked. "She has six pups," he explained, then added in justification, "two dogs, four bitches." A pause. "I hid 'til all was still, but the fires cut me off. I waited whilst the Spaniards withdrew. When the coast was clear I came hither where I knew you and the Squire to be. All else is ablaze."

"All for a dog." Keigwin laughed a laugh from which all humour was not quite lost. "Take the boy upstairs, Teek, and hide him. Perhaps the great bed, aye, and take the terrier

280

too. Still I fear they will return and least one must live to tell our tale."

Silence. Silence and the waiting fear, and the guilt of being fearful.

"Safely hidden, sir. Not long now, the tide is ebbing fast. They must be away or have a last attempt."

From the street, men's voices. Spanish voices. Yet English too.

"English voices, sir."

"Traitors' voices, John Pearce. Traitors. The most vicious of all are those that sell their country for enemy coin. Their guilt drowns all compassion."

"Keigwin, do you hear me, 'tis I, Richard Burley."

"I hear the voice of a traitor."

"You hear no such voice, for I am true to my faith. 'Tis you Keigwin are the betrayer. Now I am come to avenge my name and my honour that you would have taken from me. Yield yourself, Keigwin, and your men will be spared. If you do not, all will be put to the sword. Long have I awaited this day."

"I must surrender, Teek," he spoke softly.

"That we might live a lie? Never! To know you are paraded as a prize, Squire Keigwin? Tortured, or even worse?" With booming voice he called: "May you roast in hell, Burley. 'Tis I, Teek Cornall, speaks."

A less cultured voice. "Cornall of the *Golden Hind*?"

"The same and proud on't."

"The saints be praised! For Thomas Nicholls too will be avenged."

"Be damned for your treachery."

A volley fired the reply, bullets from Spanish muskets spattered the wall and thudded into oaken door. Keigwin cocked his loaded matchlock. "I'll go upstairs to the drawing-room," he whispered, "the better to see what they are about."

Outside, and order was shouted in Spanish. The Keigwin musket roared reply.

"They have a spar as a battering ram. Burley has pikemen in reserve. I have no time to prime my musket. John Pearce, by the door, slide back the bolts when I say. They will charge

281

in, Jacob, Teek and I will spit them from the fore, you, John Pearce, will slam the door to come at them from the rear. Make the first seconds count!"

Decision, then to action. Fear yielded to anger, anger outraged became courage.

The patter of running feet, a cheer, a crash that shook the door. The footsteps retreated. The patter of the charge, the bolt slid back, the door burst open as the rammers hurtled into the dark, low-ceilinged room, to be blinded for a moment by the changing light, as the bolts once more slid home.

For a glorious moment Keigwin sloughed the sloth of age, temper revived the vigour of departed youth. Man for man pikeman and musketeer were no match for the fury of the flailing sword in that dim confining space. Rapier in right, dagger in left. Thrust and parry. A scream in gurgle ended, blood spurted from a slashed throat, another run through the groin where the breast plate did not reach. From behind with furious roar John Pearce struck, near severed a Spanish head with a mighty sweep. Teek, back to the wall where two assailed him. Open-mouthed, Ben watched through the banister above, in speechless horror. In the gloom he saw his brother beaten to his knees by Nicholls and another. Jacob saw and shouted to distract, pike thrust hesitated for a second, half turn of a soldier's head that never saw the upward thrust as from the floor Teek struck home. The boy sank his head upon his hands.

Steel on steel, no time for breath or oath or word. From without again the door was battered, the bolts finally to yield. Old muscles tired, outnumbered in the new onslaught, Keigwin and then Jacob gave up ground before the press of pike. Teek, now with one arm, the other dripping blood, pinked by Nicholl's point.

"Leave me the old man," Burley cried as Keigwin faltered, yet raised his sword once more to parry. Back to the wall, he summoned his strength's dregs to feint and thrust at his agile foe. But the reach of Burley prevailed as the rapier ran through the Squire's right breast. Unhurriedly Burley withdrew the blade, to laugh as with buckled knees, his enemy slid slowly to bloodied floor. The traitor's sword poised for the final strike, John Pearce stepped between to parry for his master, but too confined to ward the fatal thrust that took him through the heart. A sigh, his sword clattering to the floor, he sank to fall atop the Squire he died to save.

Jacob was now forced into the far corner. His sword struck time and time, the ancient steel finally shattering against a Spanish pike. Defenceless and erect he stood, eyes closed in dignity to await the mortal blow.

One against four, steel rang on steel.

"Let me have him," roared Nicholls. Spanish soldiers pulled aside. Cornered, Teek leapt forward in attack, a flash of blade took Nicholls above the guard of his rapier's hilt. Toledo steel clattered upon the bloodied granite, in disbelief he looked upon the bleeding stump where once had been his hand. A piercing scream of anguish, while others struck, where he had failed, to run his enemy through.

A cannon's roar.

" 'Tis the last signal. Run or be left." He paused to speak in Spanish. "Leave no son of Spain behind. A man apiece upon your backs, haste ye now." Supporting arm around the bearded Nicholls, Burley made for the door with those left alive to follow with their grisly burdens down the slope, to where the last skiff remained to board the waiting galley.

Keigwin heaved John Pearce from off his chest, to grope for his sword and stagger to the open door. The stench of smouldering filled the air and a pall of smoke drifted lazily in the soft breeze. Three galleys rounded the arm of the harbour wall to make for the open sea.

Burley helped Nicholls aboard, his men to clamber after. Thence to the foredeck for a final sight. Alas, no treasure. Through the haze of smoke Burley saw the stout figure, that raised his sword to shake aloft, in a gesture of defiance. Keigwin was alive! For what purpose had God spared him?

The prow swung in a gentle arc. The coursier cannon came to bear upon the narrow hill where the lone figure stood. A flash of flame, a roar. Recoil, reload, sight, and fire again. The shot sped forth, to strike on pave and granite wall. Confined. To funnel in an alleyway of death. The drum beat. The oars fanned. The galley continued in her turn.

A doll of rags, scarlet-clothed, was flung into the air to

fall in crumpled heap as the galley made her way to join the waiting squadron. At last the Squire had fallen and Burley praised his God. All resistance quenched in one brief moment of bravery, to which none but a boy bore witness.

He waited. The bloodied bodies lay in the hallway beneath, broken and smashed upon a granite floor. Tears streaked the grimed face, as with hands a-tremble he closed unseeing eyes and arranged the still warm bodies into some semblance of Christian dignity, their weapons by their sides. Then finally the Squire, the cannonball by his side.

A dish of milk for Skilly, left in a basket, her fat blind puppies suckling. Where to go? What to do? What would Teek have advised? Keep inland lest they return, make for the high ground, circle, thence to Madron and Landithy.

Sebastian clapped his hands in glee. Visitors that would break the peace and quiet so favoured by his mistress. Bearers of news and gossip, to him the finest of fare. Into the courtyard the brothers rode, to swing their legs over nags' quarters and slide easily to the ground.

"A fine day, Sebastian," Richard called. "Have you stabling for two tired horses?"

"Indeed, master and for their riders too." The brothers ignored the familiarity.

"How fares Mistress Elizabeth, and Lady Anne?"

"Well, master, very well. As a rose in full bloom." He postured with thumb and forefinger held together near his nostrils in elegant gesture, eyes closed as to smell the fragrance of a flower. Then to giggle at his own conceit.

"Be off with you and tell her Ladyship of our presence."

Martin aimed an imaginary kick at his departing rear as Sebastian scuttled laughingly away.

At the sound of voices the elderly groom, arrived to relieve them of the nags and packhorse.

Elizabeth's loving greeting for her husband was at contrast to Martin's words of warning. She made no effort to conceal her joy at the reunion with her husband; Lady Anne looked on, a smile of contentment upon her lips as she witnessed their embrace.

They dined upon cold capon, cheeses and fruits, Richard satisfying his appetite with difficulty since Elizabeth held his hand so tightly throughout the repast, whilst Martin amused the ladies with tales of the journey.

"And what of you Richard?" asked Lady Anne as he wiped the final morsel from his mouth.

"Ah, my dealing with merchant and gentlemen gives me a new insight into the devious nature of mankind."

"And what of your own devious nature?"

"I too plumbed depths of my nature that I never knew existed, as I played the game."

"What game husband?"

"As you play me at chess and care not to lose, so it is the same with trade. It is a form of game and yet 'tis more meaningful. For upon the winning lies the profit and upon that we depend. Fat-bellied, middle-aged merchants of superior mien would oft-times treat me in a patronising manner, regaling me with their own importance and wealth whilst I was made to listen. Hiding as best I may my boredom behind a mask of interest and respect." He paused to sup. "There was an occasion, I recall, with a gentleman of vast girth and even greater conceit, who in a manner of extreme condescension was to offer me but a little of what I sought. I made as to rise and bid him good day. 'Good day, good day! You cannot leave me before our business is concluded.' – 'But sir,' I replied, 'I would not dream of detaining such personage as yourself, a gentleman of wit and consequence. For such a transaction as I seek is small ale in comparison with the quality and size of trade you undertake.' – ' 'Tis true, 'tis true, but no need to hasten yet, some more ale.' – 'I drink but sparingly, sir,' I replied, 'since ale does so befuddle my mind.' "

"But Richard, you can take your ale as a babe takes its milk," Elizabeth protested.

"Ah but my dear, sometimes it pays to be simple; low cunning can oft-times defeat high intellect."

"But you are not cunning, Richard."

"As a fox when needs must! Would you wish your husband to be outwitted by such a common-bred fellow?" He continued, "At the end of the day it must be that if only a

Keigwin can deliver, so only a Keigwin can demand. 'Tis a fact that the excellence of one's table can dictate your placing within the social order."

The door banged open and Sebastian almost fell into the room.

"What manner of intrusion?" Lady Anne half rose, as the little man straightened himself to fearfully whisper in tones that all might hear.

"Milady, the Spaniards are landed."

"Where, man, where?"

"Mousehole and Pensans."

"Is this one of your notions?"

"No truly, riders have come to warn us and dare not dwell, since all fit men must rally to Sir Francis Godolphin at Pensans."

Chapter Eighteen

Once more under way, the flagship resumed her place to head the squadron. On the aft-deck, the officers were in high spirits, joking in relief at their success. Each recounted his part in the action, Burley making much of his own. He turned to frown as Nankervis pleaded for his attention.

"What do you seek? Watch your helmsman."

"He has land sightings I have given him to follow. But, Captain Burley, the church of Pol de Leon is burned?"

"It was found to be a house of heresy."

"What of the Chapel of St. Mary?"

"At Pensans? I know not for that is a matter to which Friar Domingo must attend."

"A boon Captain Burley, grant me in the name of the Virgin Mary herself, for if we are to land once more, to pillage once more. Pray you be reminded, sir, that I and others have celebrated Mass in that chapel and know that there are those who do so still."

"Is this true?" Burley now all attention, pulled his beard as he was wont, to look inquiringly at the eager Cornishman.

"Aye, sir, I swear 'tis true, for my mother celebrates Mass therein."

"Then, thank you Nankervis, 'tis possible you have prevented a mortal sin. Friar Domingo Martinez must be told."

The gaunt face smiled beneath the shaven pate.

"This is a time of celebration, Captain Burley. A place where idolators and your enemy denied their God, to worship instead the image of a horse — that temple of evil is now destroyed by our avenging hand. We are the instrument of God. The Chapel of St. Mary will be saved by the word of a true believer, heaven sent, who has given us of his knowledge. 'Tis almost a miracle in itself that we have been granted such intelligence. A blessing upon him. Who do you say? Nankervis? Why, I am moved to verse. This church will be saved as testimony of God's will and the munificence of Spain."

Upon the greensward that lay between Pensans and Newlyn, Sir Francis Godolphin, Governor and Captain General, Crown tenant of the Isles of Scilly, builder of Star Castle for their greater protection, stood at his horse's head to peer anxiously westward. The pall of death hung over where once was Mousehole. Silent witness to the evil of the preying galleys hovering off that fisher-town.

"What do you think, Flemyng?"

"Drake must be alerted with all haste. Then we should withdraw under the protection of the Barbican battery."

Godolphin grunted a laugh. "What protection? Hawkyns has taken his pick of the gunners and the ordnance too! There is little reliance on what remains, one cannon and aged gunners, too infirm to serve at sea. Tom, Tom Chiverton!" His secretary came to his side. "Write to Sir Francis Drake." He gazed up to the set of the sun. "Sir Francis Godolphin and Thomas Chiverton to Sir Francis Drake and Sir John Hawkyns, generals of the forces now at Plymouth. Four galleys are at anchor before Mousehole, their men landed, and the town and other houses in the country thereabouts are fired."

He turned to where Flemyng with hand-shielded eyes was peering west to sea. "See you other sign of sail?"

"None, Sir Francis, more is the pity on't."

"Ha, more sail could be enemy, mayhap they are part of an armada. Continue, Tom: 'No more of the fleet are in sight; fifty or sixty were seen on Monday evening and yesterday athwart off Falmouth. Pray consider what is to be done for safety and defence.' Give me now the quill." He signed with a flourish.

Godolphin looked about him at the meanly-armed men

288

who had rallied to his call. "A postscript, Tom. 'About two hundred men have assembled; we attend the coming of more so as to make stand toward the enemy.' Sand and seal, Tom, sand and seal." The ink thus dried. "Now hasten, man, by post to Plymouth. May God speed and protect you on your way."

Foot in the stirrup Chiverton swung into the saddle and with rowel of spur urged his mount eastward to the Icknield way.

"The galleys are on the move, Sir Francis, the devils are intent on further mischief. See they head towards us."

"How many soldiers are aboard?"

"Some say as many as four hundred a piece."

Godolphin laughed aloud. "One and a half thousand trained soldiers, against our band of ragamuffins! Pray to God the wind and tide favour Drake, that he is speeded hither."

Flemyng pointed. "See, sir, how they have steered outward from Low Lee Ledges."

"Aye, Flemyng, therefore they are well apprised of our sea and its dangers. Doubtless from their spies they know that Drake is ill-prepared and Hawkyns has deprived us of our defences." He sighed. "If only my advice had been heeded. The parsimony of our blessed monarch beggars all belief. Sometimes I wonder what is her magic that we would lay down our lives for her."

"Yes, Sir Francis. We may yet have to prove that point." Flemyng laughed a bitter laugh.

The sound of the drum could be heard echoing across the still of the silent sea.

The two brothers pushed through the throng in answer to Flemyng's hail: "Martin, Richard 'tis good you are here. Alas we need more of your kind."

"What news of our parents."

"You mother is safe at Landithy, Becky too. But of your father, I know not. He would remain to help the people escape and in truth I am fearful for him. But see Godolphin for his orders."

Cursorily Godolphin acknowledged the doffing of their caps. "You seem like fighting men." Both statement and

289

question.

"We have done our share, and more, Sir Francis. And have good reason besides." Richard pointed across the bay toward Mousehole.

"What are you named?"

"Keigwin, sir, Richard and Martin at your service."

"You are of the right breed if you are sons of Jenkyn Keigwin," he paused briefly. "I pray he may be saved. Now go place yourselves with the men facing seaward. Bow-men to fire when in range, muskets discharged only when they will inflict most harm." His voice dropped that none other might hear. "We are so few in number I am fearful that under cannon's fire our men will not stand their ground. Thus be prepared to withdraw into Pensans until our forces are strengthened. Messengers have gone for assistance."

"Ben."

He flung himself into Becky's outstretched arms.

"Mistress, mistress, Ben has come. What news, Ben?"

"Becky, Becky," he hugged her around the waist, his head upon her bosom, his frame shaking with the sobs he could now unleash. "Awful, awful," he lifted his tear-streaked face. "Becky, they are all dead! Killed by the Spaniards. Dead Becky. Dead!"

"May the good God have mercy on us. Teek, what of Teek?"

"Is dead, Becky." His voice lowered and was lost in weeping as he repeated, "is dead. All are dead."

Softly she held his head, her brimming, unseeing eyes looking into the distance, that her mind might envisage.

"How did he die?"

"Bravely, but bravely, sword in hand. Before numbers bore him down. Becky there were also English there. Burley they called him, Burley. The Squire too, killed by cannon. The others are also gone. John Pearce and Jacob, killed within the house."

Elizabeth and her mother silently joined to overhear.

"Squire Keigwin, Ben, where does he lie?"

He looked up. "In the open. I tended him as best I might."

290

"Of course, Ben, of course. Elizabeth, see to Ben and the children, for Becky and I must away to Mousehole."

"But Mother . . ."

"The galleys have passed beneath. They will not now return. We have done our duty to the living, now we must needs tend the dead. You must see to Landithy and your own."

Mother and daughter embraced in emotion too strong for tears.

Becky, standing alone, thought back. Those too few happy years of which she was forewarned. The one crucifix that floated in the magic stream, the wish that was denied.

"You have made yourself a valuable friend, Nankervis."

"How is that, Captain Burley?"

"The Friar sees your knowledge of the Chapel of Pensans as divine intervention. He has ordered the Chapel to be saved."

"May God be praised!"

"What is to do?" Nicholls bulled his way to the Englishman.

"Now to anchor where Nankervis has directed. See the greeting that awaits us? Godolphin has rallied the countryside about and that pitiful band is all that can be summoned! Don Carlos has ordered the course of action as before. Again we will land westward of our enemy, whilst the cannon ply their shot and contain the Cornishmen, we will take up our position on the shore. Eastward is a battery of cannon, of which we must beware."

"Gather round, gather round," Godolphin called. "Men of Cornwall, we are beset by tyrants." He shouted that all might hear. "They would pillage our homes, desecrate our churches and imprison our people. Outnumbered we may be, but yield we must not! Assistance is summoned. Be of good cheer, for Drake is coming to our call and together we will confront and confound our enemies. Eight thousand Cornishmen are to rally to the defence of our land. Lift up your hearts, have faith in the Divine Majesty in this our necessity! Now to your stations, bravely to face the foe. Bow-men, be prepared to loose when the enemy are clustered and in range. They will be most vulnerable when crammed into their launches."

"Eight thousand will rally to our aid?"

"I know not, Flemyng. Drake has some two and a half thousand men under the command of Nicholas Clifford. We must give our men hope, or they will not stand."

Whistles blew. Drums ceased to beat their monotonous message. The squadron hove-to out of arrow shot from the shore. Captain De Amelrola gave his orders. The sergeant major of the galleys watched with eagle eyes the lowered launches that ventured forward, soldier-laden, to ground upon the sandy strand where the gentle surf now only rippled. Rapier held high, Don Leon led his men ashore, the archers were held at bay as galleys plied their shot to furrow the turf and cut a swathe of havoc to reap a rich harvest of flesh and bone of Cornishmen.

Proudly Juan de Urbea acknowledged the signal of Don Dezpeleta, as he lead his men forward upon the right flank, his musketeers firing at random upon Godolphin's men, who quavered from joint onslaught of ship and shore as the Spaniards now moved to encircle their enemy.

"Out-numbered and out-gunned, Flemyng."

"And soon outflanked." Nicholas pointed to where Martin and Richard were engaged in a skirmish with the leading Spaniards, intent to cut off the prospect of retreat.

"Forty dead already. Withdraw lest we are all slaughtered. There is no shelter! To the Market Place, Flemyng and make a stand where cannon cannot reach. Prepare it for defence. Take advantage of the high ground. I will follow hindmost to observe the enemy's order. Haste, man, haste!"

Flemyng wheeled his horse, a blow as of a hammer thudded upon his back plate, to rend his doublet and throw him to the ground. Yet still he held tight the reins and swung back into the saddle. If God had meant my death, his mind flashed,

292

then that musketeer would have shot but half a second sooner. No time to dwell. The craven men needed not a signal. Their plight was too apparent. Withdrawal became retreat, retreat a rout as musket and cannon continued their remorseless fire.

How could they resist such overwhelming odds? Cowed and daunted by their bloodshed without loss of one of Spain, the English withered before the cannonade, to lose themselves amongst the houses and alleyways of Pensans. Neither persuasion nor drawn rapier would induce them to face the foe again. All were vanished save some ten or twelve loyal servants of Godolphin.

"We will make for Marazion where, if God is merciful, Flemyng, we will await Drake's generals."

"Sir Francis, permit Martin and me to return to discover the fate of our father."

"So be it. Travel well inland lest you confront the Spanish. Return to me at Marazion where we will muster and await assistance. Recruit such men as you need for there is now no purpose for the galleys to return to Mousehole. God be with you."

"And with you, Sir Francis." They doffed their caps in farewell.

Victorious soldiers burned and plundered. The fortress armed with cannon was put to the torch. Three wine-laden ships sunk within the harbour, whilst alone the Chapel of St. Mary remained unharmed. Upon the foredeck of the *Capitana*, Nankervis fingered the ring about his neck as he traced the way of friend and foe amidst the flaming town.

Startled he turned as the silent figure of the Friar came to his side.

"You are Nankervis?"

"Yes Padre."

"By God's will 'twas you that celebrated Mass within the Chapel of Our Lady?"

"Indeed, Father."

"In consequence her place of worship is safeguarded."

"God bless you Father."

A dismissive gesture from the Friar. Who turned his gaze upon the burning town. "Oft I have noticed you toy with a pendant about your neck. A symbol of your faith?"

Suddenly he grasped the clenched fingers that unwittingly held the ring within their grasp. Gently he prised open the hand to gaze upon the beauty of the black pearl.

"A mere bauble, Father."

Slowly the dark eyes raised to fasten upon those of Nankervis and delve the seaman's soul. Awhile. Then softly he spoke. "A bauble? Perhaps so, but a bauble sufficient to ransom many a king. Tell me in truth, where and how came you by this 'bauble'?"

A hesitation. The dark eyes ordered his reply.

"It would not amuse you, Father. 'Tis a tale I have never told. Had I done so none would have believed the truth on't. Then in consequence would I be branded twice, both as a thief and a liar!"

A mirthless laugh. Dark eyes continued their search of the man within. " 'Tis a tale I would sometime wish to hear for I, my son, believe you."

Long had Burley waited, his patience near exhausted, yet never had revenge been so sweet. The fire of hatred that burned his soul was now dampened by the blood of heresy. Yet there were others aboard, impatient and untried, anxious to take their turn. Still there was daylight left and more to be accomplished. Don Leon gave the orders to return his men unto the waiting galleys, prodding and poking a ragbag of reluctant English prisoners before them.

"Hawkyns, read this." In the lamplight of his cabin Drake handed his vice-admiral the letter from Godolphin. "Sixty sail sighted at sea. If they are fighting ships as is supposed, they are goodly odds and worthy of our mettle." He read again. "Vivyan is fearful lest they land along the coast." Gentlemen, remind me of the limitations of the galley. Sir Nicholas?"

"Their low waist renders them unsuited to heavy seas."

Drake ticked his fingers once. "What else?"

"With such a complement of slaves and soldiery they are

294

ill-equipped for a lengthy voyage."

"Why?"

"Lack of stowage for provisions."

"Aye, and for water. Only at Newlyn and Mousehole is there shelter and fresh water. So you Sir Nicholas must take as many as you can muster to support Godolphin's militia. Ride hard now! Send more soldiers to follow. With your captains there will be men enough to restrain their launches from returning to the galleys. Hole them when they come ashore for water. Ambush them as they return, Spaniards on English soil? God forbid they go unpunished whilst we have English blood within our veins! The tide will shortly favour us though we must beat into the wind. The same wind that hinders their return. We will make our way to cut off their retreat from sea."

His pacing ceased as he sat upon a chair to sink his head upon his chest and look up beneath his frowning brows: "Would that we knew the nature of the sail that was sighted." He thought a moment. "We must be alert and on our guard lest the attack upon Mousehole and Pensans is but a lure, that whilst we are away to take the bait an armada enters Plymouth or engages us at sea!" He paused. "I am fearful lest that be their ploy, but that is risk we have to take."

He rose from the seat, his hand held out to his captain. "May God speed you on your way, Sir Nicholas and aid you in your endeavours."

Relief at last. Against all odds the *Alcedo* had battled and won against the wildest storms that Biscay could arouse. Moonlight and William Monson, Vice-admiral to the Earl of Cumberland steered his ship into the safe waters of Plymouth Sound, struck his topsails and took in his flag in salute to the Admiral. The *Defiance*, flagship of Sir Francis gave due acknowledgement to the courtesy.

"What is she, Hawkyns?" demanded Drake.

" 'Tis a merchant's ship of the City of London, one of Cumberland's fleet."

"Who is in command? Monson?"

"Aye, he went as vice-admiral. Lost her mainmast too."

"Summon him aboard straightway. Soon the tide will be on the turn."

His weariness worn with disguise Monson climbed aboard.

"You saw nothing?" Drake paced his cabin. His brown bearded chin jutting his anger, as the *Defiance* led the squadron to work its way into the open sea. "Clear night? Calm sea? Yet you saw nothing! Vivyan of St. Mawes Castle," he held a letter aloft, "tells of forty sail sighted off the fort, whilst Godolphin tells of an armada of sixty. But you saw nothing! Nothing of the galleys?"

"We saw no Spanish ships, but we did espy a fleet of Hollanders, merchantmen and escorts making their way westwards, tacking into the wind."

"Could they have been espied from shore?"

"Aye, sir, though fishing boat more likely."

"Then by all that is holy! Lowlanders, and merchantmen withall. Mistaken for Spanish galleons!" He laughed aloud, an unsmiling laugh and slapped the letter against his thigh.

Martin halted his horse and pointed east to the darkening sea. "See Richard. Thanks be to God for the galleys are leaving."

"Not so fast, Martin, look now, they are easing to starboard."

They watched as the squadron turned into the wind.

"Hell's fire, they are intent upon Newlyn! We must ride hard before they land."

Across the combe that Jacob knew, they forded the stream, then upwards over the hill toward where Mousehole lay. Onward they pressed their tiring horses, watching as they went.

Beneath them slaves bent at their oars in the evening sun. Elated soldiers marvelled at the ease of their victory and looked towards their next adventure.

Upon his shoulders the cowl had slipped, his tonsured dome shone pale in the lamplight. Before the altar in his cabin, Friar Domingo was at his devotions. Mouth moving in silent prayer as his rosary recorded Ave Maria and Pater-noster. Today had been one of retribution, and salvation. They had departed Blavet on the eve of the feast of St. Anne, mother of the Holy Virgin and by Divine intervention had intelligence that had saved a church of her daughter, the blessed Saint Mary.

The Friar now was weary. Preparation, anticipation and responsibility had exhausted him. Faith alone had lent him strength. In his simple chair he sat to meditate. He awoke with a start from his doze. Was it a dream, or his imagination? A dream? Then surely, a God given dream was a vision! Was this a vision? To found a priory, here, in Cornwall. To teach and preach the true faith and overcome heresy. Extend the will of God in the service of Rome. To found a priory. A fountain of learning. A sanctuary from which a clear spring would flow to refreshen the spirit of those who toiled to maintain the orthodoxy of the church of Rome.

Trumpets and whistles sounded the now familiar drill. Again soldiers took to their boats to land upon the unprotected shore. Four hundred pikes and shot to pillage, to burn, to make prisoners of free men and women. A patrol was sent to the hilltop beyond to keep watch, to discover what forces or ambush might lie in wait within that heathen country. But they could only espy the meagre group that Godolphin led. Without hint of resistance the jubilant forces returned, to board the waiting ships.

The day was drawing to its close. The bitter smell of smouldering wood pervaded the evening air. The brothers, in dread anticipation, approached their town. A word of greeting, of commiseration to an occasional forlorn figure, scavenging amongst a home in ruins, to salvage what they may. They passed The Mermaid, roofless, the walls standing stubbornly, to cross the stream. The sound of hooves upon the cobbles all that broke the saddened silence of their homecoming. Through the wreckage they rode to the defiant presence of their Manor home. A pale lamplight shone from within.

Trewhella heard the sound of horses and gingerly peered around the door to see who it was approached.

"Master Richard, Master Martin!" To retreat within and call, "Master Richard and Master Martin are arrived."

The upstairs of the Manor was little disturbed, the roof and ceilings holed by cannon-fire but still within stout walls there was protection against a summer's storm.

"May God be thanked! My sons are safe!" Thomasine ran to fling herself into their arms that the three might hug and kiss in blessed relief.

The south-westerly continued a soft blow that roused the sea but little. Galleys tacked the starlit night away, keen eyes scanning lest Drake hove into view, or plunder might pass by. Unknown.

Thursday August 3rd 1595. A council of war aboard the *Capitana*, the *Nuestra Senora De Begona*. Friar Domingo stood to address the seated De Amelrola, and his captains.

"Today, Don Carlos, is the eve of the feast of the blessed St. Dominic. I wear the habit of his order. By his grace and that of St. Anne, upon whose day we sailed, our mission has been sanctified and blessed beyond belief. With such aid our expedition has been successful. Thus, upon St. Dominic's eve it is my wish to celebrate Mass on land, that heretics may witness the authority of our God, and the power of Rome."

He looked around the gathering with a zealous intensity.

"By the grace of God I have had a vision. I am directed to found in this wild country a priory of the Order of St. Dominic. I seek a hill, upon which to build. A vantage, that it may be seen from afar, and defended against those that would deny the true faith. Thus it may endure, both a sanctuary and fortress."

A silence as they pondered upon his words.

"I have seen such a place." De Maeda spoke and rose that all might hear and give attention to what he was to say.

"Pray tell, tell me Don Luis, of what you know."

"Beyond Newlyn I have seen a commanding height, a rounded hill at whose base is a fringe of woodland, whilst

298

the top is bare."

The Friar smiled and stroked his shaven pate. "It would seem you describe my head; that augurs well!"

The captains laughed at the Friar's jest, yet none too loud, lest they incur the displeasure of a man of such authority both in this life and the next.

" 'Tis God's will, Friar Domingo."

"Therefore so be it. As many as may, will celebrate Mass upon this hill, the galleys to stand sentinel, lest the enemy threaten."

And so it was agreed.

The news of the death of Jenkyn Keigwin had spread, as had the manner of his dying. From near and wide folk had gathered by the smouldering tower of St. Pol de Leon, to surround the churchyard's open wound where sons and servants had carried the Squire in procession, to lower his coffin into his final resting place.

"He cometh up and is cut down like a flower," intoned John Tremearne. "He fleeth as it were a shadow."

The dangers that beset them did naught to deter his parishioners and his peers. Fishermen and farmer, merchant and tradesman attended at his graveside. There were those who were lacking in his courage, that bravely risked much that they might attend, in farewell of him who had dared and died that they might be free.

Of such a kind was the gaunt, black-garbed figure, whose ancient mule picked at the grass upon the green without. At the fringe of the throng he stood, lace kerchief held to his face, his narrow shoulders shaking.

Bravely she stood in widow's weeds, eyes open yet unseeing. Flanked by her sons, her family about her. Bonnetted head lowered, too sad, too proud for the tears that later she would shed to dampen her pillow, unwitnessed, in the solitude of her lonely bed. There to recall days of love and happiness, tragedy and disappointment, yet, transcending all, the fulfilment of their marriage.

Fronds of rosemary strewn upon the coffin. 'Earth to earth, ashes to ashes, dust to dust'.

Now in file they passed, the mourners, to sprinkle earth which rattled upon the elm as final tribute to patriarch and Squire, laid to rest next the blaze-blackened church. A place where he worshipped, founded a thousand years before by a saint whose Celtic blood he shared.

Nearby, within another grave, another coffin. The mortal remains of John Pearce Peiton, buried that same day.

Behind the fisher-town of Newlyn, upon a rounded hill, soldiers took boards and gathered timber for carpenters to fashion a hut, with an altar within. From the high vantage a cross was planted that might be seen from afar. For the prospect was as de Maeda had stated and commanded views across all the land about.

North and west upon the hills were the watching patrols of Godolphin. East and seawards the guardian screen of galleys anchored at their station. Beyond the hills and south, but one mile and half again as the mournful curlew flies, there lingered a wisp of smoke above the church of St. Pol, in whose churchyard, even now, men were gathered to mourn their Squire. Here would the invaders flaunt their faith in very view of their enemies. Here would Burley rejoice. Here would those cleansed prisoners be released, to travel, teaching the true faith throughout the land; playing their part that the rule of Rome might once more reign.

In joyful display, Burley ordered a volley to be fired from arquebus and musket that would deter the watchers from foolhardy heroism, so that Mass might be said in safety.

Waiting, watchful aboard his flagship De Amelrola pondered. Despite days of frenzied fighting and of battles won, he had no trophy, no memento worthy of their deeds. Whilst the Cornish were distracted by the service now being held ashore, he could act. He summoned Sergeant Major Juan de Arnica to his cabin and gave orders for his mission. Down the galley's wooden walls to board the waiting launch. The Sergeant Major and twelve musketeers to carry out their captain's daring plan. A raid ashore by only thirteen. But once more surprise would be the key, to do the unexpected, that victory would result. The capture of the cannon that

300

still threatened from the fort. The piece that could fire upon them from the safety of the barbican of Pensans. The ancient gunners offered only brief resistance.

The piece was captured and dismantled, hefted aboard the launch, thence slung on board the flagship, to greet the return of those that celebrated ashore. Thus by prayer and by plunder were the priests and soldiers of Spain determined to record their triumph.

A sail sighted out to sea, off the Lizard. As hounds unleashed from the slips, off went the galleys in pursuit of further plunder. Two hours and within range of cannon, she hove to, laden with wine and salt to be left unharmed, for the vessel was Irish, to whom the hand of friendship must be extended. Friends in peace might be allies in war. The galleys returned to their haven that in the lee of Newlyn they might shelter the night away.

Stars began to prick the darkening sky, whilst beyond the high hills, unseen, the storm clouds gathered. As slowly rose the moon so swiftly did the wind, and rain began to lash the heaving seas. Gone was the calm of the days before as the spindrift flew from angry, white-veined waves. In the shallow, shelving waters of the bay rollers began to build, to roar and crash their devilish spleen to slaver upon the shingle of the shore.

At their anchors the squadron snagged and fretted to pitch and roll between wave top and trough. Into the ship's low waists the high seas pounded. Shivering slaves were drenched in the chill misery of the night.

Upon the aft-deck of the *Revenge*, Drake clenched the gunwale, hands white-knuckled, eyes restless, searching the sails for hint of a shift in the wind he sensed might come.

Frustration, the wind on the nose that held his ships in check as aided by the running tide they tacked their slow way westwards. Sails cracked to luff in the strengthening breeze. He turned to grunt a greeting to the figure by his side.

"The wind is veering, Monson." An upward cast of eyes. "Easterly, she will freshen with the moon and come round further."

"Aye, sir, then shall we have the advantage."

"Ah and should she blow strongly into the bay, she may trap those slave-ships without our aid."

Morning. Friday August 4th 1595. Devotions ended and Burley was summoned to his captain's quarters, where De Amelrola rose to greet him. Seated in the corner was the Friar, wan smile his welcome.

"Friar Domingo has interrogated certain of our prisoners and has gleaned some knowledge."

Burley raised his eyebrow in enquiry and smiled congratulations upon the monk.

"Our chaplain tells me those captured have confessed that Godolphin can call upon eight thousand men to protect this coast. What say you?"

"That is what I also have gathered, though I cannot pronounce whether or not it be true. But our captives have told us that Drake has men at Falmouth as well as Plymouth that we must suppose were alerted when we first came. By my reckoning their vanguard could well be nigh."

" 'Tis as I too believe. Drake will soon be upon us aided by this easterly wind. 'Tis but fourteen leagues to Plymouth."

"Captain Carlos, I know these waters from my boyhood. The winds that blow presently will in the morning follow the sun around. As it rises in the east so will the wind then round to the west."

"Then it may yet favour our return."

"It is most possible."

"Umh, the *Patroness* is taking in water. The caulkers report she cannot be repaired unless careened." He thought awhile. "How fare the prisoners, Friar Domingo?"

"Somewhat fearful when in my presence. My black mantle is often the key that unlocks the tongue. They have heard tell of my Order and the autos-da-fé of the Inquisition. They have been fed and fattened upon a diet of fear and lies. I have told them their own Elizabeth burns many more of our faith lest she be toppled from her throne."

"Undoubtedly," he had little time to hear the ramblings of the priest, "but are you satisfied with what you have achieved?"

302

"Don Carlos," reproved the Friar, "to celebrate Mass to which our foes were witness? That alone has been reward enough!"

"Aye, Friar," intruded Burley, "and greatly impressed all Englishmen aboard. Prisoner and Jesuit. Since only with God's blessing could we smite the heretics with such impunity. Those most devout will long praise our deeds and are content. Aye, and to such effect that when our armies again land, swarms of people of all degree will leap out to assist. For there were those who once did waver that now marvel at the length and strength of the arm of Rome."

"So be it; the booty has gone, yet punishment is now meted and our duty is near complete. Burley, set loose prisoner and priest that they may advance God's message. Take care in these treacherous seas."

He nodded in dismissal to turn to the Friar: "Friar Domingo, all we now require is for the seas to lessen, for they threaten our safe return as gravely as Drake."

"My son, once before in God's name were the seas bidden to calm, and they obeyed. I will pray that it may again be so."

"Mother, you will be safe with Trewhella awhile, the galleys' duty in Mousehole is done, unless they seek fresh water. We believe that they might do so at Newlyn's stream. Martin and I must to our duty and join Godolphin."

"Wait." Thomasine left, to return with the musket her husband prized, with pewter flask of powder and shot. "Take this and use it well, as he would wish."

She embraced them both to turn away to hide her sorrow.

On refreshed mounts they rode for Marazion, recruiting and encouraging tough tinner and timid townsman as they went, adding to the throng, all anxious for revenge. Through squalls of rain from the hills above they watched the antics of the storm-tossed galleys, tugging on their anchors. Launches were leaving, rowing shorewards with a cluster of men aboard, neither armed nor armoured.

"Do they come for water, or what else is their purpose?"

"Perhaps, but they are too far west."

"We have men enough to ambush them on their return.

Come, hurry Richard lest we are too late!"

"Too late already. The launches are returning, empty.
I have it. They have released prisoners."

"Aye, or priests of the Jesuit kind."

They drew their swords as one, calling their men to follow
as they cantered down to the shore of Gwavas Lake.

Some men were there they knew, with them at Pensans
until encircled by the Spanish. Fishermen, of Newlyn too,
taken when their homes were torched.

"Who are you?"

"I am named Barnaby Loe."

"You have neither voice nor the name of the west country."

"I am of Suffolk and hail from Ipswich, being a captive of
Spain this many month. Now we are set free."

"That you may spread the gospel of Rome?" He saw a figure
out the corner of his eye. "Where do you slink to? Damnation,
a bunch of Jesuits. Gather them up! To Godolphin with them!
Landed with the prisoners as a blind, or take me for a
Hollander! Martin, command these men whilst we fire
upon the galleys lest they return to rescue the traitors."

Muskets cracked, bows were bent, ball and arrow flew
as the Cornishmen dared the galleys to come about. But all
too late. De Amelrola ordered the squadron to repair out of
range, then to make sail for Brittany.

"Now to Godolphin," commanded Richard. "All men will
follow me. We muster upon the Green at Marazion. Martin,
take six armed men you can trust; escort those you know not,
to give into Godolphin's care. I and others ride on ahead."

"Sir Francis."

"What is it, Flemyng?"

"More men are arriving, see yonder. The captains for
whom you sent."

"Thank God."

"Godolphin?"

"I am."

A hand outstretched in greeting. "Sir Nicholas Clifford
and Sir Henry Power, captains of Sir Francis Drake who bids
us send you his compliments." He paused. "We are com-

manded to give you every assistance."

"Where is your Admiral in God's name?"

"Depending on wind and tide, lurking off the Head with his squadron, intent on teaching those galleys a lesson they will long remember."

Burley looked skyward to study the scudding cloud.

"You have God's ear, Chaplain."

The Friar gave a slight nod, a rare smile upon his lips.

"The wind is coming off the land, He has answered your prayers. By the grace of God the sea will calm and we shall be wafted homewards on His wind. There is a break in the west and the seas are already coming calmer. Is this another of our miracles, Friar? Heaven and all the saints be praised!"

In flattening seas and changing wind that aided their departure, the Spanish squadron left the bay unhindered. The English ships, helpless and unable to engage against winds that only aided the enemy.

He lay in his cabin cot taking such rest as he might to ease his tired and aching body. His head rested in clasped hands as he gazed upwards, wide-eyed. Recapturing the detail of adventure that fain would permit him sleep.

Homeward bound. But where was his home? Perhaps he could now settle. Perhaps now he could be content that his ambition was fulfilled. A squadron of four galleys had chastened a presumptuous England as was God's will. With such success others would be encouraged to follow in their wake. But also he was avenged. Ah! The sweet smell of revenge exacted! The booty from Brazil had been lost to them, but all else had been achieved.

Was that the drum-beat quickening? He felt the galley surge. A knock, a call. Quickly to his feet. A summons to attend Don Carlos.

"Burley, two ships have been sighted now hove-to in fear. Our skiffs have returned with prisoners but the Friar cannot comprehend their tongue. Pray question them for perhaps you will understand."

The bemused captives left under guard. Burley returned to make his report.

"Don De Amelrola, it is small wonder Friar Domingo was bemused, for these men who speak in a strange tongue are Scottish and as a consequence have no allegiance to the English Queen who murdered their own Mary. In return for their freedom they have given me intelligence."

De Amelrola cast his eyes towards the priest for guidance; a nod was his response.

"Continue Captain Burley."

"There is a fleet of Hollanders that sail southwards, beating against the wind, and on our course."

"How many do they say?"

"Forty or more, some of which are escort."

Again De Amelrola looked toward the Friar for instruction but none he gave, only to ease himself upon his stool.

"The *Patroness* concerns me, for she is damaged and taking in water." A thinking pause. "We have suffered little hurt, hence our victory is the more complete."

The Friar shuffled. "As consequence of the guidance the saints have given us," he murmured.

"Where did they sight the fleet?" asked the commander.

"By now they believe them to be off the Pointe du Raz."

"Those are wild waters, in which the wind will grant them no favours."

"They could seek shelter in the bay."

"True. Yet tomorrow we should sight them. Such numbers cannot hide. Then we can decide our course of action."

"We shall have the advantage of surprise — and speed also, in these light airs and thus . . . "

The Friar cleared his throat to gain attention. "Tomorrow is the Feast day of Our Lady of the Snows. That augurs well, for the saints have given us their blessing. Have faith in those who have guided us upon our mission, for with their aid we may add further glory to our venture."

"Aye, Friar Domingo, and with the cargo they bear we may yet make good the treasure that escaped us."

The ninth day of August 1595. Evening devotions were ended and dusk was falling as Burley watched the high cliffs of the Pointe du Talut slide past. The Hollanders had fought both well and bravely, enemy ships had been boarded and bloodied, two of the escort sunk. His men had fought with great spirit, yet they had suffered loss and damage. Had they presumed too much? Had they taken their God for granted? Had He sent the wind that had aided their enemies? But now they were returned to enter the sanctuary of Blavet and mend their ships. Was it only fourteen nights since they had left their haven? St. Anne's day, the 26th July? What had been achieved in that short while would delight his King.

Burley might look to further patronage. A position of privilege granted by the Royal hand. He would be favoured by his grateful sovereign, of that there was no doubt.

Chapter Nineteen

"The letter awaited me at Plymouth and I came with all haste."

The three were once more united, the brothers intent to appraise Tom of all that had transpired.

"I was prepared to see Mousehole pillaged," Tom shook his head, "but never, never did I envisage such destruction." His voice, vibrant with emotion. " 'Tis far more terrible than . . . " his speech trailed. "So Grandfather died as he had lived?"

"Yes, Tom, with a rare courage and dignity. Defiant. He lay down his life that others might be spared."

A silence, as each was lost in recollection, each embarrassed to be the first to break the silence.

"Come, gentlemen, let us to the study, there to plan." They followed Richard to the room that reeked of the presence of him they had lost. "Here shall we feel my father's hand to guide us. Tobacco gentlemen? The wine when we have agreed upon what course to take."

"Tell me, Richard, what is to do, for I have come post-haste, yet at Plymouth none could tell me of events."

"Few do know, for Godolphin and others have suppressed the news on the wishes of Queen Bess."

"Why so?"

"Because she dare not let it be broadcast lest it hearten the Papists and threaten the throne."

"Which, doubtless was part of their intent," added Martin.

"When changing my mount at a posting house upon the moors I near came to a duel, but the fellow bluffed and played it by the text, else he would have felt my steel."

"In the name of God we have had our fill of fighting."

"True, but the insult was too great to bear."

"Insult?"

"Aye, the coxcomb accused the Mousehole men of cowardice."

"I am afeared that is a slur we shall have to live with."

"Not for me, brother," Martin spoke with gravity, then turned to his nephew. "See you, Tom, all our fighting men were with Drake at Plymouth, or with Richard and me escorting the treasure."

"Treasure?" Ears were pricked as they told of Lancaster and the booty he had won from Brazil.

"This was another cause for the Spaniards to come, if they but knew on't."

"They knew, be assured, for so the prisoners revealed: as also they told of Burley."

"Burley?" Tom's hand stole to the dagger on his hip.

"Let me tell the tale from the beginning, and should I forget Martin will fill the gap." And so Richard told his nephew all of that which had occurred, with Martin recalling and enlarging where required.

"Now, to hold a council of war, for there are matters that we must address and course of action to be decided upon. Firstly, the well-being of Mother and the family."

"Aye, Richard, and of Elizabeth. When is the baby due?"

"Very shortly, Tom, and she is well suited by her condition. Second to ensure the prosperity of the family, and of Mousehole. Third to see as best we may, that Mousehole is restored. Then, I come to the fourth point." He paused awhile, drawing upon his pipe, to fix the ceiling with his stare.

"What may that be Richard?"

"To be avenged upon our father, Tom!" He leant forward, hand on knee, to gaze deep into his nephew's eyes. "Are you with us?"

"To the death, Uncle!"

"Death needs not apply and does not feature in the plan."

"What plan?"

"The plan that we have hatched."

"With the guidance of Solomon Fernandes."

Richard nodded to acknowledge Martin. "But first is the family and our fortune. For if we be strong then so is Mousehole."

"There is no doubt on that, brother. But you are the new head of the Keigwin household and must don our father's mantle."

Richard shook his head. "I fear it will envelope me, for I lack the stature to step into his shoes."

"So you may, for a while, but you learnt at his knee and have the support of the family. Take heart, brother, take heart. Time will ensure you grow to fit the role."

"If we stay united then I have less to fear."

"But we are and so shall remain. You have the family here, Dick, but also my father and your sister at Madron to lend support — and there is Fernandes too!"

"I count on you all, for there is so much to be achieved and without your aid I would despair. There are also those who would needs take advantage of my father's death and seek to steal our trade." He mournfully looked into the bowl and tamped the tobacco.

"Never fear Dick, shake off the melancholy. If we are united we shall not be defeated! Reveal the plan."

"To the plan. I will act the merchant as best I may, with such knowledge as my father imparted. I will also play the steward of our lands." He paused a moment as they nodded to agree. "So be it. Then our mother and Elizabeth will give succour to the distressed; that will give a sense of purpose to their being and fill the void left by my father."

"But shortly Mother will have another grandchild to dote upon," said Martin.

Richard nodded. "How she tries not to presume upon us, but she has love to spare and a need to cherish now she is without a mate. My wife loves her as well as might my sister."

"As one generation is shorn another is born."

"God's hand at work."

"Then there is Becky."

"Rebecca will relieve Mother of the burden of the household, for she is as near to being family as maybe, and with Teek gone," his voice trailed a moment and he pointed the stem of his pipe at his brother, "but Martin is the key."

"The key?"

"Aye, Tom, the key. For 'tis for him to create new markets, new opportunities. For there are now more mouths to feed. Mousehole is dependent upon us and we must needs create wealth with which to aid her."

"To provide work that all might profit." Martin nodded his agreement.

"Hence to seek those new markets, those new opportunities. 'Tis for you to travel, Martin. To link with those merchants of France and Spain, as well as further afield; Africa, aye and India too! Learn to speak their language; you are the key."

"I shall not fail you, brother."

"Then the final matter. To be avenged on Richard Burley. Tom, there lies a task for you."

His nephew nodded in anticipation. "The traitor must not go unpunished."

"Richard and I have spoken with Fernandes and have devised a plan."

"Exactly so. Now," Richard prodded the air with his pipe stem, "who else do we know who has suffered at the hands of this Burley?"

"Why, Dick, the merchant John Donne was betrayed."

"Indeed. Now who do we know as men with authority?"

"Hawkyns? Drake? Godolphin?"

"Sir Francis and John Hawkyns are adventuring in the Indies."

"Godolphin?"

"Yes, he is made the scapegoat and methinks would prefer to let sleeping dogs lie."

"Yet 'twas no fault of his."

"True, but think again, Tom."

His nephew shook his head.

"Why, Hoby, Tom."

"Edward Hoby?"

"Aye, recall his promise. He has the ear of his Uncle, my Lord Burghley. And, I am assured, Edward is held in high esteem at Court. He is a man of consequence and your true friend. Now this is the plan which we wish to implement

311

and so we seek your sanction."

"Pray continue, for I am intrigued," said Tom.

Richard paused awhile, to toy with the tobacco, then to suck and cause the bowl to glow once more.

"In France there are those who serve two masters, Mendoza and Lord Burghley. Donne is well-travelled and has knowledge of such a one, Edmund Palmer, a merchant of St. Jean de Luz with whom he trades. Yet, so Donne does swear, he gives intelligence to whomsoever pays the most, and is a man no one may truly trust."

"What part do you wish me to play?"

"Spies are everywhere. Martin and I dare not venture abroad, unless it be to sea and trade. Yet you, Tom, are so seldom here your absence is understood. And should one so enquire, why to Oxford have you gone, a visit to your brother. From there, follow the Thames, travel by post to Bisham, for there lives Hoby, 'tis on that self-same river. Prevail upon him to seek the assistance of his uncle that he may write a letter to Richard Burley, praising him for his loyalty to our Queen and thanking him for his services."

"But Burley is a traitor. There is no such cause to be grateful."

"Heed me! We shall ensure that Palmer is entrusted to transport the letter to Burley. Fernandes has kin who know his whereabouts in Lisbon. Such letter to be writ in a cipher we know to be already discovered. Perhaps that self-same cipher as Father Parsons employed. Then Palmer will betray the confidence and so ensure Burley be punished and disowned by him he serves."

"Will such ploy achieve its task?" Tom enquired of both.

" 'Twill depend upon Hoby, and your chore is to convince him."

"If he but prime the musket, our aim and fire may strike true."

"That is the task for Martin. 'Tis agreed he will act as factor for John Donne."

"Aye, Tom, to sail from Marazion to St. Jean de Luz with goods to sell to Palmer. I shall give false name and give him monies to ensure Burley is safely delivered of the letter, and impress upon this Edward Palmer its importance, and let it be known it is from one of high esteem in England."

"Thus we calculate, Tom, the curiosity of the merchant will lead to the betrayal of Burley."

Over and over they turned the project, until every point was satisfied.

The scent of incense hung heavy on the air. Before Burley, the elaboration of the high altar dimly lighted by an unwavering flame. The ritual of the liturgy was ended. He knelt, blue eyes wide opened across clasped hands. His soul at peace. Other communicants now departed, he was quiet and alone. Here might he saturate in the love of God, to be filled with the tranquillity of the Holy Ghost: the turmoil of his mind soothed in prayer and benediction.

By his King he had been both summoned and received. In his presence they had knelt to praise God for their triumph in His name. He had received his reward. By worship was he refreshed. Here in Lisbon he would await such further service of which King Philip might have need. He rose, to make obeisance and cross himself before his Christ.

She sat beside the window that close overlooked the little harbour. The sea gently lapped the great stones that lined the wharf. Her home was complete. Her nest was made. Would she ever be accustomed to this many-mooded sea? What a contrast to the tree'd combes of her girlhood. Forsaken the sweet music of the song birds, exchanged for the gull's harsh cry. Lost, the scent of wild flowers beside the cooling stream, instead, soft rain fell upon the charred timbers of the little town. Still there lingered the pungent smell, remnant of that dreadful day. Gone was the peace, all was hustle, as under the guiding hand of Richard men were rebuilding their shattered world.

Another stab. Sharper. Elizabeth reached for the silver bell that brought Becky to her summons.

"Is that a pain, Mistress Elizabeth?"

"A twinge, Becky, but a twinge."

"All is prepared, never fear. I will go tell Mistress Keigwin,

313

o

for your labour will soon be started."

She bustled with importance from the room.

"Do you permit me?"

Elizabeth replied with a nodded smile, as Thomasine lifted the infant from the oaken crib.

"Once his father slept in the self-same cot, did he not my treasure?" She cooed at the bundle held in her loving arms.

"He has the likeness of his father — and his father before him."

" 'Tis true. That forehead. The set of his chin foretells the same determination. Yet his eyes," Thomasine looked keenly into those of Elizabeth. "His eyes will be as his mother's." She rocked him in her arms as her own began to brim. "The Squire would be proud that such a babe as this will follow in his line."

"Doubtless he knows, my dear mother-in-law."

Thomasine nodded in silence, adjusting and fussing the clothing of the infant, that her feelings might be hid.

"Now Tom," Richard forewarned, "where'ere you may, travel in the company of others of your kind, and take a stout man with you. I hear tales of bands of footpads and vagabonds that wait upon an easy prey."

"Alas, too many good men have been turned adrift. Brave seamen that are no longer needed now the Spaniard is beat." He spoke with feeling. "Without their aid the Don would be in London town, the Queen in the Tower and a papist on the throne of England."

" 'Tis as may be, Tom. But keep your tongue well tied, or your head will be paraded on a pike."

"I am watchful what I say in company. But there's many as think as I."

"There's many found guilty of treason for less. Let your man be mindful of his words, lest his tongue be loosened when in drink. Who goes with you?"

"Pentreath."

"A good man with a sword in his hand, but not I fear with

ale in his belly."

"He will do as he is bid. Married men are less impetuous than rash youth."

"Aye, 'tis time enough you made a fresh marriage. Now, you will go by Bodmin?"

"Such was my intention unless you wish me otherwise."

"Not so."

"There I was intending to overnight at some inn."

"Mmm. Thomas Cocke is Mayor of Bodmin and a man of substance. You will be a welcome guest in his house. Did he not entertain us right merrily, Martin?"

"Aye, brother, as did his ladies!"

"He purchased much of our spices; give him news that he may relish, Tom, except the reason why you travel."

" 'Tis but to see my brother in Oxford!"

"And enquire as to his needs, for he keeps a fine cellar that may well need replenishing. Let him know what wines we have in store, and we will deliver as soon we may."

"That mantle will fit you ere very long, Dick. As hounds are bred to scent their quarry, you are bred to sniff for trade."

"I was but thinking of your welfare," protested Richard.

"Nonsense! You were thinking to take advantage of my journeying and where's the harm in that? 'Tis right and proper that you should."

"And, Tom," Martin interrupted, "beware the cyder! Thomas Cocke will quaff it as 'twer his mother's milk. Stay by the grape or by his ale. But be wary of his cyder, for unless you are weaned upon it, you are bound to succumb."

"So you travel to Oxford?"

"If my nag can bear the burden of me." He turned to his hostess. "Mistress Cocke, I was forewarned as to the excellence of your comestibles, but fear that I have over-indulged."

"Whilst we, Captain Flemyng, have delighted in your company. Why to Oxford?"

"I go to visit my brother." He turned toward his host. "For, sir, it is some years since we have met."

"And pray, sir, what is his vocation?"

"He is a scholar."

"And in what subject is he versed?"

"Why, sir, theology."

"Theology, by Jove."

"Indeed, sir, he is a doctor of divinity."

"Then should he ever pass this way and wish to break his travels, we would be honoured to welcome him as our guest, is that not so, Alice?"

"Why yes, for it is a subject of regret that oft-times we lack for stimulating conversation. Here we are isolated and fear that others may find us but boring bumpkins who know little of the outside world."

"Fear not, Mistress Cocke, for such unworldliness is as refreshing as the dew upon the rosebud and so encourages the bloom of conversation."

"Prettily said, sir, prettily said." The Mayor drank deeply of his jar. "Whilst I know of your uncles and indeed have sat in session with your father, I know not if you have a family of your own, Captain Flemyng?"

"Sadly, sir, whilst once I was wed, I am now a widower."

"I am saddened to hear that of one so young."

"But I have no fears for her, in the certainty that the soul of my Jane now rests with Almighty God, as is that of the child she was about to bear."

The hand of Mistress Cocke reached forward to touch and comfort that of her guest.

"My daughter Elizabeth frowns at my clumsiness. I pray your forgiveness for my intrusion."

"Nay, sir." Tom turned to where Elizabeth sat, a tapestry upon her knee. "I am the most fortunate of men to have been wed to her even but a brief while. For whilst at sea I was without her presence. Ashore, I could revel in her company. Do not concern yourself, Elizabeth, I am no longer sad, for she is forever at my side and oft-times I feel it is her hand that is shielding me from danger." He lifted the pewter to his lips. "Thus I have no regrets."

"Is it your intent to seek a wife?" The Mayor probed.

"Father!" Elizabeth looked up from her work, aghast, cheeks a-blush. "I apologise for my father. Not oft-times is

316

he so rude and I know not what is his motive."

" 'Tis simple, Captain Flemyng."

"Thomas, sir, and Tom to my friends."

"Then I shall call you Tom for, if that is the privilege of friendship, I would wish to claim it."

"I am honoured, sir."

The Mayor waved dismissive hand and once more the pewter jug was raised. "I drink to you in affection, Tom." He looked at his guest's empty jar. "Elizabeth, Captain Flemyng will now drink with me. Pray tell the servant to bring more cyder."

"No, thank you most kindly sir, but this March ale well suits my palate."

"Never be daunted, Tom, try the cyder."

"Forgive me, sir, I crave you excuse me."

"Wisely spoken, Captain Flemyng, for I fear my husband is over generous with his drink to the point of folly, and I fear he has already drunk his fill."

Her husband waved his hand with dismissive air.

"To continue, Tom, my daughter seeks a reason for my enquiry."

Flemyng looked toward Elizabeth, her head lowered in unnecessary concentration, as Cocke filled his jar from out the foaming flagon.

" 'Tis all a matter of breeding." He spoke with the seriousness of the slightly tipsy. "For don't you see, we are but a small country in a world that daily grows with new discoveries. Spain is large. Her people are many, whilst we are few in numbers." He paused to fumble for a kerchief and wipe some froth from out his beard, and then to ponder.

"Pray continue sir."

"New horizons. New colonies. Spain is populating the Americas with her stock. The Portuguee is in Africa, India and perhaps beyond." He leant forward with an earnest expression. " 'Tis for the likes of you, Tom, of good family, both fair in form and feature, to play your part. Of courage there is no doubt. And if your uncle be a guide, not without some semblance of intelligence." He warmed to his theme. " 'Tis for the likes of you, Tom, to breed. Produce sons and daughters of which your country may be proud, lest Spain

317

be let loose to dominate once again." He sat back, drawing upon his pipe, an invitation for Flemyng to respond, but Tom hid his face within his tankard's brim.

"Captain Flemyng," she spoke with some degree of hesitation, "no words of mine can express with due sufficiency my shame and chagrin at my father's thoughts." With pleading she sought his eyes with hers. "Pray will you forgive him and know I do not share his views?"

"My husband has drunk too well of the cyder." Mistress Cocke excused. "But do you not see, it is the pleasure of your company that encourages him in this vein?"

"Vino veritas, Tom. I speak truly. Now daughter the same to you applies. You are of the stuff to breed!"

How wide were her brown eyes. How the blushes enhanced her features. But the Mayor would not be stayed. Again the cyder pot was raised to his moist lips and lowered.

"You are fit and strong and accomplished in the womanly arts."

"I am not of your flock that graze upon the moor. How dare you discuss me so!"

"Husband, please do not embarrass our guest."

"Embarrass my friend Tom? Certainly that was not my intent, eh Tom?"

A pause.

Tom sipped that he might think. "Any views of yours, sir, must be treated with respect."

"Well said, Tom. Pray tell me, when do you expect to return this way?"

"Of that I am uncertain but perhaps a day or two either side of three weeks."

"Then you must bide here awhile, to break your travels and tell us tales of Oxford. Leastways on that the ladies and I agree."

The soft bed eased his aching back. Seamen should ride upon the water, not upon a nag. He had partaken of ale in plenty at the insistence of his host. Yet he was sober, craving for the balm of sleep. He lay back, wide-eyed in the darkness. A vision of Jane conjured in his brain. "Oh God, only You can know how much I miss her company, her merry laugh, her teasing wit." How she had pleasured him beneath the secret canopy of their bed. Had she been bearing him a son or would the child have been a daughter? No point in surmise.

"Lord, I never knew such loneliness." Oft, he would enquire of her advice, that she might answer in his head. She was smiling down upon him, no longer was he alone, she was nodding as to encourage and say 'Yes'. She blew him a kiss. Was it in farewell? Her picture faded from his mind. Then came the image of another. Elizabeth. She of the nimble fingers and the blushing cheeks.

Chapter Twenty

They reined in where the roadway breasted the steep hill, and paused to rest their nags and gaze upon the expanse that stretched below. The lazy sweep of the river that gently flowed between water meadows where fat sheep grazed. A mellow cluster of red brick and flinted cottages, the church and abbey beyond. Behind, gold and rusting in autumn splendour, the beechwoods that climbed the scarp.

The Abbey at Buckland, mist-shrouded moorland home of Drake, had given him cause to wonder. But never had he seen a home such as this. Such magnificence. Had his uncles but realised their temerity. Yet he must not fail.

Pentreath led the horses to the stabling. Tom stood alone, outside the ornate iron-hinged door. Above towered the stepped gables of chalk and rose-red brick. The setting was of peace and tranquillity. The softness of the scene, a contrast. All was contrast with the harshness of the land from whence he had come. The door creaked open, the servant enquired as to the nature of his visit.

Rested and refreshed. He sat with Hoby and related to him the account of the Spanish sacking of Mousehole: of the valiant death of his grandfather, and the need for revenge, lest others be tempted to follow in the footsteps of the traitor, Burley.

How strange, thought Tom, here am I in august company. Haughty portraits looking down in their finery and condescension, yet I am at ease. He voiced his thoughts aloud. "You and I are as opposite as the countryside in which we live. Yet, seemingly we have much in common."

"It is that which separates us that gives depth and interest

320

to our friendship, Tom. When I first set my eyes upon you I realised that here was one of character. One with whom I would wish to forge a friendship. Whilst there is much that is different, there is more that binds. That which distances us gives cause for enquiry."

"So we may learn a viewpoint from another angle."

"Precisely. I daily meet with those who share the same views as me, who have the same education, wear my style of clothes, eat similar dishes, sup like wine, and as such do I reflect their image and their thinking, as they do mirror mine. As a consequence, they bore me! But you, Tom, are the same age as me and a man of rank, but your life bears little semblance to my own. And yet, we see the world the same, albeit sometimes from a different view. But enough of my prattle. What do you propose?"

Tom told him of the brothers' plan, by which Burley would be portrayed as an agent, who served two causes that he might doubly profit.

"The plan is well conceived. But I need time to ponder on how best I can assist, for assist I will, of that you may be content."

Across to where the lazy Thames lapped the dew-drenched lawns, they strolled, side by side, heads down, yet in earnest conversation with the occasional guffaw of friendship renewed.

"The Mayor did not jest, Tom, he spoke in truth. 'Tis time you were wedded once again, a fellow of your years. Why, your manhood is being wasted. Lest you take your pleasures elsewhere, eh Tom?"

"No, I am not inclined to do so, once married to Jane, I had no thought for another."

"Yet now you feel perhaps a need for the companionship of a woman?"

"Aye sometimes, Edward, but in truth 'til now I had thought but little on't."

"The evenings are falling in, the nights are longer now. 'Tis the time of year to bed a maid, Tom!"

"Mayhap, but we neglect the reason for my visit."

"Indeed, Tom. Let me think out loud awhile, since you so readily dismiss my brotherly advice."

321

"I well remember what occurred when you went about disposing of your own unwanted favours!"

"I recall it well and perhaps you do right to ignore me." Edward rubbed his cheekbone in remembrance. "Yet," he wagged his finger at his friend, "you and bachelordom are ill-suited, sir! However, we digress."

They paused in their walk then continued with a serious air.

"Come, Tom, to where we may sit and talk in private and you shall try some tobacco I have but lately acquired and tell me how it suits your palate. 'Tis of the London fashion."

With elegant toe, Edward prodded the glowing logs that straddled the iron dogs. "My uncle is of seventy-five summers and devotes his time and such energy as he has to his estates and to his Queen. His spies are legion and yet," he paused, "he is a man without rancour who sees his duty clearly and simply." He paused. "If I asked him to do as you propose I cannot vouch for his reaction. Can Burley harm her Majesty directly? I doubt it. Does he pose a threat to the realm? Perhaps, but only as agent for the King of Spain and when given a duty to perform."

"For such alone he should be made an example."

"Indeed, but my uncle may regard this as personal revenge which lessens his own dignity. No, Tom. Though there is another whose help I can seek in due course. My cousin will doubtless soon enjoy high office. Albeit the second son, he is sorcerer's apprentice of Lord Burghley. He is well versed in the intrigues of court. Such a proposition would appeal to him."

"Then may I meet with him?"

"Not so hasty." He paused. "This I tell you in great confidence."

His guest nodded in recognition of the honour.

"Our intelligencers report the expedition of Drake and Hawkyns appears ill-fated. The Spaniards are prepared for him. De Brochero, you recall? One time commander of the galleys?"

Flemyng nodded in reply.

"De Brochero prepared and strengthened their defences. Why, a month or more Sir Francis bravely spent at Great

Canary, but was beaten off. I am fearful for the outcome, as are others." A moment as if to consider to what degree he should entrust his friend. "Sir Francis is no longer in his prime," he reflected. "Of some fifty and more years."

"Aye, and there are devils that guard those alien shores that can overcome our English flesh and bones."

"Devils, Tom?"

"In the guise of disease, Edward. In a form that we do not encounter in England, at his age he might succumb."

"Should Sir Francis be thwarted in his expedition it will give heart unto the King of Spain. Together with their successes against our friends in France, there is so much of concern. Then there is the raid upon Mousehole. Compound these factors with the indecision of our Queen as she sways from side to side in the wind of flattery, to favour such courtier as praises her the most." Hoby sighed aloud.

"All this is known to our enemies?"

"So I believe and with Drake adventuring they have a new found confidence that once more breeds designs upon our land."

"Whispers of intelligence waft the way of Mousehole. We glean that the ships of Spain are gathering once more."

"In Cadiz?"

"So we have heard."

The seated Hoby leant toward his guest. "Whilst the Queen is the receiver of much contrary advice, when the time is crucial she will, I am sure, follow her instincts and those she trusts the most."

"So what is to do?"

" 'Tis the desire of the High Admiral that we should strike at Spain before once more they strike at us. Attack their ships 'ere they leave port. My Lord Essex holds likewise. Yet . . . ."

"Yet?"

"Yet I am troubled that there are those in high office who oppose such a ploy. Who hold that with Drake abroad and our navy at sea, our coast would be left naked and unprotected. They would contend that the raid upon Cornwall was but a rehearsal and forerunner of a greater expedition upon our shores. That with knowledge gained

323

Spain would muster another Armada, not to venture into the trap of our narrow seas, but to land in Ireland or upon our western shores. That is the dilemma." He paused and in solemn voice said, "My uncle adopts this latter view, for he is old and overly cautious, and no friend of Essex and the Lord Admiral, who propose the other course."

"And of you, Edward, what is your opinion?"

"That," he spoke in tones of intensity, "that we should strike and strike hard, sir! Land our own invading force and acquaint the world that we will suffer no threat to our independence lest we become the thrall of Spain. Twice armed is he whose blow is just, thrice armed is he who makes first thrust!"

"May God be praised! I and others like me are with you Edward. Let us prove that their defeat was not as they would claim, by freakish chance of weather."

"Aye and England has other sons blessed with courage and seamanship anxious for the chance to prove themselves in war."

"Yet will your views prevail?"

"Yes, even now my Lord Burghley begins to waver in his view."

Each sat back, to puff their pipes awhile in quiet meditation.

"Then what is to do, Edward? Is my journey in vain? Shall my grandfather's murderer go unpunished?"

"No, Tom, never! This is my advice." He rose to pace the room. "Our need is for a spur to convince those that falter, we should attack Cadiz. Garner such intelligence as you may on the preparedness of Spain. Ensure such news you glean is well sourced and founded, not tittle tattle or conjecture. Then deliver it to me by post from Plymouth. Not Mousehole. For beware of spies. Then from me to my coz, Robert Cecyll. Thus may he know direct the debt we have to Keigwin and to Flemyng, and is thereby obligated."

"But this will take time."

"Perhaps until the spring, or even later for we are the wrong side of winter and no one will dare venture the seas to Spain direct."

"Yet my uncles will still trade across the narrower

waters."

"And thus may gather news of Ireland or of France, for such an Armada will needs link with an anchorage on a friendly shore."

"Whilst Burley still goes free."

"Patience my friend, for your plot is worthy of the master himself and as a consequence we should follow his advice."

"Which master, I pray and what advice?"

"Machiavelli, the Florentine, for are we not similar in some small respect?"

"How do you perceive that to be?"

"Why, he was a patriot, as are we."

"And?"

"No lover of the Jesuit."

"But neither of us would advocate the treachery that he proposed."

"That is true, but oft-times he would contend the end justifies the means."

"The betrayal of one's friends can never be justified. There is always another way to achieve the end."

"One cannot be precise in the absence of circumstance."

"There speaks the devious voice of politics."

"Tom, I welcome the time when we can debate this more fully. How did we commence upon this discourse?"

"The advice of Machiavelli."

"He would advocate we plan and bide our time delighting in the knowledge that vengeance will one day be ours; whilst our unwitting victim rests in false comfort, knowing not of our designs. As to Burley, his deeds will dim to but a petty greatness, and less gratitude will be afforded him. For, Tom, in truth it is revenge you seek. And as the Master once declared, 'it is a dish best served cold'."

"I shall return, my good friend, and so remind my uncles whilst they gather such well-found evidence as they may."

"Then we shall convince. Cecyll will be persuaded to thank Burley for his assistance, being the evidence that Richard and Martin have gathered."

"That," Tom slapped his knee, "has a certain irony that will cause Squire Keigwin to chuckle in his grave."

"It will appeal to Cecyll also for he has humour in abun-

325

dance and the wit of it will add a relish to the dish."

The two rose to their feet.

"Then it is agreed, Tom. The sons of Keigwin have been dealt the hand, I merely suggest the manner it should be played. That way, we win the trick!" He placed his hand upon the shoulder of his friend. "One further piece I proffer."

"Pray what may that be?"

"Return by Bodmin. Has this Cocke any other chick?"

"Elizabeth is all the brood so far I know."

"Then pluck him, sir, wed the maid and, I vow, you will never want!"

This life of ease suited him. Leastways for a while. Forty crowns a month was his reward, never could he receive such recompense in England. Soon it would be November. Days of rain in Melcombe Regis. The contrast. In Lisbon was bright sunshine and warmth. Light and shadow. No dull days of England in the bright colours of his adopted land. Darkness and light, the drab and the vivid. Contrasts that reflected the ups and downs of his life. Now he was secure, basking in the favour of his King, with confidence might he plan his life ahead. But in the cool of the day he must still make to the new found fencing school, there to practise, that neither his sword nor his skills should rust.

Clouds were draped low above the moorland lending murk to the early dusk. Fine rain dripped from jerkin and from cape as the two horsemen leant into the westerly wind.

Pentreath broke the silence: "My crotch is so soaked, Captain, my organ is fearful lest the gribble worm start a'boring."

"When we make safe anchorage, dip it in boiling pitch that it may be sheathed, safe from attack."

The seaman bent his head low above his groan. "Do you hear my faithful friend?" he whispered confidentially, yet that his captain too might hear. "Well have you served me and this I vow, if sheathed you must be, it will be in sweeter, softer bed than boiling tar!" He looked up at Flemyng. "Aye,

326

and I pray the time is soon!"

The grin slid from Tom's face, his nostrils flared, as the rough road dipped into a combe, where a ribbon of bent trees straddled the road. "I smell woodsmoke." His nose again wrinkled. "And I smell treachery."

"Draw swords Captain?"

"Aye, silently as shall not be seen nor heard. Be ready to loose the pack horse." He leant further over the withers, his eyes peering from under raised brows.

"Footpads?"

"The Lord only knows."

"Then let me address them, Captain, for your voice will betray your rank and give them an appetite for booty."

Near through the woodland, a figure stepped from the shelter of the trees to grasp the bridle of Pentreath and halt the mount. In whingeing tones it spoke with other palm thrust out.

"Spare a groat for a party of starving seamen, now cast adrift. Have pity on us."

Shadows rose from out the gloom.

"What kind of seamen be you to waylay me thus?" replied the gruff tones of Cornwall.

"Those whose duty done, have naught to feed their children!"

"With whom did you serve?"

"Why, Sir Francis himself."

"You lie in your beard!"

"Have them . . . " The words ended in a moan and knees buckled as the heel of the sword crashed down upon stockinged head.

Sharply Pentreath jerked the left rein to turn his mount, as with backward beat he parried a thrust, to slash in return with a swing to near sever his assailant's head, as his steed came round, that flank to flank he might guard his captain's back.

Flemyng rowelled blood deep, his mount plunged forward to lend weight to the rapier thrust that pierced the yielding rib-cage half way to the hilt. A musket clattered to the bouldered earth as back the body fell releasing the bloodied blade. Two men dodged between the oaks, running from the fray. The pack-horse regained, they trotted tired horses to mount the rising ground.

Safe within the bounds of Bodmin town they clattered beneath the archway into the stableyard.

" 'Tis we that look as vagabonds, soaked thus in wet and blood."

"Aye, Captain, thank God 'tis His rain and their blood."

The sound of hooves upon cobbles. A whicker of greeting from another stabled. A lantern shone, as the household of Thomas Cocke was alerted to their visitors. Bolts were slid and the door flung wide, for a light to glow dimly to give direction.

"Greeting, Tom, more so on such foul an evening." He grasped his visitor by the hand. "Welcome to our home, sir, welcome. Ladies!" He turned his head to call within: "Captain Flemyng is arrived." He turned back to the yard-lad, "Ensure the nags well tended." And, as Pentreath appeared, "See the serving maid gives you victuals and a cot on which to lie, for you are indeed wet and doubtless famished. Look to him well, Sarah."

Flemyng caught the wink, the smile, the whispered words of his compatriot, "With fortune I will keep that promise, and sooner than I thought." As the housemaid led him on his way.

In the excitement of his pleasure he eased his guest toward an inner hall that opened to a drawing-room, where from the high ceiling the brightness of a wrought-iron candelabrum lighted hanging tapestries and the rich carpets strewn beneath. The ladies rose from stuffed chairs beside where logs blazed within the open fire.

"Mistress Cocke, Mistress Elizabeth." He bowed for each to curtsey in return. "A thousand apologies for my appearance. Pray," he turned to Cocke, "may I retire to make myself presentable?"

"First, warm yourself before the fire whilst your bedchamber is made ready. Your cloak, sir." Cocke reached to remove the garment. "By Jupiter! Muddied and bloodied, and that newly spilt."

"Ladies be not alarmed."

Elizabeth had caught his broad hand in hers, and wide of

328

eye and pale of face looked at him close, in unfeigned concern.

"Pray God you are not harmed, Tom?"

Why was he pleased at her familiar tone? "Nay, mistress," he smiled to dispel her fear and hold both hands in his own. "Pentreath was my protector."

"And God."

"Aye, mistress," softly, "and God. For surely it was by His design that we have met and meet again."

An afternoon in the February of 1596

"He is a bonny child." It was the turn of his aunt, Elizabeth, to hold him and dance the babe upon her lap. "What name is decided for him?"

His mother looked toward Thomasine. "We had wondered what of Jenkyn, but 'tis too soon, so let his name remain his solely, and be recalled by a later line."

"Besides, Richard daily grows in the likeness of his father, both in manner and in countenance."

"Aye, Elizabeth," she laughed, "in girth as well."

That caused all three to titter.

"There is already a Thomas, after Thomasine."

Thomasine smiled, pleased that she had not been overlooked, but nodded to agree.

"And so he is to be called after his godfather."

"And pray, who will that be?"

"Why, his Uncle Martin has agreed."

"Martin."

Thomasine and daughter smiled approval.

"And is there to be another?"

"Upon his return, we shall ask Tom to be so."

"He will be proud to play the part for such a bright and healthy soul as you. Won't he my little beauty?"

"Tom should, please God, be safely home within the week."

The door opened and Becky peeked around and entered. "Excuse me, mistress, 'tis time the young master had his rest."

"You cluck like an old hen about your chicks."

" 'Tis well I do, mistress, then no harm will befall."

His old habits still held fast. Instead of the father, it was the son he visited, on the same week-day as before. But now there was no market, no voices crying out their wares as through the ravaged town the money-lender wound his way.

Within the room Richard and Martin were informed of his arrival. "Welcome, Solomon, welcome old friend. Sit yourself upon your favoured chair." Richard looked intently at his guest. "But pray, why so doleful? Do you shoulder the woes of all the world?"

"I am the bearer of sad news. Unless you have already heard?"

"What news?" asked Richard.

"Sir Francis, aye, aye," he shook his head slowly, from side to side, "and Sir John Hawkyns too."

"Drake and Hawkyns? We have long been fearful for their venture, but tell me what, Master Fernandes?"

Solomon seated with a sigh to lean forward on the chair's edge. "Sir Francis, taken by fever, dead!"

"Dead!" Martin repeated in surprise.

"And John Hawkyns claimed by a pestilence."

"Dead as well?" questioned Richard.

"He was the first to go."

"Is your intelligence from a source upon which we may depend?"

"Were it otherwise I would not tell the tale."

"Tom told us their adventure was forewarned and was faring ill, but Drake and John Hawkyns both lost to us!" Martin shook his head in disbelief.

"Aye, and Clifford too! You recall it was he that came to aid us at Marazion. Killed whilst in the cabin of the Admiral, at supper. By a Spanish ball fired from a battery ashore," said Solomon.

"This will lend heart unto the enemies of the Crown."

"So I am afeared, Master Martin, but there is more."

"You had best tell us all."

"The wars in France bode ill for their King. Despite our aid Henry of Navarre derives no great advantage against the

330

Spaniard."

"Aye, so have we learned." said Richard.

"Yet, son of my friend, this is what I have been newly told. In the Netherlands the Archduke Albert is intent on raising a great army," he whispered intently. "He will portray that as being for another purpose, then will feint, to march on Calais."

Richard rose to his feet. "You know this for certain, Solomon?"

"When soldiers go to war for a foreign cause, their loyalty must needs be bought. Where money has to pass, those of my kind are oft-times the instrument by which it is achieved. Yet, we keep our silence, that so we may be trusted, and seek not to know the reason. In this instance my cousin discovered the truth and, worried for my welfare and for trade, shared his secret with me, that I might return to Spain in safety."

"Are others privy to this intelligence?"

His black eyes glowed with an inner fire. "No, I share it only with you that you may use it as you will. You sought intelligence of Ireland and of France. Mayhap it will help to avenge your father, and if so, then I have repaid some small portion of my debt to him who made a friend of a Jew." He wagged a slender finger. "Pass on this intelligence. If it comes from you, it will gather credence Richard Keigwin. For it is the truth I swear. Pass it to whomsoever will use it to advantage. Dwell on't. An Armada once again, if it should but link with Calais." He shook his head in dismay. "Drake is lost, as too is Hawkyns. With Calais taken!" He buried his dark head in his fine hands.

"Forgive us old friend if we quiz you further." Martin glanced at Richard for approval. "For we must have all such detail as you can give."

An April morning. Arm in arm, earnest in conversation, across the high Hoe they strolled. Beneath, in the calm waters of the Sound, merchantmen left a wake upon the water as they made for the open sea. Behind, in the sanctuary of the Hamoaze, the gathering fleet were fed by a flotilla of little

331

boats plying to and fro, to lade their sisters with victuals and with ordnance.

"I have witnessed such as this before."

"Aye, Tom, but now it is we who shall attack, and thanks be to God have had time in which to prepare the action we shall take."

They watched the scene awhile in silence.

"It was the letter that was the trump. Cecyll had spies that hinted, but none was certain until Richard Keigwin wrote. I was quizzed as if it were the Inquisition." He laughed with a snort as he recalled. "Yet 'twas the detail gave authority to the missive, and I could vouch for the integrity of the sender."

"And as consequence," Tom spoke as together they turned to retrace their steps, "we sail against Spain."

"Aye, and with a vengeance. One hundred and fifty sail, so Lord Howard says."

"And Essex?"

"Why, fourteen thousand of our soldiers are his to command!"

"But what of the ensnaring of Burley?"

"I have his word."

"Of Cecyll?"

"Aye, of Sir Robert. But much will depend upon this venture."

"Why?"

"It is his intent to praise Burley for intelligence he gave for this mission and dependent upon the size of the victory, the size of praise that may be heaped upon the traitor's head."

"The greater the victory, the greater the praise, the greater the punishment!"

With a smile Hoby nodded. "Machiavelli would indeed envy such a plot!"

"On the morrow Martin is proposed to join me aboard the *Charles*. We would welcome you to dine with us."

"That will be my pleasure, and to relate to him of what is proposed?"

"Yes, God willing, he is to deliver the letter."

"That is to be encased in a code so feeble, even a child might break the cipher."

"And all will come to be with the aid of a Jew who loved

332

my grandfather."

"And of love," he said with sly smile, "pray tell me, Tom, what of love?"

"I fail to comprehend," Tom replied with puzzled air.

"Do not play the simpleton, Tom, it doesn't suit. Tell your friend how fared you with the maid?" He poked his companion as they walked. "And what of her father, that man of substance?"

A flush of colour now tinged his cheek. "I admit to finding pleasure in her company."

"And she?" he prompted.

"Seemingly is likewise."

"She gives you pleasure does she?"

"And what of it?"

"So she is well practised between the covers?"

"Buffoon, she is a pure maid, not one of your brainless harlots of the Court that do aught else save spread gossip and the pox. Besides, I have yet to be left alone with her."

"Sometimes, Tom," he shook his head and uttered a mournful sigh, "I truly do despair of you. Methinks you would wed her before you bed her."

"In truth I would," he answered with asperity.

"Then I must suppose you would pay good silver for a nag before you rode it?"

"Mine are the ways of the country," he mumbled, "whilst yours the way of the Court."

"And, pray God, never the twain shall meet."

Chapter Twenty-one

June 1596. Thomasine sat where oft-times her husband had sat, which was now her favoured place. The great fire kept her warm in winter and in summer the window commanded a view of the sweep of the bay.

"Would that his grandfather might see him."

"Oft-times I pray he does."

He had pulled himself by her skirts and now was clinging to her knee.

"He would be so proud." She looked lovingly down and held her grandson's tiny hand.

"Come to me my robin." He turned his head to where Becky knelt, her arms outstretched and took his first tottering steps as Elizabeth silently clapped his progress.

August. Daybreak. Richard yawned to rise from his knees. His devotions completed in accord with his morning ritual, he turned to the window, splattered with the soft rain of the night that now was clearing; a band of blue streaked the western sky.

Without the harbour wall within the island shelter, a ship at anchor. His practised eye noted her lines and set of rig. A longboat lay alongside into which figures were now clambering.

"Elizabeth," he said softly, then louder, "Elizabeth. Stir yourself. See!" He pointed to the man-of-war.

Quickly donning his morning garb and with a dignity retained, he hurried to the quay, to embrace Martin and Tom in turn.

Arm in arm to the Manor they returned.

"Becky, when my mother wakens, tell her who has arrived, and bid my wife to join us."

Up the great staircase to the cool of the drawing-room where the family listened as Tom and Martin vied with each other in the telling of the tale.

" . . . from fort and battlement their cannon blazed, yet on we sailed returning fire with fire, I shall forever recall those Cornish cheers as our shot struck home."

"And then within the harbour where their great galleons towered, fifteen there lay. We raked them with our broadsides and tumbled their yardsmen from the rigging lest they loose their sails and flee."

"So Mousehole was avenged." Richard sighed with relief.

"Avenged? And to spare, for that is but the part of it. Why, we took three of their finest ships to plunder and fired some further fifty."

"Fifty? Surely not so many?"

"Brother, fifty I tell you, but there is even more. When by midday our battle was won, our Lord Essex landed part of his soldiery."

"We watched from the harbour, such a blaze as was never seen before."

"The following day, the island fortress was perforce to surrender and all wealth abandoned to us."

"Their people to pay 12,000 crowns for their lives!"

"Aye, how we looted, how we burned on the anniversary of our own pillage, and cried aloud 'Remember Mousehole!' Such was the victory Essex would have remained to take all Andalusia.

"Aye and would have done so, but was over-ruled and had to be content with the razing of the city and the fortress."

"Yes, but the reckoning of their loss beggared all belief, for in total it was 20,000,000 ducats."

"May God be praised for such a victory."

"Aye and we shall share in the bounty with which He has rewarded us!"

"Now I am content your father is avenged." Thomasine spoke calmly. "But what of the churches? Did you also avenge our loss?"

335

"No, Mother," Martin's voice was serious, "for we were ordered to be merciful. Essex would suffer neither insult nor injury to people or to church. We were implored not to demean our mission by undue wantonness."

"Thanks be to God." Thomasine nodded her satisfaction. "It is well we do not follow the example Burley set."

"And what of Burley, Richard?"

"In your absence Robert Cecyll is made Secretary of State, as Hoby rightly foretold. I am assured the letter will be writ for Martin to deliver, thanking Burley for the intelligence he gave that enabled us to take Cadiz."

"For what purpose is this letter I pray?"

"Mother," Richard solemnly replied, "the time has come when you, and Becky also," he cast his eyes toward her, "may be privy to our secret. But secret it must be, else all is for nought and the life of Martin put at risk. For we have plotted further that my father, Teek, Jacob and John Pearce also, may rest in peace within their graves, our duty to them complete." And he told of what they had agreed.

"Now, enough of this maudlin talk, eh Mother?" Tom refreshed his glass. "Becky, fetch more wine and beer that we may celebrate the success of Cadiz and a safe homecoming. Let Mary bear such comestibles as will suit! Now do I propose a long life and all success to my godchild. Let us drink a bumper to him!"

"Well said, Tom," as glasses were raised.

"May my namesake be as wise and brave as me!" Martin spoke.

"Humph. Wise? Never. Brave?" Richard laughed, "Nay, foolhardy mayhap. I prophesy he is cast in the mould of me, his father, and is therefore destined for great achievements." He bent to lift the child from his mother to hold him in the crook of his left arm.

"Ah, see how he attempts to steal my ale." Tom stood close. "He is indeed a true Keigwin!"

"Silence, Tom. Tell me, husband, what else do you prophesy?" Elizabeth made jocose enquiry.

"Ah, the same Celtic blood that flowed in the veins of Merlyn runs also in mine own. If that ancient sorcerer can prophesy then so may I. Now listen with care, whilst I,

Richard Keigwin, foretell what is to be. As surely as my son grows, so will the fortunes of the family of Keigwin, aided by my brother and myself, eh Martin?" He placed the goblet arm about his brother. "Also we shall ensure that Richard Burley is sorely punished for his misdeeds: and, with God's help we shall secure the Keigwin line that it may flourish." He drank, that Mary might replenish.

"And what of me, Uncle, what of my life, my future?"

"Ha!"

He addressed the laughing family.

"As for this rascally pirate, let me ponder awhile." He raised his head to still the merriment, and in earnest voice continued, "In God's own time the wounds of your sorrow will be healed. Aye," he chortled that jollity might return, "and once again you will lose your freedom, trapped in the snare of matrimony by the maid of your choice, that under her loving influence you will give up your life of adventure."

"Perish such dull thought."

"Pray be silent whilst I continue." In serious voice. "Loved by your wife and surrounded by your many children you will lead a goodly and prosperous life, dedicated to justice and the call of duty."

He held his goblet high and drank a draught in smiling salute.

And as Richard Keigwin prophesied, so it came to be.

P

POSTSCRIPT

And what of the cast of this story?

The battle scars of the Manor have been concealed by subsequent extensions. Upon a granite plinth within sits the large cannonball that has been handed down from generation to generation, since it is this ball that is believed to have killed Squire Keigwin. By its side is another, smaller rust-encrusted cannonball, found in 1984 during restoration. It was buried some eighteen inches below the old floor and at the foot of the staircase.

Thomasine Keigwin, matriarch of Mousehole, dedicated her life to her family, the needy, and her church. Richard and Martin applied themselves to trade and to scholarship as their father had before them. Their large families would seem to have inherited those same facets of this character that epitomised their father. Fear of God; duty to sovereign and country; service to ones fellow men; courage in adversity. These were the precepts by which Jenkyn Keigwin lived and died, and that are to this day inherited by his heirs.

And of Thomas Flemyng? His life of adventure was to continue awhile, for in 1598 John Watts invited him to take command of his man-o'-war, the 120 ton *Affection*, to sail with the fleet of the Earl of Cumberland and pillage the Spanish main. On the 6th March they left Plymouth and plundered the Canaries, and thence to Puerto Rico, taking San Juan. Flemyng was to return with prizes and booty of £16,000.

The traitor Burley was restored to favour after undergoing torture when he was found to be innocent of the complicity with England that Cecyll had suggested. Burning with bitter-

338

ness, he commanded seven thousand, five hundred Spanish soldiers in October that same year of 1598, sailing aboard an Armada of eighty-six ships intent to put Falmouth to the sword. Once again the weather of those western waters came to our aid and scattered the Spanish fleet without shot being fired.

Was it merely coincidence that in 1599 Sir Robert Cecyll purchased St. Michael's Mount from Queen Elizabeth?

Don Diego Brochero, he who had persuaded his King to unleash the galleys upon Mousehole, before voyaging to the Spanish colonies to successfully prepare them to repulse Drake and Hawkyns, what of him? In 1601, he commanded a fleet of thirty-three ships that landed a force of 5,000 men in Kinsale, and in December of that year an English squadron fought its way into the harbour, a great battle ensued and all the enemy shipping at Kinsale was destroyed or sunk. In command of a man-o'-war was Thomas Flemyng, once again avenging Mousehole. The rebellion itself was crushed by the land forces of Lord Mountjoy.

The following year in recognition of his services to the Crown, Flemyng was given command of the *Merlin* and appointed Admiral in the West. But all that is another story.

Now Flemyng lies buried in his beautiful Parish church at Madron, with Elizabeth his wife. In the south-east corner, an incised slate tablet bears silent testimony to their being. Their figures are inscribed below those of Thomas and Alice Cocke. He who once was Mayor of Bodmin. Elizabeth holds an open book, perhaps to symbolise her knowledge, whilst Thomas wears an ornamental purse and a short but empty scabbard. At his side is a Justices' staff. Surely these accoutrements are intended to symbolise the man. The purse for charity, the scabbard bereft of sword, to confirm his days of adventuring were ended. The staff to remind us that he served the cause of justice. Beneath them are the figures of their ten children.

There is another slate tablet. The Epitaph to Thomas Flemyng, Gentleman; the last lines of which conclude thus:

'His neighbours soldiers Kinsman and ech one,
Doe deck his herse with sadness mournful mone.

Saying Hees gone whome we must needs commend
A true peace maker and a faithful friend.
Beloved of all not hated once whose pure
And good report for ever shall endure.
Concludinge thus his soule to Heaven did fly.
That well did live and ended gloriously.'

No mean epitaph for a pirate!

And Mousehole, ancient port and market town? The carnage and destruction wrought upon her was so complete that her days of market, fair and feast were lost forever.

Other harbours and towns seized upon her vulnerability and adversity to their advantage, assuming her trade and industry. Under the watchful eyes and influence of the family of Keigwin, gradually Mousehole was rebuilt into the higgledy piggledy, enchanting town of today. A town that the pace and stress of modern life has kindly passed. Where there is still a time to dream. To lean with others upon the harbour rail and gaze over St. Clement's Isle to the distant Lizard Head. To reflect upon this proud community of fishing and flowers, to whom grief and hardship come not as strangers. To walk the streets where the Captains walked, abreast, the length of the deck, then turn about with rolling seawise tread.

Thus it was that Mousehole became the ultimate beneficiary. Her people jealously preserve their heritage and way of life, innate possessors of the importance of their history, determined that the simple unadorned beauty of this working village shall remain unsullied by the trappings of greed that in the name of progress so hideously adorn the sea fronts and harbours of those less fortunate communities.

In the warm uncluttered days of autumn we sit upon the quayside bench. Willie and Alan, Cyril and me. I listen to the tales of the sea and meadow I have oft-times heard before. Of storms and disasters. Of chill wind on the trumpet and red spider on the violet.

Here, one has time. Time to gossip. Time to care.

HISTORICAL NOTES

Since a full year cannot be divided precisely, small discrepancies of minutes and hours accumulate until by the 16th century the Spring Equinox occurred ten days earlier than at the time of the Council of Nice in 325 AD. In March 1582 Pope Gregory XIII sought to resolve the irregularities in the calendar by scientific reconciliation, calling for the advancement of existing dates by ten days whereby certain leap years became common years.

A Papal Bull was issued to this effect and the New Calendar was immediately adopted by Spain, Portugal, parts of Italy and later that year by France and the Low Countries. English Protestants, suspicious of, and inflamed by, any edict that emanated from Rome, believed this to be a Papal ploy to steal ten days of their lives, and refused to comply. Scotland adopted the new reckoning in 1600 but it was not until 1751 that the English parliament passed the Act 'for regulating the commencement of the year and for correcting the calendar now in use' which brought conformity of the English calendar with that of neighbouring countries.

In an endeavour to simplify the dates recorded by the protagonists I have used the Gregorian calendar in use today. Being ten days in advance of those dates mentioned in English manuscripts of that time.

In a charter of 1292 the town is referred to as Mosehole, and in 1414 Bishop Stafford exhorted all persons within the diocese to aid an appeal to rebuild the chapel of Mosal. This is not to be confused with the chapel that sat somewhat precariously upon the guardian island of St. Clements, depicted in paintings of the period, and in 1540 was described by Leland as 'a Lytle Low Island With A Chapel Yn yt.'

Mousehole was a port and commercial centre of considerable importance in the Middle Ages. One of the western ports to which Letters Close were addressed for summoning ships to augment the fleet, for regulating imports and exports, and for searching vessels for letters prejudicial to the authority of the Crown. Furthermore

341

it supplied the courts with suits involving claims for the restitution of the goods of plundered vessels.

One cannot but think it could well be this authority that might have given credence to the subsequent actions of Thomas Flemyng.

Such was the consequence of Mousehole that it was granted both a Tuesday and Thursday market and two annual fairs, being on the vigil of St. Barnabas and for six days on the vigil of St. Bartholomew.

Penzance was but a village at this time and I have used the spelling 'Pensans' in the form of Carew. Marazion or Thursday's Market, was then named 'Marcaiew' or 'Marhas Diow', that seemed too obscure from the present-day spelling to use in the text.

The Elizabethans were a demonstrative people and given to displays of affection and anger, as I have endeavoured to portray.

Chapter One

I have endeavoured to construct the characters in this story from such knowledge that one can glean including their wills and inventories of their chattels. The spelling of names often varies, but I have spelt Flemyng in the manner of the man himself.

The principal bankers of the time were of Italian and Jewish origin. A merchant 'A' wished to make a payment to a trader 'B' in a distant town or country. A local firm 'AA' had an account with a firm 'BB' in that same town or country. At 'A's' request 'AA' would write an order, being the bill of exchange to 'BB', authorising payment from 'BB' to 'B'. In this manner would 'A' pay and 'B' collect. In time these bills were to become a form of currency in themselves, traded at discounted prices, whilst delays in transportation meant that such transactions also could become a temporary loan upon which interest was charged.

The report of John Donne of January 2, 1581, and his betrayal by Burley, is broadly as I have recorded, albeit there is no record of any part played by Richard Keigwin.

The *Golden Hind* is sometimes referred to as 'Bark Flemyng', also she is sometimes called a pinnace — a term usually reserved for a smaller vessel. However, pinnace is derived from the Latin, pinus, or pine. Thus she may have been a barque built of pine or spruce. She would certainly have been fast and handy. She was of fifty tons and was armed with cannon and carried a crew of thirty.

The *Hope of Newhaven* was a hoy, being a merchantman of eighty tons and often used for carrying passengers, whilst Newhaven is now the French port of Le Havre. It was from Newhaven that William Wollartone reported to Robert Cecyll that books for Mass, printed in Rouen, were sent to Ireland.

Chapter Two

The prayer is the short prayer to be said before a fight at sea.

Oaths were a form of expression often used to denote a person's calling. Scholars used scholarly oaths such as 'By Jove' to advertise their learning. Priests would invoke the saints, and soldiers would employ blood-curdling language.

The Topcliffe to whom Martin Keigwin refers was the licensed torturer of the Privy Council. Many English Jesuits bore his attentions with remarkable courage in a ritual of martyrdom.

The Jesuit priest Robert Parsons (sometimes named Persons) had three printing presses at Rouen, producing books for Mass and inflammatory tracts. Since Newhaven was the port that serviced Rouen I have made various assumptions which are incorporated in the story. It would not be unreasonable to suppose that the *Hope* could be carrying such as these to inflame the Irish, since this truly did happen. It was three years later that John Snowden provided Lord Burghley with the intelligence that: 'No sooner shall he (The King of Spain) land an army in England, that swarms of people of all degrees will leap out to assist him; for Parsons has published in a book that there are 3,000 or 4,000 professed Catholics in England who are wonderfully affectionate towards the Spaniards. . .'

Dr William Allen, Fellow of Oriel College Oxford, Principal of St. Mary's Hall, a devout follower of Rome, finally left England in 1565 never to return. Receiving priests' orders in 1567 he founded an English College at Douai in France, of which the principal aim was to preserve the Catholic faith in England. To this seminary came young men, students and soldiers of Catholic tendencies, who would return to England pledged to undermine the Protestant cause. It is conceivable, even likely, that Burley was one of their number.

In 1587, Allen was created a Cardinal. At this time he signed the 'Admonition to the People of England', in which he declared Elizabeth to be deposed and encouraged the Catholics to take up arms that she be overthrown. It was intended that he would return to England where he would represent the Pope and it was about the time the *Hope* was taken that the Pope's legate was placed in England, in anticipation of a successful invasion.

In August of 1588, the Lord Admiral Howard, himself a Roman Catholic, complained to Lord Burghley against the town of Newhaven: 'It is a great dishonour, so much favour is shown to that town, which is at the devotion of Her Majesty's greatest enemy, the Duke of Guise.' Since this letter also contained mention of Thomas Flemyng might not Flemyng himself have occasioned this complaint as a consequence of his discoveries?

Chapter Three

Drake and Hawkyns were cousins. Flemyng was related to Hawkyns through the latter's wife Katherine, daughter of Benjamin Gonson, treasurer of the navy, as was his father before. Thus there is every likelihood that Flemyng would have known Drake personally.

The Flemyng family were obviously people of some consequence. They had their own coat of arms, as did Keigwin and whilst they came from Munster, Southern Ireland, they had been granted by Queen Elizabeth the Advowson and Landithy, their Manor home; where Nicholas Flemyng, father of Thomas, son-in-law of Jenkyn Keigwin, was also a Justice. Sadly the Manor has long since gone, being replaced by a farmhouse of that name. The courtyard became a farmyard in which modern stone houses have been built. But one can still see traces of the quoins and granite stones that would have formed part of the original house.

On the 7th June 1588 the Privy Council issued 'An open placard of assistance, to all Vice Admirals, Mayaurs, etc . . . for th' apprehending of Thomas Flemyng and the searching and enquiring after anie goodes and merchandize taken out of a hoy called the Hope, of 80 tonnes or thereabautes, apperteyning to Thomas Nicholls of Newhaven.'

John Smith, that extraordinary soldier adventurer and founding father of Virginia was also an acquaintance of Sir Richard Grenville. It will be recalled, incidentally, that his life was saved on two occasions by Pocohantas the beautiful Red Indian princess. Smith records that Flemyng was 'as much sought for as any pirate of the Queen's reign'.

Invisible ink and highly complicated ciphers were often used in the composition of secret messages. As every schoolboy knows the ink I have described is quite effective and together with the cipher I have mentioned, was, I believe, in use at that time.

344

Chapter Four

Monson, later Admiral Sir William, was at the time a young lieutenant aboard the *Charles*, and in his Naval Tracts of 1588 records:

'The first land they (the Armada) fell in with was The Lizard which they took to be Rams head athwart Plymouth and the night being at hand they tacked out to sea making account in the morning to attempt our ships at Plymouth. But whilst they were thus deceived in the Land, they were in the meantime discovered by Capt. Flemyng a Pirate who had been pilfering and upon view of them, knowing them to be the Spanish fleet, repair'd with all speed to Plymouth and gave notice to our fleet then riding at anchor.'

The Spanish version is somewhat different.

In his report of August 28th to Lord Burghley, Admiral Lord Howard also reminds us that 'The first discoverer of the Spanish Fleet was Thom. Flemyng only'.

It is also recorded that on June 20th, a bark of Mousehole encountered 'nine sail of great ships between Scilly and Ushant, bearing northeast . . . their sails were all crossed over with a red cross.' Godolphin sent this intelligence to the Lord Admiral. It would seem that the bark had spoken to a French ship at sea, that had seen the Spanish ships and talked to them, and also to some Englishmen aboard.

Edward Palmer later wrote to Walsingham: 'Many English rebels went in the fleet and amongst others, Richard Burley.' His name is also recorded in Spanish state papers as being amongst the few Englishmen that sailed with the Armada.

Other reports indicate that the Armada was widely scattered by storms, and the Andalusian Squadron was the first to be sighted by Flemyng, sheltering off the Scillies, and a Richard Brierley (surely a corruption of Burley) was indeed aboard their flagship, the *Rosario*, as was Stucley (an English pilot) and four other Englishmen.

The nonchalant call by Drake to continue with the game of bowls is not recorded until 1624, but would have been in keeping with his character.

The weather is well documented, and I have endeavoured to portray accurately the scene, the conditions and the strategy of the English and Spanish fleets as they are recorded to have happened.

The name Skillywidden that was to be given to the puppy is the name of certain mischievous Cornish sprites. Whilst at sea the mention of an animal, especially a four-legged creature, was believed to be unlucky.

345

Chapter Five

I have endeavoured to give an eye-witness account of the manner in which the battle was waged as portrayed from the view of both Spaniard and Englishman, together with the ships involved, and where appropriate, the damage they suffered and the manner in which it was obtained.

Burley, Stucley and others were transhipped from the *Rosario* to the Flagship as I have described. The *Rosario* was taken by Drake, who forsook leadership of his squadron at night in order to do so. Had he not been so successful he would doubtless have been severely reprimanded. The *Rosario* was believed to be carrying some 52,000 ducats and much plate and private treasure belonging to the noblemen aboard, who were themselves valuable as ransom.

This action of Drake's so angered the piratical Martin Frobisher, the no-nonsense Yorkshireman, knighted during the Armada campaign, that he addressed one of Drake's officers, Mathew Starke as follows: 'Sir Francis Drake reporteth that no man has done any good service but he . . . then like a coward, he kept by her all night, because he would have the spoil. He thinketh to cozen us of our shares of fifteen thousand ducats, but we will have our shares, or I will make him spend the best blood in his belly.'

The Englishmen who remained aboard the *Rosario* were hanged.

Don Pedro de Valdes, however, spent agreeable years as Drake's prisoner. He was held in such esteem that when he was ransomed for 3,000 ducats and exchanged for an English prisoner, Edward Wynter, of a well regarded family, the Lord Mayor of London gave a banquet in his honour.

Drake protested against Frobisher to Lord Howard, who reported: 'Account of the money taken out of the ship of Don Pedro by Drake, of which he himself had received 3,000 pistolets, for he had not 3L left in the world. Energetically protests he had not one crown more.' This is the note of the money Sir Francis Drake found on board the ship of Don Pedro, with the appropriation of certain sums out of it, signed by Howard and Drake.

The *San Salvador* and the taking of her and the involvement of Thomas Flemyng was broadly as I have described. Lord Howard records: 'The stink in the ship was so unsavoury and the sight within board so ugly, that they (Hawkyns and Lord Thomas Howard) shortly departed.'

The *Bark Flemyng* was ordered by Hawkyns to take her in tow and

I have recounted how it might have been.

Chapter Six

It is recorded that Richard Pitt, Mayor of Weymouth and Melcombe Regis was required by the Lord Admiral to ensure that the munitions aboard any captured vessels were delivered to the fleet. Pitt consequently wrote to the mayors of nearby harbours:

'His Lordship hath taken two great carracks or ships from the enemy, sent to the shore, wherein great store of powder and shot in either of them; and requireth that all the said powder and shot be sent unto his Lordship with all possible expedition, for that the state of the realm dependeth upon the present supply of such wants. These are therefore, in Her Majesty's name, straightly to charge and command you, forthwith, upon receipt hereof, you make diligent enquiry to what place the said carracks or ships are gone.'

A week after Flemyng towed the *San Salvador* to Weymouth, inspectors arrived to prepare an inventory and they noted part of their duty was to record ' . . . the notable spoils that were made upon the ship'. They also reported that part of the reason for their delay was 'the far distance of the ship in the bay from the town of Weymouth,' and that, 'in the stealing of her sails and cables the disorder was very great. Of some 200 Barrels of Venetian powder each of some 120 pounds in weight, and yet but 141 were sent to the Lord Admiral.'

It is fascinating to note that George Trenchard and Deputy Vice-Admiral Francis Hawley also recorded:

'This very night some inkling came unto us that a chest of great weight should be found in the forepeak of the ship the Friday before our dealing, and all such search hath been made sithence our coming, but no treasure can be found, and yet we have removed some part of the ballast. We find here no Spaniards of any account, but only one who calleth himself Don Melchor de Pereda, and nine others of the common sort; two Frenchmen, four Almains, and one Almain woman; and since there landing here, twelve more are dead. We humbly beseech your Lordships to give some speedy direction what shall be done with them, for they are here diseased, naked, and chargeable.'

However a chest such as that missing from the *San Salvador* is on display in the excellent historical exhibition at Brewers Quay, Weymouth.

In the town records of Weymouth and Melcombe Regis compiled by

Moule there is reference to the union of the two boroughs in 1571. There are also records of the enmity that existed between the two, and their inhabitants, who would hurl stones at each other across the river.

The names of the first aldermen are recorded as being 'J. Burley and T. Samwayes'. There is an earlier record of 'Francis Lawse Mayor of Melcombe Regis and J. Burley and Owen Grigory Bailiffs of the same . . .'

At the time of the Armada, Edward Hoby was twenty-eight years. He had matriculated at Trinity College, Oxford at the age of fourteen, was a bachelor of arts at fifteen, and master at sixteen. His uncle was, as I have stated, Lord Burghley (William Cecil or Cecyll) Secretary of State, Lord High Treasurer, confidant and close advisor of his Queen, and Knight of the Garter.

Hoby became a man of importance a Member of Parliament, Justice of the Peace and in 1594 was granted letters patent for the buying and providing wool for sale in England. Widely travelled, he was also sent on a number of missions and impressed those he met, including James VI of Scotland, with his affability and learning.

In July 1588 he was sent on a confidential mission by Queen Elizabeth to report on the state and availability of ships to augment the fleet and since Mousehole was a port of some importance, it would not be beyond the bounds of possibility that Hoby would have visited the town in the knowledge that here were letters close addressed to summon ships to augment the fleet.

Chapter Seven

Once again I have endeavoured to interpret the battle scenes, as they were recorded by both English and Spanish chroniclers. Indeed the two fleets were at times so close, that the men aboard could shout insults at each other that might be heard above the noise of the battle.

Some Spanish did regard the shift in wind as being truly miraculous, and Sidonia did prepare himself for death, as I have recorded.

The bravery was not one sided. Envisage the privations of seamen and soldiers crammed between decks on unaccustomed storm-tossed seas. The sickness, the rotting food. The shortage of shot and powder. Yet as the English fleet followed them to the Firth of Forth (the Frith) still the Spanish offered to fight in the manner I have attempted to describe.

The plight of the German gunner and his revenge is recorded by

Calderon, an officer aboard the *San Salvador:* 'It is said that Captain Priego had beaten a German artillery man who went below, saying one of his pieces had got wet, and would have to be discharged. He fired the piece and then threw the port fire into a barrel of powder.'

Petruccio Ubaldino, a Florentine historian and scholar, who came to England in 1545 wrote a narrative of the defeat of the Armada for Lord Howard and recorded: 'An army captain (i.e. Priego) had insolently beaten a Flemish gunner, it is not known whether on account of his work or of the wife of the gunner who was with him, as is the custom of his country; whereupon the poor wretch, despairing of his life and that of his wife, and perhaps even more of her honour, and that of his daughter, set alight to a barrel of gunpowder, thus avenging himself and his dear ones.'

The fact that in defiance of the King's orders German women were on board, would seem to confirm the account.

The seamen of that time had to sleep where they could, for hammocks had yet to be introduced. It is said that Drake himself had a great four post bed fixed in his own cabin.

Roast goose, stuffed with sage and onions, was a favourite dish of Queen Elizabeth. Indeed, she was at table on Michaelmas Day when news of the final defeat of the Armada was brought to her. Doubtless the food was accompanied by the ale that she much preferred to wine. And so it was that the Queen decreed that 'This glorious occasion be commemorated by serving roast goose on this day every year.'

Chapter Eight

Hounds may be divided into two groups — hunting by sight or scent:

Those that hunt by sight and are reliant on their speed and agility, being sight or 'gaze' hounds of which 'grey' is believed to be a corruption. Usually they hunt or course in couples. Three white gaze hounds feature on the Keigwin coat of arms. Sight hounds may well be of Eastern origin, of which the Afghan and Saluki are examples, and may well have been introduced to Britain by the Celts. Our 'gaze' hounds include the Greyhound, Whippet, Irish Wolfhound and Scottish Deerhound.

Hounds that hunt by scent usually do so in a pack, and were introduced to Britain at the time of the Norman Conquest being clearly depicted on the Bayeaux Tapestry. The Bloodhound of St. Hubert being an example and so called through the purity of its ancestry or 'blood' line.

In Tudor times hares were by no means plentiful in England and were imported alive from the continent. Furthermore Cornish countrymen have assured me that whilst many villages had coursing clubs, the hares were imported into the county since they did not breed freely.

The sport of deer hunting was a favourite pastime of Queen Elizabeth and the nobility, and it was during her reign that deer parks were introduced, being populated by the imported fallow deer.

Whilst Carew contended that the native red deer did not breed freely in Cornwall, they were widespread on the west country moorlands, to which the granite uplands of West Penwith are a part. A herd of red deer introduced some years ago onto the Lizard seem to be thriving, consequently, I have taken the view that the red deer could well have been found in this location.

The action the *Golden Hind* saw is evidenced by her damage. Flemyng was forced to write to Lord Burghley, the Lord High Treasurer, in the following terms:

'Right honourable: whereas, by warrant and commandment from the Lord High Admiral of England, I was charged to serve Her Majesty at the seas for the space of five months against the Spaniard, in part whereof I received by the appointment of the Lord Admiral only for three months and a half; and for the other six weeks, having charge of 36 men in a small bark of mine own, to be furnished with all necessaries, as of victuals as wages, I have hitherunto received no allowance, the which, with his loss of cables, anchors and masts, amounteth to the sum of 70L at least. My very good Lord, for as much as my charge in the said service hath been very great and chargeable unto to me, and my attendance since my return from the seas, by these 15 weeks past, very tedious, I beseech your honour therefore, to have regard for my present state, and to take some good order for my present satisfaction in respect of this said charge, to my further encouragement in service, and daily prayer for the continuance of your honour in all happy state. And so I must humbly take my leave, this 27th of December, 1588.

Your Honour's most Bounden
Thomas Flemyng'

If one compares the claim for £70.00 with the annual pay of a skilled labourer as being less than half that amount; and a merchant or man of substance at £100.00 per annum, the sum owing him was no mean amount. He claims his crew numbered 36 whereas other records state the number as being 30. Who was right? Or, was Flemyng claiming a little extra in lieu of interest? I know not. Neither do I know if Martin and Richard served with him. However, at that time they were described as fishermen and featured upon a list of those liable to be called into the service of the fleet.

The *San Martin*, flagship of Spain arrived in Santander on the 21st September 1588, with Burley and other Englishmen aboard her.

The Duke of Medina Sidonia was disgraced. His grand fleet broken and destroyed, only some half of those great ships that ventured against England made a safe return. Whilst on the other hand Drake reported that the enemy 'did not in all their sailing round about England, so much as sink or take one ship, bark, pinnace, or cock-boat of ours, or even burn so much as one sheep-cote in this land.'

Chapter Nine

Mystery or Miracle plays were often performed to educate and entertain the populace. They were essentially dramas, founded upon historical parts of the Old and New Testaments, or the lives of the Saints. During the Middle Ages they were firstly performed in church by the clergy and choristers to which lay people were recruited. At that time it was unseemly for women to participate and boys were required to play female parts.

Currently the principal surviving play is 'The Passion of Our Saviour' which is presented every tenth year at Oberammergau in Bavaria.

Cornwall's mystery cycle — 'The Ordinalia' — is believed by many to be the oldest of the British mystery cycles.

Chapter Ten

From the researches I have made I believe the legendary beliefs in Madron Well to be as I have described. It was also thought maidens would drop a straw into the water, and the number of bubbles it produced would be the number of years they would wait until wed. Not only is it a place of considerable historical interest, but one of magic and beauty.

It is a sad reflection upon those entrusted to safeguard our historical inheritance, that they lack the wit to grant to this place the subtle sympathetic conservation it so richly deserves.

The use of herbal remedies is broadly as described. It is interesting to note that sixty percent of medicines in common use are plant derivatives. A further thirty percent now synthesised artificially were originally obtained from plants.

The warning I have attributed to Hawkyns would have been justified, as Queen Elizabeth vented her spleen upon the Roman Catholics. Within a period of three months, thirty were accused of being traitors and executed with embowelling and other atrocities being committed upon them. Their only crime being the practice of their religion. Fines were rigorously imposed, and many gentlemen financially ruined, for a year's imprisonment or the fine of 100 marks could be imposed for every time Mass was heard. All this despite their loyalties to the Crown and their contribution towards the defence of their country.

Fearful of threat of invasion from Ireland, the persecution of Irish Catholics was increased, with fines and imprisonment a daily occurrence, together with the added frequency of capital punishments.

Chapter Eleven

I have used the legend, and the history of Saint Pol de Leon as being an appropriate subject for a miracle play. Recognising that John Flemyng was in truth a Doctor of Divinity and second warden of Wadham College, Oxford, becoming Chaplain to James I, he could indeed have been an author of such a work.

It is interesting to note that John Keigwin (1641-1716) who I believe was the grandson of Richard Keigwin of the story, received a classical education and was taught the Cornish language by his father, in which he had a profound knowledge. He was also a master of Latin, Greek, Hebrew and French. He is described as a merchant of Mousehole. Furthermore he translated from the Cornish 'Pascon Agan Arluth', the mystery play 'The Passion of our Lord' and also 'The Creation of the World' by William Jordan.

I have drawn upon what is known of John Keigwin to fashion the character of his forebears, as indeed I have of Richard Keigwin, who I believe was also a grandson of Richard Keigwin. This Richard was a Colonel of Marines, and following many amazing adventures, was killed when leading his men in action. Once again one witnesses the Celtic contrast of the soldier and the scholar.

Hawkyns was the architect behind the new race design of English ships that defeated the ponderous high-castled vessels of the Armada. He had experienced many adventures and witnessed many sights, some of which I have attempted to describe, but was principally a merchant, ship owner, and Admiralty official.

The integrity of Hawkyns was always suspect. It is believed that it was Sir Robert Mansell, who claimed to know him, that said of Hawkyns: 'He had malice with dissimulation, rudeness in behaviour, and was covetous in the last degree.' I have attempted to reflect this into his character. His wife Katherine died in 1591 after a long illness, and he later married Margaret Vaughan of Herefordshire.

Chapter Twelve

I have assumed the type of hound to be of the old Southern breed. A heavy ponderous animal with an excellent nose, that would so rejoice at the scent, it would sit on its haunches and bay in ecstasy! I suspect the breed was improved by the addition of cross breeding with a lighter, faster animal such as the greyhound that would lend greater dash and thrust to the offspring.

At about that time, Flemyng was patrolling off Ireland in a Queen's ship the *Charles*, preventing the export of corn to a hungry Spain.

Burley had been at Court in Cadiz attendant upon King Philip. He did bring the Kings' orders to the galleys. The plan for the raid was hatched by Don Diego Brochero de Anaya and Don Pedro de Zaubiaur who 'proposed the organisation of a combined squadron of galleys and fly-boats for transportation of men and stores, to ravage the coasts of England.' The intention was known to Fuenterrabia, but the warning letter did not reach England in time. Was this deliberate?

In 1591 Captain Flemyng had sailed on a special mission to victual the fleet of Lord Thomas Howard in the Azores. They were lying in wait for a fleet of Spanish treasure ships. In 1598 as Captain of the *Affection*, Flemyng sailed with George Clifford, Duke of Cumberland, to raid Puerto Rico. They took prizes worth £16,000. The *Affection* was owned by John Watts, who with others of worship in the City of London, victualled three good ships; to wit, the *Consent*, the *Saloman* and the *Virgin*. Thus I have construed that both Watts and Lancaster could have been well known to the merchant of Mousehole.

John Watts had commissioned and served aboard the *Margaret and John* in the thickest of the fighting during the Armada campaign. In 1601 he was elected Governor of the East India Company (in which

353

also served, as earlier noted, Richard Keigwin, who I believe to be a great grandson of Jenkyn Keigwin). His eldest son, also John, was an active member of the Virginia Company, and would doubtless have known John Smith, the founder, whose comments on Thomas Flemyng I have already recorded. Knighted in 1603, Lord Mayor of London 1606/7, Member of the Cloth Workers Company, he was described to the King of Spain as 'The greatest pirate that has ever been in this Kingdom'.

Lancaster was also active in the Armada campaign commanding the *Bonaventure* in Drake's squadron. He lived a life rich in adventure. In 1600 he was appointed to command the first fleet of the East India Company. Knighted in 1603, he died a bachelor, and with the exception of some small family legacies, left his fortune to the Skinners Company, and 'Mistress Thomasine Owfield, widow, for distribution amongst the poor'.

It was reported by Sir Thomas Baskerville, who served with Drake and Hawkyns on their venture, that Cornwall had been de-nuded of arms and munitions since they had been commandeered for the expedition. Thus I have concluded that Mount's Bay would have been ill-defended. No mention of this is made by Carew in his Survey of Cornwall which details the English version of the invasion. Since Queen Elizabeth was sponsoring the fleet, was it for fear of incurring her displeasure?

The delays that Drake incurred in fitting his ships for sea are, I believe, as I have recorded. The method of sheathing that I have described is that invented by John Hawkyns.

State papers record that in May 1595 'a shallop from Blavet manned by sixteen sailors and twenty-four soldiers, captured a fisher-boat of St. Keverne, carrying the men over to Brittany. There they were examined but could tell nothing of Drake's objectives; only that they knew of a fleet which consisted of one hundred ships under Drake.' An English gunner from Bristol, whom the Spaniards would not release, told the fishermen 'to report to the first Justice of the Peace that there were four galleys and ten ships of war at Blavet'.

On August 2nd, 1595, Edmund Palmer, the double agent — whom I have introduced later in this book — wrote to Lord Howard as follows: 'Subiacoe came back from Bluett (Blavet) 26th July, having landed such monies and provisions as he carried, and brought back some horses, pigs etc., as also his General Don Diego Brochero, who was in the galleys there, and who landed in the Passage Road and went by post to the Court at Madrid; when he returns, he will go as General of six sail and four pinnaces, now in the Passage and bound for Lisbon to join those there. Their pretences are to follow Sir Francis Drake, who they understand has gone to sea . . .'

Chapter Thirteen

It is known that there were a number of Englishmen aboard the squadron. In my opinion the Spanish raid was so very well planned that it was probably well rehearsed beforehand.

Having researched the various English raids taking place at that time, there would seem no doubt that the booty from Brazil which the Spaniards record they were intent upon recovering, was that taken by Lancaster. Indeed in his letter to Lord Howard, Edmund Palmer goes on to state: 'The Spaniards are advised that certain English ships have taken wondrous great riches at Pernambuco, in Brazil.' I have endeavoured to give an eye-witness account of that raid, which I have interpreted from *Voyages and Discoveries* by Hakluyt.

Chapter Fourteen

The passage of the Spanish squadron is adapted from the translation from the original Spanish by Robert Dickinson contained in the Journal of the Royal Institution of Cornwall 1988.

Food and beverage were important features of the middle and upper class Elizabethans. Ale was a most popular drink and came in several forms, as indeed it does today. There was single beer or small ale and double ale, having double the quantity of malt and hops. But double double beer was twice as strong! The names were even more enticing to the male ego than those of today, with names such as 'mad-dog', 'angel's food' and 'dragon's milk'.

'Never', it is said, 'did Romulus and Remus suck their she-wolf with such eager and sharp devotion as these men hale at huff-cap, till they be as red as cocks, and little wiser than their combs.'

Gentlemen, however, brewed an ale for their own consumption called March ale from the month in which it was brewed, but which was not brought to the table until it was matured at two years old.

It was about this time that the *Charles* was patrolling off the south coast of Ireland, it will be noted that the family of Flemyng had come from Munster, which forms part of Southern Ireland, including Kinsale, an important port of that time.

Chapter Fifteen

The journey and adventures of the galleys were broadly as I have interpreted, and the state of the weather is also well documented. Barnaby Loe came from Ipswich, being an English prisoner later released by the Spaniards.

Sailing aboard the galleys, maintaining the fighting capabilities of the vessels, would have been shipwrights and sailmakers. The well-being of the crew and soldiery also had to be considered, hence cooks and surgeons were aboard to nourish and repair the body. But of greatest importance was the soul, and to ensure God's favour, priests were in attendance to conduct prayers and purge the soul of heresy. Friar Domingo Martinez was of the Order of St. Dominic: a Black Friar, bound by a solemn vow of chastity, poverty and obedience, to whom the eating of meat is forbidden. One of an order of preachers and teachers, missionaries in foreign lands — strict guardians of the faith. In this role it was the Dominicans who presided over the infamies of the Inquisition and the autos-da-fé. Armed with this power, Friar Domingo would have held the final authority aboard the flotilla, and as a consequence would, I believe, have been much feared and respected even amongst the highest command.

The apparel of the Dominican is a black robe — hence the Black Friar — and they also popularised the use of the rosary.

My comments concerning rough cyder and attributed to Martin come from bitter personal experience. The ingredients were told to me by local farmers in the back bar of a certain hostelry in Okehampton where, not wisely but too well, with a number of friends we were celebrating the successful completion of Army exercises on the moors.

There is a contemporary map showing the route of posting houses along the principal roads; en route from London to Marazion there is shown a post house at Crewkernewell.

Chapter Sixteen

From what I can determine, I believe some of the Keigwin land extended to the west of Mousehole towards the hamlet of Raginnis, then spelt Reginnis. The stock and contents of the house can be discovered from the inventory attached to the will of Martin Keigwin.

The prophecy is one of many attributed to Merlyn. It is specifically mentioned by Richard Carew in *The Survey of Cornwall* written in

356

1602:

'In fatis, they say (and not in fatuis) it was, that the Cornish people should undergo this misfortune; for an ancient prophecy, in their own language, hath long run amongst them, how there should land upon the rock of Merlyn, those that would burn Paul's church, Pensanz, and Newlyn: and indeed so is the rock called, where the enemy first stept on shore. The prophecy is this:

> Ewra teyre a war meane Merlyn
> Ara Lesky Pawle Pensanz ha Newlyn.'

Carew was a friend and cousin to Sir Francis Godolphin from whom he doubtless obtained a first hand view of the Spanish attack. I find it difficult to conceive that the incursion occurred exactly as Merlyn the Wizard had predicted nearly a thousand years before. What I can and do believe is that the Spanish, through their English spies, or through the English that lived in Brittany and Spain, would know of the prophecy, and enacted it to strike the greater terror into the local inhabitants.

The description of what happened has been adapted from the Spanish account of De Amelrola (or De Amelzola) and that of Richard Carew. They are remarkably similar, albeit Carew estimates the number of Spanish soldiery that attacked Mousehole as being two hundred, whereas De Amelrola, who would know precisely, gives the number as four hundred. The detail I have reconstructed by tracing the likely footsteps of the participants. The names of the commanders are as recorded, as are their individual roles; so far as can be reasonably assessed.

In his *Short Account of the Ancient Church of Paul*, Mr Cecil Aitken says that a tradition in the Parish states that a number of country people were intercepted carrying bundles of furze. Why? I have made an assumption and written it into the story. Similarly it has always been believed in Mousehole that Squire Keigwin himself killed six Spaniards before he himself was slain. This may be a slightly extravagant claim consequently the story has given him some assistance.

In the translation by Dickinson, Paul Church is described in the original text as a 'mosque'; that confirms the view that this battle against heresy was an extension of their own wars against the Moors who had occupied their own country. In the 'mosque was a horse carved in wood and greatly embellished, serving as an idol to be worshipped by the people'. One can only assume this was a hobby-horse, of the sort used throughout the land at times of festival and

357

merry-making.

Chapter Seventeen

In the hands of a skilled archer, the longbow was an excellent weapon. The Jacob I have envisaged would be well-practised as would have been required in the early days of Elizabeth's reign. Four hundred yards is sometimes mentioned as the distance at which a skilled archer could cleave in two a slim wand of hazel. By an act of Henry VIII no person was allowed to shoot at a mark nearer than 220 yards at which distance a broad arrow would easily pierce the stoutest armour.

The Falcon was a cannon firing a ball of two and a half inch bore. The point blank range was 'fifteen score paces' and random shot one thousand, five hundred paces. A Falconet was of two inch bore with the same range.

I know not the manner of Jenkyn Keigwin's dying. Nor is any mention made of it in the Spanish account, or of their losses other than to claim later that there had been no 'loss or bloodshed on our part'. The cannonball that is believed to have killed is of 5½" bore and would, I suspect, be more likely to have been fired from the galleys that we know were very close within the harbour. It would seem too large to have been fired from a cannon man-handled ashore, the smaller cannonball discovered during restoration would appear to be of 3" bore. This cannon would have weighed about five hundred pounds.

There are various accounts of the death of Keigwin. The most common is that he was killed by a cannonball. I have no wish to disturb local legend, rather to envisage how that legend may be encapsulated in the story in a possible or probable form.

Chapter Eighteen

The church of St. Mary is believed to have been saved consequent upon the intervention of Richard Burley who claimed that Mass had been celebrated there. Friar Domingo was so moved, he wrote two verses in English in which he declared his reasons for not burning it and his belief that Mass would again be celebrated there.

The letter that Godolphin wrote to Drake is factual. I have also continued to write an eye-witness view of what might have happened based on English and Spanish accounts.

According to Carew: 'Upon their moving, Sir Francis Godolphin moved also, to enter Penzance before them: and as soon as that weak number were entered into the open green, being of three quarters of a mile length, the gallies ceased not to ply them all that way with their ordnance from their prows, as busily as they could: of which shot, though none were hurt, but only a constable unhorsed without any harm, saving the shew on his doublet of the bullets sliding by his back, yet many in fearful manner, some fell flat to the ground, and others ran away.'

From the English prisoners, the Spaniards had been told that Godolphin was on his way to defend the coast at the head of 8,000 armed men. Yet Drake had but 2,500 soldiers under his command. Carew records that of the Cornishmen, 'in number something above a hundred, wherein were about thirty or forty shot'. The Spanish claim that 'more than fifty Englishmen killed at one assault'.

One can imagine Drake's concern. Not only did he receive the letter from Godolphin but also from Vivyan at St. Mawes fort:

'Hanibal Vivyan to Sr Francis Drake and Sir John Hawkyns, generals of the fleet at Plymouth.

'I think you are informed of the Spaniard's landing this day in the western parts; they have burned Penzance, Newlyn, Mousehole, Poole Church and Church Town, and other villages adjoining, without resistance; I speak it to the disgrace of those people. The only ships there are four galleys, but there are forty sail seen to seaward. There is a great want of leaders; the Spaniard's conquest without resistance may give them greater encouragement to land along the coast, as well as to the east and north. I beg you if your ships are not fit to fight, to send into these parts some of their leaders who have commanded in war, as they are greatly needed now, and will be more so if the Spaniards should land. If you lack mariners, I think one hundred could be procured in ten hours in Falmouth harbour. Noted by Sir Francis Drake and Sir John Hawkyns that this letter came to hand as the post was ready to take his horse, and that some captains are getting ready to go westward.'

Both letters had told him in effect that a fleet of ships, presumably an Armada of Spain, lurked over the horizon. The wind was veering easterly, and should he, even if his ships were seaworthy, sail into the shallow waters of the great bay, the wind could drive his ships to founder upon the rocks; whilst the oared galleys escaped. Drake's fleet mustered twenty-seven, thus he would be heavily outnumbered and if by wind and enemy action he was defeated, what a victory it would be for Spain!

Monson did arrive in Plymouth, as I have recorded, and joined with Drake to sail. No mention is made of any sightings.

The Spanish celebrated Mass in the manner in which I have described. It is believed this took place on a hill known as Mount Misery that lies on the outskirts of Penzance. Barnaby Loe confirmed, 'they had a Mass next day on the western hill where they vowed to found a priory when they had conquered England.'

The Spanish account records the concern that the Queen's fleet would come in search of them, which was indeed well justified. Furthermore, Robert Dickinson's translation states, 'in addition he (Carlos De Amelrola) was satisfied that part of the booty from Brazil, which would have justified staying longer in that bay even at the risk of damage to the galleys, had arrived in London.'

The repairs needed to the galleys is also my interpretation from the translation; as indeed is the shift in the wind that enabled the Spanish to escape.

There is an accurate account of the Spaniard's return and their pursuit and engagement of a fleet of forty-six vessels of Dutch Flanders off the Point du Raz. It would surely have been unusual for two fleets of similar numbers to have been sailing in similar waters at the same time. Consequently against a westerly wind this fleet could well have been sighted from headland or fishing boat when on a broad tack, neither Vivyan nor Godolphin state the fleet is Spanish, but that would seem to be the obvious implication that would justifiably have caused Drake to react with a degree of time-consuming prudence.

All previous parish records being destroyed in the conflagration, the first entry in the Parish Register of 1595 is as follows:

'Jesu spes et salus mea!'
1595
'Jesus my hope and my salvation!'
1595

'Jenkyn Keigwin of Mousell, being killed by the Spaniards was buried the 24th of Julie.

'John Pearce Peiton was buried on the 24th daie of Julie.

'Jacobus de Newlyn occisus fuit per inimicos, et sepultus est 26th die Julie. (Jacob of Newlyn was killed by enemies and buried on the 26th July.)

'Similter Teek Cornall, et sepultus, the 26 Julie.'

The characters of Jacob, John Pearce and Teek Cornall and the part they played have no bearing on any facts that I can discover. I trust they will forgive me and excuse the liberty I have taken in their inclusion in the story.

An examination of the English prisoners revealed the galleys would have stayed longer and done more spoil but were in fear of Drake's fleet. The change of mind and tide enabled them to make their escape. They decided to forego attacking St. Ives and Padstow, and also the Scillies, where they could keep the galleys under the protection of the fort.

Chapter Nineteen

It is believed that Queen Elizabeth did suppress news of the success of the Spanish raid for fear of the effect upon her people.

To 'play it by the text', derives from the popular text book of 1595 *Of Honour and Honourable Quarrels* by Vincent Saviolo. The publication was read by coxcombs of that period who would demonstrate their social status by conceit and rude offence. Saviolo defines the exact grounds of a duel and hence the precise line at which to stop if one had no appetite to digest cold steel after dinner.

Sadly, when the Armada was defeated and danger no longer threatened, as all too often happens, those that one day had been branded heroes, were dismissed, left in their hundreds to fend for themselves when the fleet returned to their home ports.

Thomas Flemyng married Jane at Madron on the 16th September 1593. I know not who were her parents and I presume she died.

Chapter Twenty

I have endeavoured to portray some of the indecision that took place, and the flattery of the courtiers that affected the opinions of the Queen. However, at the end of the day the decisions she made were invariably correct, and her parsimony was occasioned by the fact that in comparison with Spain, England was a small and relatively poor country. Hoby did indeed live in some comfort at Bisham Abbey near Marlow, where he entertained the Queen, and the Court, when plague threatened. He was to serve on the raid to Cadiz. He had no issue by his three lawful wives, but by Katherine Pinkney he had a son, Peregrine, who adopted his fathers name and rose to some prominence.

361

Bisham Abbey is indeed a magnificent building steeped in history, a house of the Knights Templar, founded in the reign of Stephen. In 1947 Miss Phyllis Vansittart-Neale offered the Abbey to the youth of England in memory of her two nephews, Berkeley and Guy Paget, who as subalterns in the Kings Royal Rifle Corps had given their lives in the last war. In 1963 the Abbey and park were sold to the Central Council of Physical Recreation, where it is now used by many of our national sports teams in their preparation for major events.

As I have earlier hinted, the expedition of Drake and Hawkyns to Porto Rico seemed doomed from the outset. Delays, as I have indicated, enabled the Spanish to prepare their defences in anticipation, and, as earlier stated, de Brochero who had master-minded the galleys foray, had already set sail to thwart Drake's intentions.

Chapter Twenty-one

The English attack upon Cadiz was successful beyond the wildest expectations and is as I have described. Indeed, the youthful and impetuous Earl of Essex, who had himself fought with great gallantry, would have held Cadiz but was overruled, after razing the fortifications and reducing the town to ashes.

The invading English were restrained from shedding blood in wanton manner, and behaved with moderation to such an extent that by his conduct Essex received the plaudits of the enemy, and the Spanish King.

As Monson records: 'The plotter was Captain Burleigh who afterwards was well requited for his treachery for to be even with him for so foul a fact, Sir Robert Cecyll, the Principal Secretary, writ a letter to him residing in Lisbon, pretending he was employed as a spy, and gave him thanks for some particular service he named he had done, when indeed there was no such cause, for the man was ever too honest to that side. Sir Robert Cecyll so ordered it that this letter fell into the hands of some ministers of the King of Spain, whereupon Burleigh was apprehended, close imprisoned, and cruelly tortured, when he deserved no such ill usage. I speak this because I would have the world judge how justly he deserved it, and how prettily the Spaniards were imposed upon it.'

William Resould, the pseudonym of Giles Van Harwick, a spy of Robert Cecyll wrote in 1598: 'Captain Burley is not executed at Ferrol, as reported, but strangely racked.' Whereas in July of this year

Edward Conyers wrote to Cecyll: 'Capts. Burley and Cocke were apprehended, tortured and condemned to the galleys for ten years, and Brooke executed.' Whilst in September Resould again reported: 'Brooke has been hanged, and Burley beheaded and Eaton the traitor is dead at Ferrol.'

Yet Burley was to be reprieved and prove his innocence, perhaps by firstly being racked. He lived to serve his King and continue the fight against his homeland.

KEIGWIN C

RESCUED AT BIRTH

An Adoptee's Journey to Closure

Jeff Eddins

RESCUED AT BIRTH

PREFACE

We're going on a journey that I think you'll find fascinating. What makes being on a journey so potentially intriguing? You may not know what you'll discover along the way, what you'll do with what you find, or more importantly, *what you find will do to you.*

I could never have imagined the impact my quest to identify my biological family would have on me emotionally. Nor could I know just how much frustration I would experience from the many obstacles I faced during the process. My journey has been very cathartic, shedding many tears of sadness and many tears of joy along the way.

When I was young, I was only slightly curious. But as I got older, I found myself on an unstoppable mission to identify with someone who resembled me. From start to finish it took nearly twenty-two years with most of that time sitting in limbo with no visible pathway to complete my task.

My motivation to share my story is to help fellow adoptees identify with someone of like kind, and to help non-adoptees understand what it feels like to know nothing regarding one's genetic origins. My hope is that you will be greatly moved by my story.

ACKNOWLEDGEMENTS

I want to give thanks with a grateful heart to the people in my life that loved and cared for me. My greatest appreciation is clearly directed toward my mom and dad who loved me unconditionally. I'll never have adequate words to describe the depth of love I have for them. If there's anything to reincarnation, I'd want to return as an adopted child in the arms of the parents that deeply loved me.

I was very fortunate because all those within my adopted family loved and considered me the same as any other family member. Although my grandmother and many of my aunts and uncles have passed on, I am forever grateful for their acceptance, inclusion, and love.

I also want to thank my wife Debbie for tolerating my obsession as I sought to identify my birth family. She knew how important this search was to me, and she always supported me during my journey. Along the way, she also challenged me to consider a few ethical issues I was oblivious to. And because she has such a caring heart, she wanted to make sure that I would, in no way, hurt my adoptive parents. We had the same interests, but as a non-adoptee, she could see things differently. As I helped others with their searches, she often offered her perspective to ensure I considered the feelings of those who might have become exposed to information they may not have wanted to know.

TABLE OF CONTENTS

INTRODUCTION

FOR MOST OF MY LIFE, SOMETHING FELT AMISS. SOMETIMES, WHEN looking into a mirror, I asked the question, "Where did I come from?" But, of course, I didn't have a magic talking mirror like the evil queen in *Snow White*. For so many years of my childhood and young adulthood, I felt like I came from nowhere. But I had to come from somewhere. Who was responsible for the color of my eyes and the shape of my seemingly bridgeless nose? Where did my hair texture and color originate and which one of my birth parents was responsible for my big feet? I certainly didn't have many of the physical traits of my adoptive parents and I doubt anyone could have found any significant resemblance between us.

During the first thirty-six years of my life, I quelled whatever desires I had to search for my biological parents. Perhaps I didn't start searching earlier because I worried that doing so could have made my adoptive parents feel inadequate. And they were way more than adequate. Or maybe I was afraid that if I found my birth parents, neither of them would want anything to do with me, resulting in yet another rejection. But there came a time when I was in my late thirties, while both of my adoptive parents were still living, when I felt this deep desire to find the people who created me and identify with someone who shared my physical traits.

Have you ever wondered what it would be like to spend nearly your whole life not knowing anything about your biological origins? Most people who were raised by their birth parents have not given this much consideration, and understandably so. At some point, early in their lives, they identified with specific physical traits of their parents. Or perhaps another relative brought it to their attention, or they realized they looked like their siblings. There is a sort of subliminal validation and sense of confirmation that, for most, becomes something taken for granted.

For the adoptee, there can be a sense of incompleteness. At big family gatherings, at times, they may feel like an outsider because everyone else is connected to each other in a way they are not. Unlike non-adoptees, there are no family pictures on the walls of their house for them to identify with. And no matter how well they were loved and raised by their adoptive parents, or accepted by their extended family, there's something of great importance missing.

For many adoptees, the desire to identify their origins begins at the moment they learn they were adopted. For others, it can be a delayed desire. But make no mistake about it, most adoptees have some degree of curiosity that eventually drives them to want to find their biological family.

There are other considerations that lead adoptees to search for their birth family. We want to understand the circumstances that led our biological mothers to surrender us. Why didn't she keep me? Was it a struggle for her, or was it simply that legal abortion wasn't an option for those who were born before the landmark case of Roe versus Wade in 1973? Perhaps she wanted to abort me, but she was afraid to? Was there a religious belief that made her carry me to full term, while knowing the entire time of her pregnancy that she would not keep me? What life circumstances led her to release me? Was she too young to provide for me or did her parents force her to give me up? Was I the product of a one-night stand or rape? Did my birth father know about my existence, and if so, why didn't he choose to keep me?

Some adoptees carry a deep sense of anger and bitterness toward their birth mothers, especially if their relationships and experiences growing up with their adoptive parents were not ideal. Some wish to find their birth mother to express their hurt and frustration.

"Why did you tempt fate? I had no say in any of this. Did you get rid of me out of convenience? Maybe you shouldn't have been running around having illicit sex and then simply tossing away your unwanted trash. I'm fully aware you could have sent me to a medical waste bin. Am I supposed to be grateful that you didn't? You've left me wondering all my life just who you were and fantasizing about what it could have been like to know you. I wanted to be hugged and loved by someone who shared my DNA. I wanted cousins and uncles who looked like me and could clearly identify themselves in me. I wanted a grandfather to look at me and appreciate that I was biologically related to him. But you took every opportunity for that away from me."

To be clear, the feelings and thoughts I've just shared in the previous paragraph are not mine. But I have heard those kinds of expressions of bitterness from many others who struggled with their adoption.

As a parent of two children, I know the depth of love I felt the moment each of them entered this world. It's unfathomable for me to have ever considered living my life without them, never knowing what became of them. But that's an easy thing for me to say because during the time my children were conceived, my life had structure and stability. My wife and I loved each other, and we'd already committed to a lifelong marriage that included wanting children. For many unwed, expectant mothers who are in unstable life situations, keeping a newborn child is not a viable option. In most instances, adoption is the best choice for the child.

Moving forward, to eliminate any confusion, I want to define a few terms. Throughout the book, the terms "dad," "father," "mom," "mother," and "parents" will always be in reference to my adoptive parents. I will always use the terms birth father, birth mother, or birth parents when referring to my biological parents. While I intend no disrespect toward my birth parents, I only have two parents, the ones who loved and raised me. I will also only provide the complete names (first and last) of those who are deceased. To protect the anonymity of those still living, I will use either their first name or a pseudonym, unless granted permission to do otherwise.

Now, I want to take you through the details of my journey to identify my birth parents and the emotional roller coaster I rode for many years. I liken my search to going on a scavenger hunt, where figuring out one puzzle led me to the next clue and then the next. Of course, my story is unique and not every adoptee has a similar experience or outcome. This book is autobiographical and attempts to describe the events of my life from early childhood as an adoptee through today. It's also deeply personal and perhaps I'll be sharing intimate feelings about things I probably shouldn't. But if you're an adoptee, or even someone who discovered later in life that one of the parents who raised you was not biologically related to you, I'm sure you'll be able to identify with many parts of my story. If you're not an adoptee, I hope you'll gain some insight into what it's like for others out there like me.

[1]

DROPPING THE "A" BOMB

HAVE YOU EVER TRIED TO RECOLLECT THE EARLIEST YEARS OF YOUR life? If so, how far were you able to go back? I think it's difficult for most of us to recall any of the details of our lives before, say, the age of five. And if you believe you remember anything from your earliest years, how can you be sure you're not confusing what you remember with photos you've seen that captured specific moments of your childhood? If your parents have also given you details about your early life that coincide with any of those pictures, they're probably not actual early memories, but imagined recollections of life events that were constructed based on what you learned about them.

That said, I'm going to tell you about an early life event that I can picture so vividly that there is no question that it happened. It's not just that my mother has corroborated the event; I can picture it down to the exact shirt I was wearing at the moment it happened. I'm sixty years old now and can barely remember what I've eaten for lunch, but this memory has stayed with me since sometime before the age of six.

I was sitting on the edge of my bed, wearing a long sleeved red turtleneck, getting ready for school. My mother was bent down on her knees as she helped me tie my shoes. I can't remember how we got on the topic, but I clearly remember her standing up, then sitting next to me on my bed and telling me that I was adopted.

Adopted? What did that mean?

My mother began describing the adoption process. She wasn't being truthful with me, but what she said to me came straight from her loving heart. She explained that she and my father were unable to have kids of their own. I find it strange now that she would tell me that at an age when I knew nothing about the birds and the bees. She then went on to explain that she and my father wanted to have children so much that they went to an adoption agency to find me.

Here's the part that's a bit sketchy, but I now understand my mother's motives for offering me a misleading explanation of the process. She told me that after they arrived at the agency, they searched through all the available children that were there. I think she had me believing it was like a smorgasbord or buffet of some sort and they simply went down all the rows of children that were laying in bassinets until they found me. "We'll take that one!" She clearly told me that they handpicked me from all the available children, and I was the only one they wanted.

The most important part of our discussion for my mother was that she wanted me to know that I was special. I wasn't some throw-away kid or someone who wasn't greatly desired by both of my parents. Irrespective of how I landed in their arms, they were going to love me as if I was their biological son. And that had a huge impact on me. My mother's words have stayed with me through the entirety of my life and may have been what deterred me from searching for my birthparents until much later. I never questioned the love my parents had for me.

In fact, I even remember that when I was a few years older, I told all my friends that I was more special to my parents than they were to their parents. I almost felt sorry for them because their parents just got what they got through the natural random chance of reproduction. I was different. My parents *chose* me. It's funny to me how I took that information and ran to an illogical conclusion. Perhaps I just wanted to reassure myself about just how much I was loved and wanted.

It wasn't until I was in my early teens that I questioned what my mother told me that day regarding how they "handpicked" me. I eventually learned that my parents had nothing to do with choosing me. They simply applied for a Caucasian male baby and the adoption agency assigned me to them. I learned later that the first time my parents set eyes on me was the day they took me home. But that didn't bother me in the least. I knew however random the path into their loving arms was irrelevant. I knew the depth of love they had for me and that's all that ever mattered.

It wouldn't be until decades later that I would come to realize that I had hit the "family lottery" compared to what my family life would have been like if my birth mother chose to keep me.

Adolescence

I was born in Los Angeles, California, on May 19, 1961, and raised in West Covina, California, a middle-class suburb located about twenty-five miles east of downtown LA. We lived in an eleven hundred square foot two-bedroom house. My father worked hard as a tool and die maker, and my mother stayed home and cared for me.

At nearly the age of six, not long after my mother explained the adoption process to me, my parents told me that soon I would have a baby sister. I probably assumed they were going back to the "adoption store" to pick her out. I recall people from the adoption agency coming to our house multiple times to interview my parents and observe our home environment and how well my parents were taking care of me. On one occasion, while the social workers were meeting with my parents at our house, I slammed my bike into the rear corner of a parked car on our street. Over the handlebars I went. I hit the asphalt headfirst and had a huge egg-shaped lump on my forehead. I'm sure that didn't look good for my parents, but that didn't railroad their efforts or prevent them from bringing my sister Sharon home a few months later.

I don't remember the day they brought Sharon home from the agency. What I do remember was that she was given my bedroom and I was moved to the den and slept on a bright red roll-away couch. At the time, I thought it was more fun to sleep on a special bed like that. And because I thought I was so special, a special bed was appropriate.

I remember thinking my baby sister was cute, but we weren't that close growing up, mostly because of our five-year age difference. It certainly wasn't because I didn't love her—Sharon has always had the biggest heart for animals and people, and I always felt a warm feeling toward her. But I was busy playing with the other boys my age in our neighborhood, and G.I. Joes just didn't play well with Barbies.

My father was raised in Mississippi and my mother in Minnesota. They were introduced to each other by my mother's sister and married in Las Vegas in 1951. Although I grew up in LA, you'll discover many people involved in my story spent time in Las Vegas, but they didn't always stay in Las Vegas.

My dad served in the Korean War and as much as I tried to get him to divulge stories about his war experiences, he rarely would go there. I've continued to wonder what horrors he was exposed to during his time serving. I do remember it was a requirement to always finish my dinner—even as I gagged on the disgusting vegetables my parents put on my plate. He explained to me that on many occasions in Korea, he had seen dead Korean children who'd drowned in the fifty-gallon drums outside of their mess tents while trying to get to the discarded sloppy food muck inside those containers. He wasn't the type to open up about too many things, but I remember him telling me on numerous occasions that I should always come to him first with any of my life problems. He told me he would always be there to help me, no matter the issue. That was important to me, solidifying just how much my dad loved me. Having a safe foundation for help if or when I would get into any trouble provided me a sense of security. Knowing how important that comfort was to me motivated me to extend that same offer to my own children many years later.

I wouldn't fully realize until my late teens that my father was an alcoholic. Each night after work he sat at our kitchen table and drank two six-packs of beer while smoking filter less cigarettes before retiring for the night. My dad was not a "fall down" kind of drunk, and he was never verbally or physically abusive toward anyone in our family. Perhaps he was traumatized by his war experiences. Or maybe he was just a hard-working, blue-collar guy who found escaping from reality as a way of survival.

My dad smoked so heavily that there were times he would have intense coughing spells where it sounded like he was dying. More than once, during a coughing spell he passed out and fell to the ground. One afternoon when I was about ten years old, he passed out on our kitchen floor, and it looked like he wasn't breathing. My mom was on the floor holding him, screaming his name, trying to wake him, and that's the last thing I heard. I ran out our front door as fast as I could run. I finally stopped two miles away, sitting in the hallway of a local junior high, wondering what I would have to face when I came home. I stayed there for over two hours, until it got dark, before returning home. When I got back, my dad was seated at his chair at our kitchen table as if nothing happened. That one incident stands out, but there were others that were just as traumatizing. Even at night, when my dad was sleeping, he would wake up and cough like that. I always closed the one door in my bedroom / den that was the closest to my parents' bedroom. If I heard him coughing, I would also wrap my pillow around both ears and hum to drown out the sound. I honestly lived in fear of my dad dying as far back as I can remember.

My mother was a "reformed" Christian who was raised in a Midwestern Lutheran church. In her later years, she told me that she had struggled with the "fire and brimstone" style of churches she attended as a child. When I was younger, she took my sister and me to a non-denominational church that replaced organs and hymnals with guitars, keyboards, and drums. This church played worship songs and older hymns that were more in line with the kind of music I enjoyed.

When it came to the spiritual side of life, my dad was not present. His "holy roller" Southern Baptist upbringing discouraged him from ever wanting to have anything to do with church. I can't remember ever discussing spirituality with him, and he never attended church with the rest of us. I'm sure he thought religion could provide a person with moral rules and help teach them how to be a better person, but nothing past that.

Unlike my father, since I was a child Christianity has played a very important role in my life. Although I have major issues with the idea that there's an interventionist God who acts on this Earth at the request of others, I agree with most of the core values of Christianity. It wasn't until I was in my mid-thirties that I began to doubt that God was manipulating any of the events on this Earth. I've written a book entitled *Trading Miracles for Grace* that investigates miraculous godly interventions and the collateral damage created by those who claim God actively favors them. After reading about my journey here, I'm sure some might be convinced that God was intervening on my behalf, but I do not support that notion. My existence and the circumstances leading to my adoption involved many random events, and I deeply doubt God controlled those outcomes.

My father worked hard at his blue-collar job, but never seemed to get ahead. Because of this, he told me from an early age that I would be going to college, and that my parents would help me financially as much as they could. For as long as I can remember, he told me that I needed to study hard in school to ensure that I would be afforded the opportunities he never had. He wanted to see me use my mind, not my hands, to earn a living. So, taking my schoolwork lightly was never an option. I excelled in math and science and always wanted to make my parents proud. I wasn't a straight A student, but I certainly held my own.

Growing up, my parents told both me and my sister numerous times that if we ever had a desire to search for our biological parents, they would do whatever they could to help us. That always seemed strange, even awkward, to me. I wondered if they were only saying that to let us know they didn't feel threatened by the possibility that we might yearn to meet our biological parents, but I doubt they hoped we'd take them up on their offer. Unlike my sister, their offer didn't interest me, but it did open the door, for if or when I ever desired to search while they were still alive.

When I was nine, I began to participate in organized sports. I played Pop Warner football, basketball, and baseball, and I loved every minute of it. I played most of these sports through high school, and even played a year of college football. My position was quarterback, and I hoped to someday make it to the NFL, but that dream ended my second year of eligibility in college. Up until that point, nearly everything in my life was centered around athletics and school, and I believe that the hard work I put into them helped me become the person I am today.

During the early parts of my life, I remember having a dull, curious wonder regarding the physical traits of my birthparents, but it never consumed me. My sister Sharon, on the other hand, struggled with not knowing the origins of her life. She always seemed to be in a state of uneasiness and bitterness about her adoption. I remember that during a few of their arguments, she told our parents that they weren't really her parents, and that they had no right to tell her what to do. It seemed to me that Sharon always felt a deep sense of abandonment, whereas that never crossed my mind.

There was something else about Sharon's adoption. It wasn't until I was in my later teens that I discovered that she knew the circumstances that led to her adoption and the original name her birth mother gave her on her birth certificate. She knew that her birth mother was only sixteen and that her parents pressured her into giving up Sharon. I never gave that much thought until much later, when I was in my late thirties, and I learned that the adoption agency provided some limited information to my parents about my birth parents.

I met my first serious girlfriend and future wife, Debbie, in high school when I was sixteen. She was a year younger, and we dated off and on for most of my junior and senior years. We decided to break up when I was leaving for college, as we would be separated by four hundred and forty miles and neither of us could imagine trying to navigate a long-distance relationship. Saying goodbye the night before I left was heart-wrenching. I loved that girl deeply, and little did I know at the time that our separation wouldn't last very long.

Some of my high school friends threw a big going away party a few days before it was time for me to leave. I had a little too much to drink that night, but I will never forget saying goodbye to my closest friend Mark. We grew up together on the same street, and we stood there at about two in the morning in the middle of that street, hugging for the longest time.

I can vividly remember the day I left for college. My uncle Vic who lived in Northern California drove to our house with his pickup truck. We loaded all my clothes along with the heavy wood-framed bed that replaced my red roll-away couch when I was in elementary school. That entire morning was filled with anxious tension as my parents and I prepared to say goodbye. I remember giving my mom a long hug as we both began to cry. But saying goodbye to my dad crushed me. I'd never seen him cry before. The instant I let go of my mother, I caught him from the corner of my eye trying to hold back his tears. We stared at each other face to face before our final embrace. I can still hear him saying, as he fought through his tears while we hugged, "You're gone, boy." He didn't say, "I love you" or "Take care of yourself." That sentence was a demarcation, indicating our lives would never be the same. It was time for him to let go and time for me to become my own man.

I was a wreck as I drove behind my uncle in my car that burned and leaked eight quarts of oil on the seven-hour drive to the UC Davis campus. I was mourning the loss of everything that had been so important to me. Did I make the right decision to leave home for college? Was football that important to me? How was I going to live my life without the girl I loved so much? Would I be able to make new friends? I only knew one person at UC Davis, the football coach who recruited me to play there. During that drive, it was beginning to set in that my life was about to change forever, and for the most part, I was taking that risk in the blind.

[2]

THOSE COLLEGE YEARS

I NEEDED TO BE AT THE UNIVERSITY FOR FOOTBALL PRACTICE about six weeks before classes began. But I had applied to UC Davis so late that there was no availability in the dorms. So, I asked my coach if he could help me find a roommate. Luckily, he found some message boards on campus that had fliers from people who were looking for roommates. A few weeks before leaving home, I called a guy named John, and made a verbal agreement with him over the phone. But I didn't meet John until the day before school began—five weeks after I'd arrived in the city of Davis.

My uncle helped me unload everything from his truck into my upstairs apartment, took me to dinner, and then he was on his way home, about two hours away. So, there I sat all alone after my uncle left. The electricity had been turned on, but there was no TV or phone installed yet. Long-distance service charges were expensive in the late 1970s, so I couldn't afford to call my parents, or vice versa. The only way they would have known that I'd arrived safely was if my uncle called them after he returned home. I didn't have money to buy any furniture, but luckily my new roommate had an old couch and a couple of bean bag chairs to sit on.

I did have a bed and a cheap stereo system with two speakers. I used a box that I had brought my clothes in as a stand for that stereo. I didn't have a dresser for my clothes, but a few drawers were built into the underside of my bed. Debbie had made me a cassette tape of some of our favorite songs about three months earlier, and I decided to listen to it. That was a big mistake. I sat on the edge of my bed, alone in that two-bedroom apartment, and cried for hours. All those songs made me miss her so badly I seriously considered packing up my clothes and stereo, leaving my bed behind, and returning home.

Football practice started two days after I arrived, and it didn't take me long to find new friends. Most of my teammates lived on campus and ate in the dining halls. My parents paid for me to have access to the dining halls during my first year. So not only did I see my teammates during practice, but I also ate breakfast, lunch, and dinner with them. I had one of my best seasons and enjoyed being part of the team.

In November, I hitched a ride back to LA for Thanksgiving with one of my teammates. It was great to see my family and I was very tempted to call Debbie. But I'd heard through the grapevine that she was seeing someone else and I didn't want to get in the middle of that, so I didn't call.

I returned home again only a month later for the Christmas holiday, and for some reason, Debbie's sister came over and invited me to their house for a New Year's Eve party. She hinted to me that Debbie would be okay with me being there and it wouldn't be awkward to have me there. I wasn't sure how to take it. Did it mean that her sister thought Debbie wanted me there? Did Debbie put her up to it or not know that her sister had extended the invite my way?

I showed up to the party with a few friends from high school. I talked to a lot of people for a couple of hours and saw Debbie walk by a few times, but we didn't speak to each other. That is, until I saw her walk into one of the back bedrooms. I startled her a bit when I walked in and I'm not even sure we said, "Hi." We stared into each other's eyes and the next thing I knew we were hugging and kissing. I'll never forget how beautiful she looked and how it felt like all that time I had been missing her had come full circle. But we still had a big problem. I was leaving again in two days, and we'd be back to where we were five months earlier. We had to figure something out.

Debbie was still in high school and taking technical classes at a trade school to become a registered dental assistant. She wouldn't be finished with all of that until the middle of June. So, we started to make plans for her to move to Davis that fall. She found a studio apartment and a job in dentistry, and we were set.

I "redshirted" my sophomore year of football and was only a participant in practice. Our varsity coach had recruited a quarterback from a rival school who was extremely talented. In fact, he was so talented that he went on to be a quarterback in the NFL for ten years. Although I had an extra year of eligibility over him and could wait until he graduated to try to be the starter, I was pretty sure it wasn't worth it. So, my junior year, I decided to hang up my cleats and focus on my studies.

I also decided to change my major to physics, although that would add another two-and-a-half years to college. I dropped out for a couple of quarters to get my head straight and earn some money. I couldn't keep asking my parents for financial help, as they had already given me as much as they could.

In late fall of 1982, I proposed to Debbie, and to my surprise she said, "Yes." We started planning a formal wedding for the following fall, but were so anxious to get our lives started as a married couple, that we only made it about six months before we eloped! On May 21, 1983, we went to the home of the father of one of my close friends. He was an ordained minister who lived on a ranch about ten miles outside of Davis. In that rustic place, with a couple of good friends, Debbie and I said our vows and made it official.

Everyone knew we were going to be married, but no one expected us to elope. Her parents were helping plan the wedding, and were greatly disappointed with our surprise news. I don't blame them—I would have been extremely angry too if one of my kids did that. In place of the wedding, her parents still hosted a beautiful renewing of vows ceremony for us in a local church, and a nice reception at their home.

After the ceremony in West Covina, we returned to Davis for my final two years. Debbie continued working as a dental assistant and I was attending classes, studying, working part-time in an auto parts store, tutoring, and grading exams for money. Our lives were extremely busy.

And that's when it happened the first time.

Debbie and I were watching a local Sacramento TV talk show called *The Sally Jesse Rafael Show*. The host, Sally, had a guest on who owned a company in Las Vegas that helped reunite adoptees with their biological parents. The woman who owned that company simply asked adoptees to send her an application that included their birthdate, ethnicity (Caucasian, black, Asian, etc.) if known, the city or hospital where they were born, and their contact information. She also invited any mother who might be searching for a child they gave up to mail her the same information. Her company sorted through applications, and if they found a match, they would inform both the adoptee and the biological parent as well as provide their respective contact information. The parties only needed to pay a fee if her company found a match. In hindsight, this was quite a rudimentary method for reuniting adoptees and their birthparents, but it could certainly be effective for adoptees who were lucky enough to have a birth parent searching for them.

And just like that, that feeling returned, that dull curiosity pulling at me again. But this time it pulled at me a little harder, and for good reason. Debbie and I had been discussing when we would start trying to have our first child. I wanted to wait until after I graduated because I wanted to be more financially established. But what could the decision regarding the timing of our future children have to do with identifying my birth parents?

People who've grown up with their biological parents know about their family history. They know if heart disease, specific cancers, or diabetes are prominent within their genetic lines. Adoptees have no clue. Although for most adoptees, knowing about their genetic medical history is low on the totem pole for search reasons, they still would like to know. They want to know if they're potentially a carrier of some lethal disorder, and want to risk passing it along to their children. Moreover, it can become frustrating every time an adoptee tries to fill out a doctor's medical history form and has no answers. If a doctor asks them something about their family medical history when attempting to find the cause for some alarming symptoms or test results, the adoptee's answer is usually, "I don't know—I'm adopted." I wanted to know if I was a carrier of some rare disease before deciding to have children. Perhaps I could kill two birds with one stone—find a birth parent and obtain background medical history.

After watching that talk show, Debbie and I agreed it would be worth a shot to send my information to that company in Vegas and see if I was lucky enough that my birth mother was also looking for me. I didn't get my hopes up too high because I knew that could easily end in disappointment. I wasn't going to allow myself to go there, but it was the first time I remember having a strong desire to know something.

Months and then a year went by and nothing but the sound of crickets. My birth mother most likely wasn't looking for me. I felt a sense of disappointment, but that was only temporary. Sometime in the late fall of 1984 Debbie started feeling under the weather. You guessed it: despite our best efforts to wait until we were a bit more financially stable, she was pregnant. My slight disappointment about being unable to identify my birth mother quickly was overshadowed by excitement and fear. Not knowing my genetic history was a small concern compared to the fact that our baby was due only a few weeks after I would be graduating, and I didn't have a job lined up.

I mailed out applications to at least ten companies all over the Southwest, looking for employment after graduating. A few months later, I received a call back from the aerospace company Hughes Aircraft in Los Angeles. They flew me to LA, interviewed me, and gave me a tour of their facility. Two weeks later, I received a call informing me I had an engineering position. Whew! It was such a relief to have found steady income with a baby due in three months.

I finished my last college class in late May, and Hughes sent a truck to move all our stuff to a storage facility in Los Angeles until we could find a place to rent. I didn't even attend my graduation ceremony; the rush was on to get started at my new job because I needed to have been employed there for a month before my health insurance would cover the costs of delivering the baby.

Debbie had our daughter two weeks early, six days before I completed my first month at Hughes, and we had to pay cash for everything. I clearly recall handing over all the bills I had in my wallet, even counting out a few pieces of loose change to pay in full. It wasn't the best way to start parenting, but no price was too high for my cute little daughter.

Taking Midlife Risks

While I was still working for Hughes, and twenty-two months after our daughter was born, we welcomed our son into this world. We were living in a small condominium in a city adjacent to where Debbie and I grew up, so we were able to spend more time with our parents. Since we couldn't afford the rent for anything close to my office, my one-way commute through the heart of downtown Los Angeles was exactly forty-two miles and took about two hours each way on a good day. If there was an accident, I could spend as long as five hours total commuting. I enjoyed my job at Hughes and was later promoted to be a member of their technical staff, working solely as a physicist. But I was becoming burnt out from the traffic and knew I couldn't keep running on that kind of wheel and continue sacrificing so much time with my family.

In 1987, a close high school friend of mine named Kevin started a new communications business that sold pagers that received sports scores every five minutes. That pager also provided wagering odds for every major sport, horse race results, and served as a regular pager. Younger people may need to Google the term "pager," but they were cutting-edge technology in the late 1980s. This "Sports Pager" was mostly marketed toward the gambling community as well as those who wanted up to the minute sports results. The monthly subscription fee for one of these devices was $65, which was very expensive in 1987.

Kevin bought the franchise for Southern California from the parent company, who disseminated that information via satellite from Las Vegas. He was looking for someone to help him get it off the ground and asked me if I would be willing to "sell" those pagers to people in my spare time for a commission. I always liked having extra money, so I agreed to do it. He advertised in the sports sections of a couple of newspapers and when he received an order, he sent me to meet with the new client and complete the sale.

My first "sale" was at a pancake house in Beverly Hills at six in the morning on the way to my office. It was eye-opening to me because it revealed just how successful Kevin's business could become. I parked my three-cylinder car next to a black stretch limousine. A very pregnant woman, dressed in what appeared to be some Victoria's Secret lingerie and high heels, stepped out of the back of the limo and I met her at the front of her car. I later found out she was a Penthouse model. She asked me to confirm the total amount due if she prepaid for a year. I told her it was exactly $1,000. Before I could remove the pager from its box to begin explaining how to use it, she laid ten $100 bills on the hood of her limo. She seemed in a hurry, and was already getting ready to return to her car. Stunned that she had no questions about the product, I asked, "Don't you want me to show you how to use it?" She answered, "This is a gift for my husband. If he can't figure it out, he can call you, right?" I affirmed and she quickly slid into the back of her limo and her driver whisked her away.

That morning, I sat in my work cubicle with those ten $100 bills sitting on my desk. I'm not sure if I'd ever seen a $100 bill before. A coworker walked past my desk, saw the money, and asked, "Where did you get all that cash?" I reminded him of the startup business that I'd told him about weeks before and explained that the money was from my first sale. Kevin's business seemed headed for success, and I was certain to make a little extra money for myself.

I didn't really have to sell these devices to anyone because they sold themselves. All I did was deliver them to the customer, collect the money, and show them how to use it if they asked. I delivered them to movie and rock stars, as well as sports broadcasters, and even illegal bookmakers. I was sent to Frank Sinatra's house in Beverly Hills by his daughter Tina, who ordered one for her father as a Christmas present.

The business took off so fast that there was no way Kevin could efficiently handle it by himself. Two weeks after he bought the franchise, he called me at my office and asked me if I would meet him in downtown Los Angeles at the headquarters of the now defunct *Los Angeles Herald Examiner*. The newspaper wanted to run a big story about the revolutionary pager and Kevin wanted me to be there with him.

Two days later, the article ran on the front page of the sports section, complete with a huge picture of Kevin and me. I walked into my office at Hughes, and there were at least five cutouts from that morning's newspaper taped to the shelves of my cubicle. Every picture had been marked up with Sharpies by my coworkers; they added mustaches to my face and funny speech bubbles springing from my mouth. Although I had never mentioned my title at Kevin's company to the article's writer, the article listed me as the sales manager.

There was also a note on my desk asking me to report to the division manager immediately. I walked into his office, feeling intimidated, and he asked me point blank if I was selling these devices on company time. I honestly told him that I was not; I was merely delivering them before and after work.

In the next two weeks, things got more and more out of hand. Kevin was overwhelmed with phone calls, trying to meet the demand, and I was running all over LA before and after work, making deliveries. We couldn't just ship the pagers to our customers because many people needed us to show them how to operate it. Two weeks in, Kevin asked me if I would be willing to leave my job at Hughes and work with him full-time.

Leave my secure job that had taken six years of blood, sweat, and tears preparing for in college? I can still picture the look on my father's face when I told him what I was considering. He tilted his head slightly downward, and looked at me over the top his reading glasses, eyebrows raised as high as they could go. I remember him saying to me, "Are you crazy? You're going to just throw away everything you learned? You have two very young children and a wife to support. Are you really considering putting them at risk?" Remember, he had told me that college and a well-paying, secure job was my only option. He didn't want to see me working the way he did only to earn a modest income. I was worried about disappointing my dad, but I was even more concerned about my wife and kids if Kevin's business went under. But I had also seen just how lucrative Kevin's business was after only a month, and trying this new venture wouldn't diminish the skills I'd learned in college. I figured that if it didn't work out, I'd simply find another job in the aerospace industry.

22

I soon left Hughes to begin working full-time for Kevin. The work was fun, challenging, and I could schedule my deliveries around LA traffic so that my time on the road was greatly minimized. I worked for Kevin for about two years, until we discovered that the parent company was not collecting enough revenue from its other distributors. If the parent company went under, Kevin would lose everything, and I would be out of a job. I had stayed in contact with some friends I'd worked with at Hughes. They informed me that Hughes was losing many of their government contracts and that people were being laid off. I realized that if Kevin's company went down, it was unlikely that returning to Hughes in any capacity would be an option.

Kevin decided to protect his investment and sold his franchise back to the parent company in Vegas. He also convinced the company that they needed to hire me to ensure a smooth transition because I was the main contact point for all the customers in Southern California. Debbie was worried about what our lives would be like in a place like Las Vegas. We were very close friends with our next-door neighbors and leaving them was going to hurt. But I believed this would give us the opportunity for a better life than we could have in California, so I picked up my family and moved to Las Vegas in April of 1990. Most people perceive Vegas as "sin city." It's certainly never been known for its wholesomeness or as a good place to raise a family. But, after living here for thirty-one years, I can tell you that most neighborhoods here are no different from any neighborhood in the US. I remember just how difficult it was for Debbie when we first moved, and how she cried many times during that first year. After that, we made some good friends and life got much better for her.

I worked for them for two years before starting my own business in 1992. My new company remanufactured, repaired, and sold new and used pagers. The pager business was booming in the early 1990s and my company grew quickly. I went from being the only employee to having fifteen within two years. I owned that business for twenty-nine years before finally selling it.

I wasn't just taking risks by uprooting my family, taking a new job, moving to a new city, and starting a new business. I was also doing something that seems unthinkable to me today. From the moment we moved to Las Vegas I began gambling. My drug of choice was video poker. Like most addictions, it began with what seemed to be harmless short intervals of pleasure. Before I knew it, I was thinking about playing those machines throughout my workday and even when I was home with my family. I knew the odds were overwhelmingly against me. Even with my extensive math background, I was certain that the longer I continued to play, the more I would lose. But that head knowledge didn't quell my desire to play. Maybe I was looking for an outlet to escape the pressures of work and my responsibilities at home. Perhaps I was following in my dad's footsteps, finding something to escape the realities of my life. I could sit in front of those machines for six to eight hours if I got lucky, and only an hour or two after the wall-mounted ATM refused to provide me with another dime. I rarely left a casino with more money than I had entered with. It was lucky we didn't have a lot of money the first few years we lived in Vegas, because there's no telling how much I could have lost. As much as I am ashamed to admit it, I continually lied to Debbie, telling her that I was meeting with clients through the late-night hours, while losing hundreds of dollars we didn't have.

I continued to attend church with my family, and nobody knew about my secret gambling habit. In early 1993, our church on the east side of Las Vegas birthed a new church in the northwest, closer to our home. They hired a pastor from Kentucky and another from Ohio to lead it. We met on the gym floor of a local YMCA with the other three hundred and fifty people who had left our parent church.

About four months after we started our new church, our pastor invited one of his friends from Kentucky to give his testimony at our Wednesday night service. This guest speaker had spent four years in a Kentucky prison for embezzling from the bank where he served as vice president. Why did he embezzle? He needed to feed his gambling addiction.

He was an elder in my pastor's former church in Kentucky at the time of his arrest. He wrote over $250,000 in fraudulent loans to fuel his habit. He told us how he'd written a suicide note, then sat in his car in a vacant parking lot for eight hours, where he stuck a gun in his mouth and urinated on himself, waiting for the authorities to show up. I sat in that auditorium with tears streaming down my face as I listened to him give his gut-wrenching testimony. I related in so many ways to his suffering and addiction.

I could identify with many of his struggles, and the emotional toll gambling had taken on my own life. I remembered that on many occasions after the ATM cut me off, I frantically ran back to my car and desperately dug through my seats to find loose change, hoping to parlay that into winning some portion of my money back. I was always watching the clock to make sure I was home by midnight or one, so that it was somewhat believable when I explained to Debbie that I'd been working late.

My wife told me that our seven-year-old daughter once asked her, "Is daddy's car going to be in the driveway tonight, or is it going to be out all night like it always is?" I was living in guilt and shame. My world was caving in, and I was completely lost as I sat in that church at my emotional "rock bottom." I knew I was failing as a Christian husband and father and hearing this guy from Kentucky tell his story literally brought me to my knees. I knew my life needed to change.

When Debbie and I arrived home that night, I couldn't stop crying. After putting the kids to bed, we sat on our couch and I told her everything about my gambling and my lies and that I was sincerely ready to change.

My lustful desire to have a series of affairs with video poker machines had destroyed whatever trust Debbie had in me and any measure of integrity I had for myself. She deserved to be with someone better than me, and I'll never understand why she chose to stay. But I was honestly ready to get right with my wife and children. Gambling had led me to a place of quiet desperation, and it had made my life miserable.

I attended my first Gamblers Anonymous (GA) meetings at our small, portable church. For a long time, it was just me and the guy who started it. Luke was a humble pillar of strength for me. He also took me to local GA meetings around town, and then I started going to those meetings alone. I remember thinking, how could a "good" guy like me end up in a room full of strangers, introducing myself by saying, "My name is Jeff, and I'm a compulsive gambler"? My gambling addiction humbled me, and even though I've been clean since 1993, I know that I'm only one quarter and one video poker machine away from failing all over again.

As I was getting my life cleaned up and incrementally earning Debbie's trust, life in Las Vegas was becoming increasingly exciting, and not because of its attractions. Our family life was wonderful, and Debbie and I were deeply involved with our church and our children's activities. Our daughter was participating in Hunter Jumper competitions, which involved her jumping horses over fences. Every time I watched her fly over a fence, my heart stopped beating. Our son was playing basketball and I coached him during his early years before high school. We loved the weather there and our parents were only a three-and-a-half-hour drive away. Las Vegas was exploding in population and the city was growing exponentially. We moved from a modest small house into a larger home in a brand-new development. And then four years later, it happened to me again.

[3]

THE PULL OF A FREIGHT TRAIN

IT HAPPENED TO ME AGAIN IN 1997, WHEN I WAS THIRTY-SIX YEARS old. I was watching yet another TV talk show, *The Montel Williams Show*. I know it might seem I spent my days watching talk shows, but I didn't. I just happened to turn on the TV on a day they were featuring a story about two half-brothers in their late thirties who'd both been adopted, shared the same birth mother, and would be meeting on stage for the first time. I know with DNA technology today, it's common to see these kinds of reunions. But in 1997 that technology was not available and biological family reunions were infrequent.

Brothers!? Siblings!? What? In all the years after learning I was adopted, not once did I consider the possibility of having siblings. I'd only been curious about the identity and physical features of my birth parents, never about any other biological relatives.

The two brothers walked out on stage, and they resembled each other in so many ways. They had the same hairstyle and so many similar facial features. They hugged each other and began sharing the details of their personal lives. I wondered, "Is there someone else out there that may look like me? Did either of my birth parents have other children and did they keep them or were they also farmed out through adoption?" For some reason, seeing those two brothers meet for the first time rocked my world. Before I'd felt a slight tugging pull to identify my biological roots; now it felt like I was chained to the back of a freight train that was dragging me down the tracks. I had to do something about it.

At the end of the show, they provided the phone number of a national adoption searching resource. I called that number, and after telling them I was adopted in Los Angeles, they provided me with the phone number to the County of Los Angeles Department of Records.

It's important to note that the internet was in its infancy in 1997. Email was just becoming popular, and the number of websites was very limited. There wasn't a site where I could learn about their adoption record services or what I needed to obtain information. Even fancy new home computers were only using 512 baud modems and the wait and buffering times could be extensive. The telephone was still the main way to communicate and fax machines were the dominant method for transmitting documents.

When I called that records department, they informed me that all adoption records for the state of California were completely sealed. To protect the anonymity that was legally promised to one or both birth parents, no adoptee had the legal right to obtain that information. I thought, "What about my rights? Don't I deserve to know something about my genetic medical background? Don't I have the right to know where I came from or the circumstances that led to my dismissal?"

There are exceptions to the law, but they are few and far between. A California adoptee can petition a court judge to unseal their original birth records, but the adoptee's reasoning would almost always need to involve life-threating circumstances. Judges rarely grant judgments in favor of adoptees for their original birth records.

The woman on the other end of the line explained to me that adoptees were entitled to "nonidentifying" birth family background information. She stated that when my birth mother met with the agency prior to my birth, they asked her questions about her physical features, her family history, and other information that may be of interest to the adopted child if they ever requested it. But she made it clear that there would not be any information within that background document that could lead anyone to identifying their birth parents. She also explained that to obtain that nonidentifying information, I would need to submit a formal request that would require my notarized signature.

Then she told me it could take up to a year from the date they received my request to compile that information. A year! I was on fire to know something and the thought of having to wait that long was devastating. She told me they needed that time to retrieve those thirty-six-year-old records and then a case worker would review the information my birth mother had provided and either accept what was already written or rewrite a different summary.

I had no choice but to wait. I just went on with my life, knowing full well that the information coming my way wasn't likely to lead me anywhere. What I didn't know at the time was that there were experienced people out there who had knowledge and access to information regarding adoption searches. Some of them did it voluntarily and others as a business.

Discovering My Background

About nine months later, and after returning home from my office, Debbie handed me an envelope from Los Angeles County's Department of Children and Family Services (DCFS). My heart sank as I tore open the envelope. Word for word, here's the information it provided:

JEFF EDDINS

Birth Family Background Information
Adoptee: Jeffrey Brian Eddins
DOB: 5-19-1961

Your birth mother contacted our agency in March of 1961. She was described by our social worker to be a tall, large boned woman, who was striking in appearance. Initially she seemed somewhat restrained, not entering into discussions easily, but later came across as a very warm person. Your birth mother was 34 years old, born in Missouri. She was 5'8" tall, weighed 130 lbs., with green eyes and brown hair. She had fair skin, and stated she was of medium build and in good health. She is of English, German, Scotch and Irish descent, and Protestant religion. Your birth mother enjoyed music, singing, and sewing. She had completed through the 10th grade in school.

Your birth mother was a power sewing machine operator at a sewing factory. She intended to work as long as possible prior to your birth, in order to support herself and her daughter. She impressed the social worker as being very self-sufficient and ended up working until a month before your birth. She had moved to California in August of 1960. Both her parents lived in Missouri.

Your birth mother was very involved in trying to be supportive to her 15-year-old daughter (your half-sister), whose husband was killed in an automobile accident a few months prior. Your sister was also expecting a baby at any time. She had only been married a short time before her husband died. Your birth mother and birth sister lived together, and your birth mother was worried and focused on helping your sister get through this situation. She wanted her to be able to continue with her education to at least get her high school certificate so that she would later be able to get a decent job to support herself and her child. Because of their situation, your birth mother felt that adoption had a lot more to offer you.

Your birth mother was single at the time of your half-sister's birth in 1945. Your birth mother later got married (to another man) in 1956. They subsequently separated in 1957. Your birth mother was not happy in this marriage, stating that he was not a good father to her daughter. She had not had contact with him for over a year. There were no children from this marriage.

Your birth maternal grandmother was 65 years old, 5'6" tall, 160 lbs. with dark brown hair, green eyes and fair skin. She had completed through the 8th grade in school. Your maternal grandfather was 65, stood 6'3" tall, was 180 lbs., with brown hair, green eyes and fair skin. He worked as a farmer. They were both living in Missouri. Your mother had three siblings. The oldest was a sister, age 39. She was a housewife and had a 10th grade education. She was 5'6" tall, 140 lbs., blue eyes and black hair. Next was her brother, age 36. He was a high school graduate and was in the Navy. He was 6'2", 175 lbs., with green eyes and dark brown hair. It didn't clearly state whether the next sibling was male or female. I can only assume it was a male from the physical description given, age 34, 6'2" tall, 175 lbs., green eyes and brown hair. He had graduated college, and was a minister. There were no known health problems in the family. Your half-sister, who was 16 at the time of your birth, had blonde hair, green eyes, and stood 5'6" tall. She had a baby a few months before your birth.

Your birth mother was very apologetic that she did not know a lot of information about your birth father. She described him to be Caucasian of English descent and Protestant religion. He was born in 1926, was 6'2" tall, weighed 190 lbs. with brown eyes and hair. He had a husky build, fair skin, and was reported to be in good health. She did not know about his family background and believed he was separated.

On 5-19-61, you were born at John Wesley Hospital, weighing 10 lbs. 4 Oz, and 23 inches long. You were born by cesarean section.

Your birth mother seemed depressed after your birth, as the decision for adoption was difficult for her. Eventually, after giving a lot of thought, she decided that she felt adoption was best for you under the circumstances, although it was difficult for her to do so.

Since your birth mother was still married, legal proceedings ensued to give her sole custody status, which took a couple of months, delaying your adoption. She signed relinquishment papers in December 1961. Your birth mother regretted that you were not able to enter your adoptive home much sooner, and was very anxious for you to do so. She requested information about your adoptive family. After your birth, your mother found a job and began working as a waitress.

On 5-26-61, you were discharged from the hospital and placed in a foster home who cared for you prior to your adoption. You were received warmly in the home and well cared for. You adjusted to this home without crying or fussing. The foster mother felt you were a nice-looking well-developed newborn. You had blue eyes (later said to be brown), dark brown rather long hair with a tendency to curl, clear fair skin. You appeared alert for a seven-day old baby.

On 6-6-61 you saw a pediatrician since you were troubled slightly with colic and had lost some weight. In July the doctor recommended circumcision for you, which took place on 7-18-61. You healed nicely one week later. You were sleeping though the night and progressing fine.

At 2 ½ months, you were eating well. Physically you looked the same. Additionally, you were described to be robust in appearance and had a double chin.

At 6 months you were crawling and trying to walk. You were a good looking, brown eyed boy, that was said to be a very happy child, and was easy to handle. Your foster mother's children were said to "love you very much" and they enjoyed you.

At 7 months, it was observed by the foster mother that one of your feet turned out slightly and stated that you were eager to walk. You were a very friendly baby, said to be crawling all over the place. You were said to be a "good, cute boy".

On 1-5-62, your adoptive parents met you, they both took to you immediately, and you responded to them with a very broad smile. Your adoptive parents signed the adoption placement papers that day and took you home with them.

Your adoption was finalized on 3-25-63

There it was. On two-and-a-half sheets of paper, all the actions and decisions of my birth mother, her daughter, and the fatal car accident of my half-sister's husband that determined the course of my life. Not a single portion of it in my control.

I remember thinking how amazing the letter was, and just how much information was included. I immediately went into detective mode, trying to sort through the facts and ascertain what I considered to be important. I discovered later that solving these types of mysteries is in my blood. I'm also addicted to watching all those murder mysteries like *Dateline* and *48 Hours*.

During those early stages, I was feeling an anxious rush of emotions. Although it was exciting for me to discover the physical descriptions of some of my birth family, I found myself more interested in trying to read between the lines for any clues that may have helped me find my birth family. I wrote the following short summary of clues, along with my thoughts and questions about what I'd gleaned from my birth mother's claims through the words of that social worker.

- She claimed to move to California in August of 1960, and it was highly probable that she carried me to full term (C-Section). Since I was born on May19, 1961, counting back the forty-week gestation period meant I must have been conceived in August of 1960. Where did she come from, and was she already impregnated before she arrived in California, or was she impregnated immediately after she arrived? Knowing that information could possibly help me determine where my birth father lived at that time.

- My maternal side originates from Missouri. Green eyes are dominant in that family, but I have brown eyes like my birth father. I'm not 6'2" but only 6'0".

- My birth mother claimed she was thirty-four years old while visiting the agency in March of 1961. So, depending on her birth month, she must have been born in 1926.

- I have a half-sister who was married and pregnant at the age of fifteen. Wow! She is about sixteen years older than I am and has a baby (my half-niece or nephew) born a few months before me. Apparently, my half-sister kept her baby.

- My half-sister's husband was killed only a "few months prior" to my birth mother's initial intake session with the adoption agency in March of 1961. "A few months prior" could mean he was killed sometime around the holiday seasons of New Year's or maybe even near Christmas or Thanksgiving of 1960.

- I have two maternal uncles and one maternal aunt. My grandparents had surely passed away at the time I received this information, thirty-seven years after the document stated they were sixty-five years old.

- Unless there was a typo, my half-sister's sixteenth birthday must have occurred between the time in March of 1961 when my birth mother was initially contacting the agency, and the time I was born on May 19, 1961. She was initially reported to be pregnant at fifteen, when my birth mother first met with the agency, then later to be sixteen at the time of my birth. So, her birthday was likely between March 1 and May 19.

- I was likely to be the product of a one-night stand. If she was being truthful, my birth mother only seemed to know my birth father's age and his physical characteristics. She didn't appear to know anything about his family other than that he may have been separated. She claimed he was of English descent, which makes me wonder if he was from England and spoke with an English accent. Or did she mean that he was born and raised in the US, but his blood line originated from England, or merely that he spoke English? But if it was only a one-night stand, how could my birth mother have known that my birth father was a Protestant? How often do religious affiliations get mentioned during a one-time sexual rendezvous?

- Unless I locate my birth mother alive, and she knows or is willing to divulge my birth father's complete name, it's going to be an impossible task to identify him. There's really nothing to go on, given what's provided in this background document.

- My birth mother seems to have what I consider a legitimate reason to give me up. I was not a throw-away kid. She surrendered me because she wouldn't be able to financially support my widowed half-sister, her baby, and me. She also seemed to be very concerned about my well-being and claimed to be distressed when she realized I couldn't be immediately adopted because of her need to seek full custody through the courts. In some way, that makes me feel better. But I do wonder why she didn't consider requiring her widowed young daughter to give up her child for adoption, rather than giving me up.

- I was stuck in foster care for at least seven months. Did I receive the care I needed or was I placed with many other children, in a home where my needs were minimized? Did not having the love and attention of a full-time mother during that time have any effect on me developmentally?

What I couldn't know is if the claims or feelings my birth mother shared were completely true, embellished, or completely false. True or not, it was all I had to go on, and at some point, I hoped to put the pieces of the puzzle together and finally identify and meet with someone genetically tied to me.

[4]

CHASING THE CLUES

IT WAS TIME TO GET STARTED, BUT I WAS EXTREMELY BUSY WITH work, church activities, and family. Trying to fit this search into my schedule wasn't going to be easy.

After reviewing the background information multiple times, it seemed the best place to start was trying to identify my half-sister's deceased husband. If I could identify him, maybe I could locate his marriage record to my half-sister, which might reveal her maiden name. And hopefully her maiden name would be the same as my birth mother's maiden name, since my birth mother wasn't married at the time my half-sister was born in 1945.

I was hoping there would be an obituary in a Los Angeles newspaper, but how many people died in car accidents in LA from about November of 1960 to early January of 1961? That background document stated that my half-sister's husband was killed a "few" months prior to March of 1961. Since it wasn't a natural death, perhaps there was a story in one of the multiple LA newspapers that described that accident and identified the victim. In a city as large as LA, there were mostly simple lists of names and dates of death notices in the obituary sections, not detailed stories listing surviving family members or anything personal. Surviving family members usually had to pay the newspaper to post a narrative obituary. If there wasn't a descriptive obituary, I needed to find an article regarding a fatal car accident that identified my half-sister's deceased husband.

But I had another problem conducting this search. That document didn't say that my half-sister and her husband were living in LA at the time of his death. It said my half-sister was living in LA with my birth mother after his death. It also said my birth mother moved to California in August of 1960, but it didn't say her fifteen-year-old daughter lived there with her at that time. If my half-sister and her husband lived out of state, and her husband was not killed in LA, I could be wasting a lot of time. I just had to hope that they were all living in LA at the time of his death.

I went to one of the many libraries on the campus of The University of Nevada Las Vegas (UNLV) to see if I could find archives of newspaper articles from the *Los Angeles Times,* which had the highest circulation in the city. They had years of complete archives of that newspaper on microfiche cassette rolls. I began searching every relevant page of every day between November 1 of 1960 and January 31 of 1961. If you're not familiar with microfiche cassettes, they are basically film rolls of miniature photographs that are housed inside of a larger plastic cassette or even on a plastic roll. They were used to preserve newspapers and catalogs or other historical documents. A machine allowed the end user to view the images on the cassettes on a larger screen. You could quickly speed through the pages of a newspaper or go from page to page. But the machines didn't allow a person to make a query regarding any information contained on those films. Instead, the researcher had to review each page to find what they were looking for.

Finding an article about my half-sister's husband seemed like a daunting task, but I knew I wouldn't need to search every section of each daily paper. The story wasn't going to be found in the classified section, or the sports section (unless he was a race car driver). I started in November, and luckily, when I arrived on November 26, 1960, in the local community news section there was a large photo of a girl sitting on the edge of a curb. She had her head tilted down so I couldn't see all of her face, but it was a photo accompanying the story about a car accident that had occurred at night. I could see a mangled car in the background, but what shocked me was that the girl sitting on the curb appeared to be pregnant. The caption under the photograph stated that the girl and her husband had been involved in bad car accident on Fairfax Avenue and her husband had been transported to a local hospital. The photo was taken the night before the article was published on the 26th, and the article was probably written the night of the accident because the article did not say if the husband died. To my surprise, that article listed the complete names of that young married couple, which is exactly what I needed.

It was incredible! I was certain I was on my way to figuring everything out. The girl in that picture must have been my half-sister. How likely was it that other young married pregnant couples would be in bad car accidents during that three to four-month time period? I printed a grainy picture of that microfiche photo from the library and brought it home to show Debbie, convinced that the girl in that picture was my half-sister.

Now I just needed to find the marriage certificate for the couple. If my half-sister used our birth mother's last name (either her maiden name or her married name from 1956), I'd have an important piece to the puzzle. Those records weren't available online at the time like they are now. Today, if you subscribe to one of the many genealogical websites, that kind of search can be completed in a matter of seconds. But in 1998, the only place to find that information was to drive to the LA courthouse and physically search their copies of records.

So, a couple of days later, I was off on a five-hour drive to downtown LA to look for my answers. I was so excited that my detective work was about to pay off as the pieces were beginning to fall into place. I felt that in some way, I was outsmarting and circumventing the constraints they put on the background information designed to keep the identities of the birth parents anonymous.

After about an hour of searching, I found that couple's marriage certificate. My heart was racing as I perused the information on the document. But the first thing I noticed was that the age of the wife was four years older than my half-sister would have been in 1960. And they were married in LA in 1957, so it was clear I didn't have the right people. Their names were so uncommon that it was unlikely I'd located the wrong marriage certificate. The girl in that car accident picture was not my half-sister. Talk about letting the air out of a balloon. I'd just been on a wild goose chase of my own making. The drive back to Las Vegas from LA felt like the longest five-hours of my life. Now what would I do?

The only way to find my half-sister's deceased husband was to go back to the UNLV library and continue searching the *Los Angeles Times* from November 26, 1960, where I'd stopped a few days before after identifying the wrong couple. I spent the next week going through each day's newspaper, looking for stories on young car accident victims, but nothing came up. The other problem was that there were other smaller, local newspapers from different suburbs of LA that may have included that car accident story. There were too many of those newspapers to consider locating that incident. Not only that, at the time, the UNLV library didn't have archives of them available.

A few days later, I decided to reach out to the case worker who sent my background document. Her name was Grace Chan and she had seemed willing to help me. Obviously, she wasn't just going to just divulge the information I desired, but she did fax me a list of the names and phone numbers of people who helped adoptees search for their biological families.

The first and only person I contacted on that list was a woman named Gail Beckstead. She lived in Simi Valley, California, which is a suburb twenty minutes north of LA. Gail told me that she was in her mid-sixties, a fellow adoptee, and that she had solved her own case from Chicago many years ago. She worked from home and explained that she charged an hourly fee for her work. Her rate wasn't astronomical, but I had no idea just how long it would take her to give me what I needed. She appeared to be extremely knowledgeable about how to search, and we seemed compatible over the phone. So, I hired her.

Here's what still perplexes me to this day about Gail: somehow, either through legal or illegal means, she told me she possessed copies of the original California birth index records recorded on microfiche. She also claimed to have a machine to read those records. If she didn't have those records and machine, perhaps she knew and paid someone at the LA County Children and Family Services to illegally give her information as she requested it. At the time, I didn't have the courage to ask her how she "legally" obtained those records, and she's likely to have passed on by now.

The records Gail had access to were not the public records available to everyone else. These records displayed the last names of the birth mothers (the name the birth mother listed at the time of delivery), and the name assigned by the birth mother to each child born in California all the way to back to 1949. The records available to the public did not contain any records for adoptees. Today, if I showed up at the LA County Hall of Records and searched for my original birth record, it wouldn't be there, and if I used Ancestry.com's search engine, my original birth record wouldn't show up in the California birth index.

But Gail simply asked me for my birthdate and if I was sure that I had been adopted in Los Angeles. Within a matter of hours, she found multiple male babies who'd been born on May 19, 1961, in LA County. Each of the records listed the name the birth mother provided on the original birth certificates of each child. It was common practice at that time for mothers who were giving their children up for adoption to use gender terms for the names of their children. For example, many women used the term "Baby" for a child's first name, and "Boy" or "Girl" for a child's middle name. Some mothers used their maiden names after the first and gender middle names of the child, or if they were married at one time, they may have used their current legal married name.

These generalized gender names were not a requirement of the state. In fact, a woman giving up a child for adoption could give the child a complete legitimate first and middle name of their choosing, along with their maiden or married last name. Since these records of mothers giving up their children were never to be made public, specific first and middle names were irrelevant. I just needed my birth mother to have listed a legitimate (maiden, married, or former married) last name on my original birth certificate and that birth index Gail was searching to identify her.

She found many male children born in LA on my birthday. Now she needed to decipher which one of these male children and associated parent record belonged to me. Luckily, there was only one record with "Baby Boy" listed as first and middle name; that eighth record was likely to belong to an adoptee, and thus likely to be mine. If Gail had the correct record, my official name was listed as "Baby Boy Heady." Was Heady my birth mother's maiden name or her married name? The background document only mentioned her being married once to a man in 1956 and then separated in 1957, but they didn't officially get divorced until seven months after I was born in 1961.

Gail decided that the best way forward was to go to the LA County Hall of Records to see if she could find a marriage certificate from 1956 or a divorce decree from 1961 for a woman with either a maiden or married name of Heady. Knowing my birth mother hadn't finalized her divorce until late 1961 so I could be released to my adoptive parents helped narrow the search.

Gail only lived twenty minutes away from downtown LA, so it was a lot quicker and easier for her to go than me. But she was taking a chance of wasting her time as I had done weeks earlier with my car accident picture wild goose chase. If Gail couldn't find the divorce record and needed to search for a marriage record, we might have ended up empty-handed. That background document didn't say if my birth mother was married in LA or even California for that matter. And we knew she moved to California in August of 1960, which made it unlikely she was married in California in 1956. Gail and I were taking a chance that my birth mother was living in LA in 1956, got married there, then sometime after she separated in 1957 moved away, only to return to California in August 1960.

Gail's bet paid off. She searched for hours through those records and found both what she believed to be the divorce record and the marriage certificate belonging to my birth mother. She called me, sounding as excited as I was to hear it. If we had the correct woman, my birth mother's maiden name was Betty Jo Lewis, and she married a man named John Ray Heady on August 6, 1956 in Los Angeles. This woman, "Betty Heady" (I know that sounds funny) stated her age was thirty on that marriage certificate, which matched the age she would have been in 1956, according to the background document (born 1926). This was unbelievable news. But before I could really begin to celebrate, I immediately came to the realization that although this was a step forward, trying to locate her would be difficult. Was she still in LA? Did she move back to her home state of Missouri? Was she still alive? I'd already calculated that if she was still alive in 1998, she would be about seventy-two years old.

I realized that my yearning to find her had become way more intense than it had been at any other time in my life. I knew I was getting closer, and that brought waves of anxiety over me. I had so much I wanted to tell her about my life. I certainly had some reservations, too. If I found her, she may not want to have anything to do with me. I couldn't know what the feeling of being rejected for the second time would be like, but I wasn't going to let that fear stop my pursuit. Debbie believed I was becoming obsessed with this search, and she was probably right. The thought of siblings had first driven me to this place, but admittedly, I was yearning to meet my birth mother.

The End to the Beginning

As I mentioned previously, the internet in the late 1990s was barren compared to today: there were far fewer websites and the tools for searching anything in detail. There were a few websites, such as WhitePages.com, to help locate addresses and phone numbers, but even they didn't have the record capacity or personal details provided in the search tools of today. Locating my birth mother was going to be harder than finding a needle in a haystack.

A couple of days went by as I waited to hear from Gail about our next move. I wondered again whether my birth mother was alive. And, if not, was there somewhere to search records to find out? And that's when it hit me.

I wondered if there were paper or microfiche records that showed the names of all the people with a Social Security number who'd died. But I didn't know where to find that information. I called the UNLV library, but they didn't have those records on file. I was talking with my receptionist Nancy about it, and she had the bright idea to see if we could find that information on the internet. I stood behind Nancy at her desk as she used the old search engine Alta Vista (Google didn't exist yet) to look for the right Social Security website.

We found it: it was the actual government run and maintained Social Security Death Index website, and it contained a list of everyone who died with a valid Social Security number. Unlike today, it was free to search. Nancy navigated to the website and my heart started pounding because I was so afraid of what might show up on her screen. She entered my birth mother's name as "Betty Jo Heady" and within ten seconds, two records surfaced with the same name. The first record floored me, and I will never forget that sinking feeling. It had to be my birth mother because the first piece of data I recognized was her birth year in 1926. That one little moment of discovery crushed the depths of my entire spirit. If Nancy hadn't been in the room with me, I may have collapsed on the floor and broken down in tears.

There it was, right in front of my eyes: she was dead. In an instant, this recent hope of meeting her was gone. I'd never be able to show her that I had become a responsible person, respected others, and tried to live my life the right way. I'd never get to show her pictures of me growing up and in all my football uniforms. She'd never meet my family and see her two beautiful grandchildren. I'd never be able to learn if everything she told the social worker at the agency was accurate. And with such limited information about my birth father in the background document, I'd never be able to ask her who he was.

But nearly as heart-crushing was the other information provided on that record:

Betty Jo Heady

SS#: 498-24-2955

Birth Date: 22 October 1926

Issue Year: Before 1951

Issue State: Missouri

Last Residence: **89102 Las Vegas (Clark County Nevada)**

Death date: **27 July 1992**

Burial Site: **Palm Mortuary Las Vegas (Clark County Nevada)**

I was stunned. I remember thinking, "This just can't be. This can't be happening to me. She died in Las Vegas in 1992, two years and three months after we moved here in April of 1990!" We were living in the same city for more than two years. I may have walked past her on the sidewalk and not even known it. There were only 600,000 people living in Las Vegas when we moved there in 1990. I was angry with myself for not starting my search for her sooner, and now there was nothing I could do about it. It was such devastating news, and a flood of frustration overcame me.

Palm Mortuary, where my birth mother was lying in her grave, was only a five-minute drive from my office. I immediately phoned the mortuary to confirm she was buried there and after receiving confirmation, like a moth to a light, I drove there. I stepped out of my car and checked the plot map to determine the location of her grave. It was in the far back corner of the graveyard, and the lawn was not well groomed like the rest of the graveyard. The small flat concrete headstones were covered with weeds and grass, but eventually, I managed to find it.

Her name, date of birth, and date of death were listed on a small metal plaque. I stood there as tears poured down my cheeks in a violent, untamed river. I had never known her and yet I felt connected to her. I was now sobbing like a two-year-old child who's just been told "no!" This was the person who'd given me life. Irrespective of the circumstances that caused my conception (one night stand, rape, or a bad boyfriend), she had carried me to full term and made sure I would be cared for. Perhaps she gave me opportunities I never would have had with her, but at the time, I couldn't know if it was true.

I was picturing her bones beneath the metal plaque, and morbid as it was, I realized it was physically the closest I'd been to her in thirty-seven years. I squatted down and removed the overgrown weeds that were obstructing the information on her headstone, as if by doing so, I was honoring her in some way. In that moment, I began to wonder about something I believe almost everyone considers, but has no way of knowing. Was my birth mother in some spiritual realm in which she was observing me hovering over her grave and mourning her loss? I don't really believe there's any truth to the premise. But for that moment I did contemplate the possibility she'd been watching me.

Then, all alone in that back corner of the graveyard, I knelt on the grass next to her grave and began to reflect on the entirety of my life. Life had been good to me, and in one very important way, my birth mother was responsible for that. I felt I owed her some level of devotion because without her, not only would I not be here but neither would my children and future grandchildren. I wanted to call my mom and dad, but I was in no condition to try to do that. After about an hour, I tried to wipe the tears from my face, but the effort was futile. They just wouldn't stop flowing. After a moment, I finally pulled myself together enough to open my flip phone and call my parents. They knew I had started this search over a year before, and that I was getting closer to identifying her.

My mom answered the phone and through my trembling voice, I uttered, "I found her." Before she could respond, I added, "I'm kneeling at her grave." She was shocked to hear that I had found her, but even more surprised to learn that she was in Las Vegas and had already passed away. My mother reminded me just how thankful she was that my birth mother relinquished me because it gave my parents the opportunity to have me. She knew I was disappointed to find my birth mother had passed away, but she comforted me by reminding me just how much she and my dad loved me.

My mom's comments regarding her appreciation of my birth mother reminded me of a poem she had given me in my early thirties, long before I started searching. She had made me a beautiful scrapbook filled with photos from my childhood, my report cards, newspaper clippings about my athletic accomplishments, and all my sports team pictures. The poem that she included in her own handwritten calligraphy is as follows:

> Child
>
> of my heart and dreams
>
> yet not of my womb,
>
> protected and nourished by another
>
> who gave you life,
>
> yet loved and loved and loved by me.
>
> My heart says thank you to the one who gave you life,
>
> and then gave you to me.

My mother had always felt a deep sense of gratitude toward a birth mother she'd never met, and I have always appreciated that about her.

I didn't know at the time just how deep my thankfulness and appreciation for my parents would turn out to be. And, as I walked out of the cemetery toward my car, little did I know there was something else of interest in that graveyard that I was completely unaware of.

[5]

NEEDLE IN A HAYSTACK

THE REALIZATION THAT MY BIRTH MOTHER WAS GONE WAS unthinkable to me. Knowing that she had passed on only six years before I began my search was extremely difficult to accept. Why did I wait so long to start? I blew it! But I had to get over it. I needed to know more about her and, more importantly, I wanted pictures of her, and to find my half-sister who had given birth to a baby just months before my birth. I knew that if I could find my half-sister, she would probably be able to provide pictures and information about my birth mother.

When I first started my business, I spent hours each day cold-calling potential clients all over the country. Cold calling isn't easy, especially when the person on the other end of the phone knows your motives are financial gain. Although I experienced a lot of rejection and a lot of hang ups, I found I had a knack for it.

Since I knew from my birth mother's marriage certificate that her maiden name was Lewis, and I knew from the background report that my birth mother's family was from Missouri, I thought about searching for all the "Lewises" in Missouri on WhitePages.com. I also knew that my grandfather was a farmer, so that likely meant that he and his family lived at one time in a more rural part of the state. I also had two uncles who, if alive, carried that Lewis surname with them. And if they had children, I had a greater opportunity to find someone who knew about my birth mother. But Lewis is a common surname, and Missouri had a vast number of rural towns. I knew this wasn't going to be easy, but I also knew that the puzzle pieces which together revealed my story were not going to assemble themselves.

I bought a map of Missouri and had it blown up so I could clearly see all the different counties and towns in the state. That was helpful because I could also look up online the population counts of the cities and towns I wasn't familiar with. I never considered any of the larger, more populated cities. There were about five different area codes in that state and the "314" area code included the urban area of Saint Louis. So, I temporarily eliminated that area code for my initial search. I was looking for hillbillies and they weren't as likely to be found in a big city like St. Louis. My grandparents were almost certainly deceased, and it wasn't likely that all of their children were still living in the same town they grew up in. But I was hoping that at least one of my uncles or my aunt or any of their children might still be living there.

So, I ran a search on WhitePages.com and nearly burned out my old reel-driven dot matrix printer because there were so many Lewises in Missouri. I made call after call after call and made a note if there was no answer, if the number was no good, or if I left a message on the answering machine. Many phone numbers were not in service, and others didn't belong to anyone with the name of Lewis. As I mentioned, older search engines like WhitePages.com were not filled with accurate information as they are today. I repeated the same explanation to every person that I reached that I was adopted and trying to find people in the Lewis family who may have been related to a woman named Betty Jo Lewis. Many times, I let the conversation go on too long after someone I was speaking with showed a moderate amount of interest in or sympathy for me. Sometimes, people I'd left recorded messages with tried to call me back when I was on the line with others. I was becoming exhausted, but this was divide and conquer, and giving up was not an option.

I abandoned most of my business-related work for the next week. On the fifth day of calls, my efforts paid off. I reached a woman in the town of Lilbourn, Missouri. It was a rural town with a population of about thirteen hundred people. After reciting my story for what seemed like the millionth time, she seemed to get excited. She told me that she knew of my birth mother's family, and they all lived in Lilbourn many years ago. This woman's married name was Lewis, but it was her husband that was distantly related to my birth family. She said she'd lost track of all the people in my birth family, and many of the elder ones had already passed away. She told me that I needed to contact an elderly woman named Mabel who owned a pet grooming business on Main Street in Lilbourn. She was certain that Mabel would be able to help, and provided her phone number to me.

Needle in a haystack? Or was this just another set-up for disappointment? I was certainly leery of any news that appeared to be favorable. I'd seen that movie before. It seemed too good to be true that I may have struck gold after less than a week of calling. I had expected to be making cold calls for weeks and likely never getting anywhere.

But I called Mabel. I called her three times the first day and at least three times the next. There wasn't an answering machine to leave a message. Finally, on the third day, an elderly, feeble voice answered and identified herself as Mabel. She was ninety-three years old and still working as a dog groomer two days a week. Two days a week explained why she didn't answer the first two days, and in a town of only thirteen hundred people, just how many dogs or cats could there be to justify working more than that?

As soon as I began to tell my story, this apparently quick-witted (and certainly not feeble) woman cut me off and told me she'd been expecting my call, as the woman who'd referred me to her had given her the heads-up. What Mabel told me next would blow the doors off nearly everything I needed and wanted to know.

Mabel told me she had been a very close friend to my grandmother, Ora Lee Lewis, who was married to my grandfather, Matt Lee Lewis. As expected, both of my grandparents had passed away years earlier. She told me that in their later years (sometime in the early 1960s), my grandparents moved from Lilbourn to the nearby larger town of Cape Girardeau, Missouri. Then she proceeded give me the names of my aunt and two uncles. My aunt, my birth mother's sister, was named Christine Marceline Lewis and she had moved away many years ago. She was married, but Mabel didn't know her married name. One of my uncles was named Matt Lee Lewis after his father (my grandfather). She told me he was in the Navy (confirming more of my background information), but she hadn't seen him in years either. The youngest uncle was named Loran Lewis, but went by the name "Mackey," and he was a retired minister (again confirming the background document). She told me Loran was married to a woman named Irene and they had two children, one of whom was killed in a car accident. She explained that after my grandfather died, my uncle Loran and aunt Irene took my grandmother Ora Lee from Cape Girardeau back to Iowa to care for her at their home, until she died in 1980.

This woman knew so many details about my maternal birth family, all because she was such a close friend to my grandmother. In comparison to Mabel's memory of things at the age of ninety-three, I seemed like I was suffering from dementia in my late thirties. The details that she provided next would help shape my understanding of who my birth mother really was, at least through her young adult years, and how she lived her life.

Mabel mentioned many times through our two-hour discussion that my birth mother, Betty Jo, was the most attractive woman on the planet. She had multiple callers in her youth, and Mabel clearly stated that my birth mother had lived a very promiscuous life. She also confirmed more background information when she told me that my unmarried birth mother had gotten pregnant at the age of eighteen, and had a daughter named Chiquita. "Chiquita?" I had to ask to confirm what I thought I heard, thinking to myself, "What kind of name is Chiquita?" This was important information: I now knew the names of my grandparents, uncles, my aunt, and my half-sister.

Mabel said she never knew what became of Chiquita, but she did say that Betty Jo left Chiquita with my grandmother Ora during the week when Chiquita was about four years old. Betty Jo was working in St. Louis as a waitress during the week and would only come home to Lilbourn on the weekends to see Chiquita (many times drunk). After about two years of that lifestyle, Betty Jo picked up her daughter Chiquita and moved to California. Mabel wanted me to know how devastated her friend Ora Lee was after they left. After all, Ora Lee had been effectively raising Chiquita.

Mabel also told me that my birth mother was known to frequent the main military base about an hour outside of Lilbourn during the latter part of the Second World War. Although she had been raised in the church, and loved to play piano and sing gospel music, she drank too much and was quite sexually active. My grandmother had told Mabel that she was certain that Betty Jo had self-aborted children with either a coat hanger or a rat-tail comb. In fact, Mabel said that on one occasion, my grandmother had walked into the bathroom and witnessed Betty Jo performing that act in their bathtub. My birth mother was hemorrhaging so badly that they had to rush her to the closest hospital an hour away. Mabel said she knew I probably didn't want to hear that, but I had already told her I wanted every detail she could provide about my birth mother.

It was a lot for me to take in. It made me feel sick to my stomach, and it made me wonder just why my birth mother allowed me to live. "Aborted children—how many?" I was thinking as I listened to Mabel, "What stopped my birth mother from doing that to me? What made her decide to carry me to full term?" Was her body ravaged from her previous abortions, or did she fear she'd have another life-threatening experience? Before Chiquita's husband's car accident, did she actually intend to keep me? Did she struggle with that decision like a nurturing mother would, as my background information suggested? But what kind of mother leaves her daughter with her parents five days a week, partying all hours of the night? I didn't have any of the answers then, but I would later learn some information that made me suspect just how much turmoil she felt before deciding to put me up for adoption.

Before I let her go, I asked Mabel if she had any pictures of any members of my birth family. She was sorry to tell me that her house had burned to the ground about fifteen years before, and she had lost everything, including every photo she had. I knew it was a longshot, but I had to ask.

I thanked Mabel for her help in getting me a step closer to solving the mystery that had recently been consuming my life. I knew there was a lot more to do, but I had discovered so many important things during that phone call. She told me to feel free to call her back if I had any further questions.

I've always tried to live by the motto, "The harder you work, the luckier you get." I reflected on how I'd invited my luck through the many "Lewis" cold calls I'd made, and seemed to have found the preverbal needle in the haystack. Now I needed to find these newly identified relatives and obtain pictures of my birth mother. Even if I couldn't meet her, I hoped to meet my half-sister Chiquita, or perhaps my aunt and uncles, if any of them were still alive. The puzzle pieces were coming together, even if there were so many still sitting unsorted in the pile.

Piece by Piece

I knew I was getting closer and needed to keep pushing forward. Just knowing the identity and some background information about my birth mother would never be enough for me. I wanted to see her face and hopefully recognize some of me in her features. I had also started to wonder about my half-sister Chiquita and her child who was born just a few months before me. Since my birth mother died in Las Vegas, I wondered if either of them ever lived there too. I thought, if I could find them, not only would I be able to meet my half-sister, which is what had originally inspired my search, but she would also be able to tell me all about my birth mother and surely would have a ton of pictures I could duplicate. Who knew, maybe I could even have some sort of relationship with Chiquita and her family? The thought of finding her and surprising her with my presence was exciting. She certainly would have remembered that our birth mother gave a child up for adoption only a few months after she had her baby. The idea of meeting Chiquita didn't foster the same level of apprehension I had felt when I'd considered what it would be like to approach or meet my birth mother for the first time. Being rejected by Chiquita couldn't hurt as bad as being rejected by my birth mother.

It was at this time that I realized something I had never considered. If I could find Chiquita, she may be able to help me identify my birth father. She would have been fifteen (and recently impregnated) when my birth mother was with my birth father. I was hoping that Chiquita had been introduced to my birth father or my birth mother at least told Chiquita who she was "dating" in August of 1960 when I was conceived. Finding Chiquita now had even greater importance.

I didn't know Chiquita's last name, so how would I do an internet search to try to find her? I tried searching for "Chiquita Lewis" and "Chiquita Heady" in Las Vegas, but nothing credible came up. Because

Chiquita was an uncommon name, I even tried to search the entire US for all Chiquitas, but that also led me nowhere.

I was still in contact with Gail, but most of what I needed from her was finished. At least that's what I thought at the time. Without her help and access to those original California birth records, I don't know how I would have ever identified my birth mother. During one of our calls, she suggested that I look for an obituary for my birth mother in the archives of a local Las Vegas newspaper. If there was an obituary, it might list the names of the surviving family, including Chiquita with her last name. So, back to the UNLV library and another round with the microfiche machines, sorting through the two available archives of Las Vegas newspapers.

It was easy to find my birth mother's death notice from July 1992, but I couldn't find an official obituary that listed surviving family members. I'd struck out again. The next time I spoke to Gail, she suggested I go to Clark County's record office to see if I could obtain my birth mother's death certificate. She said there's normally a surviving family member's name listed as a form of contact for future reference. So, I went to the Clark County Department of Records and requested my birth mother's death certificate. I paid $20 and waited about two weeks before receiving a copy in the mail.

Most of that one-page document contained information I already knew. It did list her last known address at the time of death, and that she had died at the age of sixty-five from congestive heart failure. At the bottom of that death certificate there was a field entitled, "Informant," that listed a "Deana Jacques" as her granddaughter. That seemed strange to me. Why wasn't Chiquita listed as the informant?

I thought searching for Deana Jacques would be easy because Jacques wasn't a common name. And I was right; only one popped up in Las Vegas. There were at least five phone numbers and a long list of Las Vegas addresses for her, but every phone number I called was either not in service or the wrong number. But WhitePages.com also listed some potential names associated with Deana and they were John Lewis, Ana Jacques, and Lawrence Jacques.

Lewis? My birth mother's maiden name was Lewis. Was this "John" her cousin or maybe her nephew? I knew it couldn't be one of her brothers because if Mabel was right, their names were Matt and Loran, and she seemed very sure about that.

I went back online, to Whitepages.com again, searching for every John Lewis that lived in Las Vegas. If I was wrong about him living in Las Vegas, then the search would have been more wasted time. There was a plethora of listings for that name, but not nearly as many as my first "Lewis" search in Missouri. And there I was again, cold-calling from a long list, this time trying to see if I could find the right John Lewis. As before, some people didn't answer, and many numbers were not in service. A few people told me I must have the wrong number or simply hung up on me, which made me worried that I might have been calling the right number for John, and I'd be wasting time calling others. I don't remember how many calls I made, but it took a while before ringing the bell.

A woman answered the phone and I immediately pleaded with her not to hang up on me. I asked to speak with John Lewis, and she told me that he worked graveyard shifts, was sleeping, and that she wasn't about to disturb him. I began telling her my story and why I was searching for a man named John Lewis. The woman said she was John's wife, and that they had three young children, and were all living at her parents' home in North Las Vegas. Did I have the right John Lewis? At first, she didn't seem to be buying my story. But to my surprise, eventually she told me that John was Chiquita's son, and that she knew my birth mother Betty (John's grandmother) very well. But she'd never heard that Betty had any children other than her daughter, Chiquita. The second she said my birth mother's name and Chiquita, I knew I had the phone number for the right John Lewis.

The more I revealed about what I knew, the more convinced she became that I may be telling the truth. At some point, she asked me to hold on, put the phone down, and decided to wake up John.

He picked up the phone, and immediately I could tell he wasn't happy about being woken. His voice was hoarse and he seemed like a rough character. I could feel his resistance immediately, but who doesn't dislike being woken abruptly? I introduced myself and began telling him my story, and that I was looking for information about my birth mother, Betty Jo Heady. He was certain I was trying to scam his family in some way, and he wasn't buying my story. Just like his wife, it seemed impossible to him that his grandmother would have had a child other than his mother Chiquita and he would know nothing about it. I pleaded with him to let me meet with him so I could show him the official background documents, which should convince him I was being honest, but he objected. Although he didn't trust me, he did allow me to continue our conversation.

And just like his wife before, the more I told him about what I knew about his family, the more he seemed to realize I might be legitimate. After about thirty minutes of coaxing, he finally agreed to allow me to come to his father-in-law's house the following day after he got home from work.

Before he let me go, he said, "You seem to be referring to my mother Chiquita in the present tense, but if you know so much about my family, why would you speak as if she was still alive? Didn't you know that my mother died in a car accident twenty-four years ago, back in 1974?"

I thought, "$HIT! You've got to be kidding me! My birth mother is dead and now I'm discovering my half-sister is gone too?! Who is closely related to me and still alive from by maternal side?" Even through my frustration, I simply told John I wasn't aware she had passed and how disappointed I was to hear that news. Then I told him how much I looked forward to meeting him, before ending our call.

[6]

CONFIRMING MY SALVATION

I WAS DEVASTATED TO HEAR THAT CHIQUITA HAD PASSED AWAY. I saw her as my last chance to meet a sibling, unless my birth mother had other children I didn't know about. And that seemed unlikely because John was shocked by my existence. Her death also wiped out any hope I had that she would be able to tell me who my birth father was.

I was interested in meeting John as someone who shared my DNA, but my main goal was to obtain photographs of my birth mother. After all, she was John's grandmother, so it seemed likely meeting him could result in a treasure trove of family photos. I knew I was about to finally see the face of my birth mother and find some closure on this journey.

I remember how nervous I was on the fifteen-minute drive over to meet with John. I felt like I was about to go on trial and needed to clearly make the case that his grandmother Betty was my birth mother, his mother Chiquita was my half-sister, and that John was my half-nephew. Nothing could keep me from this meeting. I would have been willing to army-crawl naked over broken glass to finally obtain the pictures I so desperately wanted. Sorry—I know that imagery may be difficult to remove from your mind, but that's how desperate I felt.

As I pulled into their driveway, there was a man, probably in his early thirties, and not too much younger than me, standing on the grass near the edge of the front porch. He was dressed in cutoff jeans and a white tee-shirt, and he looked as though he was in a defensive position guarding his house from intruders. I could see some family resemblance to him, but it wasn't overwhelming. I could also see he was intensely staring at my face through my windshield, never taking his eyes off me. I grabbed my evidentiary paperwork, stepped out of the car, and began to approach him. I could see him perusing every detail of my physicality. Was I a threat, or was I who I said I was and showing up for the right reasons? Within five seconds, before I could introduce myself, I could see that his eyes were becoming glassy.

I reached out my hand to shake his and said, "Hi, I'm Jeff." By this time, a few tears were trickling from the corners of his eyes. He seemed to be in shock, and as he extended his hand to shake mine, he said, "This is crazy. I can see some of my grandmother in you."

Wow! That was exactly what I needed to hear, and not solely because it meant that I seemed to be on my way to convincing him that I was legitimate. It was the first time in my life that someone related my physicality to one of my birth parents. What a great feeling that was to hear that from him. I know non-adoptees can't fully appreciate that, but for people who've seemingly come from nowhere, finding that you come from somewhere feels so good. His comment also had me wondering just how much I must have resembled my birth mother that he was able to see it.

We entered his house, and he introduced me to his wife, in-laws, and his three young children. We sat down at their kitchen table, and I provided more details of just how certain I was that Betty was my birth mother, and John and I were related as half-uncle and half-nephew. I let them see the background document that described his grandmother's physical features, her place of origin, and the car accident that killed his mother Chiquita's first husband. They were finally convinced I was telling the truth. John was clear with me about just how suspicious he was of my story during our initial phone conversation; that's why he had waited for me in his front yard that day. He told me he was there to defend his turf from what he believed was an attempt to hurt or scam his family.

He then proceeded to tell me just how difficult his life was growing up in North Las Vegas. Living in Las Vegas, I already knew that North Las Vegas was not the safest place to live. It had the highest homicide rate in Clark County. He told me he took a knife to school every day and never knew if he would make it home safely. He was only four years younger than me, and had lost his mother Chiquita in 1974 when he was only nine. She was killed in a single car roll-over accident as the driver on Mount Charleston, a popular local mountainous recreation area. She was just twenty-nine at the time of her death. He reluctantly told me that Chiquita was a known heroin and alcohol abuser and that was the likely cause of her accident. She had a friend in the car with her that had been seriously injured but survived.

He explained that my birth mother Betty tried her best to raise and care for him and his thirteen-year-old sister in Chiquita's absence, but it was hard for her as a single grandmother working sixty-hour weeks as a waitress at a casino. I didn't ask John about the specifics of his difficulties growing up, but he was leading me to believe he'd been in a lot of trouble. It's what I surmised, but only mere speculation on my part, and if true, I didn't need to know anything about it. It seemed that he was working hard and trying his best to provide for his wife and three kids.

But then John gave me a strong dose of reality with what he had to say next. He looked me dead in the eye and said, *"I don't know where you grew up, or under what conditions you lived, but it had to be much better than growing up here. You got lucky to escape the horrors of my family's life that you surely would have been exposed to if my grandmother would have kept you.*" I'll never forget those words. They solidified in me my belief that I truly was rescued at birth by my adoptive parents. My birth mother could not have known before releasing me just how difficult her life would turn out to be, even if some of that was of her own doing. But it became very clear to me that her decision to give me up had saved me, and I felt a deeper sense of gratitude toward her. I needed to hear those words from John. It helped solidify my understanding that my salvation had been attained through adoption.

I also asked him about the identity and whereabouts of Chiquita's child (his half-sibling) that had been born just two months before me. I knew it wasn't John because he told me he was born in 1965. He said that it was his older half-sister, Deana Jacques, who had a different father than he did. When I asked him if she was born in March of 1961, he confirmed that. Deana was the child my half-sister Chiquita had two months before I was born, and the reason my birth mother claimed to have given me up. She was also the one listed on my birth mother's death certificate in 1992. My birth mother's story from that background document was looking more and more credible. I told John how I had tried to reach Deana before searching for him, but he told me that would have been impossible. Like their mother Chiquita, Deana was also a heavy drug user and always on the move trying escape whatever trouble she found herself in.

John told me that Deana's father was named Lawrence Jacques. His fatal car accident happened the day after Thanksgiving in Los Angeles. Of course, that made me reflect on my misguided search for that fatal car wreck and finding the wrong couple. It wouldn't be until years later that I would find the story of Lawrence's accident in the local paper of Huntington Park, an LA suburb. It was never reported on in the *Los Angeles Times* where I had searched.

He was pretty sure Deana still lived in North Las Vegas, but he hadn't seen her in a few years. The last time he had seen her, she was strung out on drugs and her life was a complete mess. He told me that Deana had two children, his half-nephew Lawrence Jacques (named after Deana's deceased father) and half-niece Anna Jacques, who both also lived in North Las Vegas. Since Deana was an unfit mother, living a drug-induced wayward life, her two kids (Ana and Lawrence) had also mostly been raised by my birth mother Betty (their great-grandmother), up until she passed away in 1992. And both of Deana's children had a lot of trouble in their lives. I'm sure most of that was because Deana wasn't much of a nurturing mother. It seemed to me that there was an intergenerational line of suffering that started at the hands of my birth mother and continued down three more generations of family. It was more confirmation of what I already suspected: that my life, if I had grown up in my biological maternal family, would have been very difficult. Absent the moral values my parents instilled in me, and the deep sense of love they provided, I doubted I would have fared very well.

I also asked John about his father and if his mother Chiquita had ever officially married him. He told me they were never married, and Chiquita simply gave John her maiden name of Lewis. In fact, he didn't know his father's identity.

But John also provided more of his mother's story. He told me that about a year or so after his sister Deana was born, Chiquita married a man named Tom Brent in November of 1962. They had a son (his half-brother) named Alan, who was born in 1963, but they quickly divorced. After that, Chiquita moved back to Las Vegas from California with her then two-year-old daughter Deana and her infant son Alan. And a year later Chiquita met John's birth father, and John was born in 1965.

So, based on what I'd already learned before meeting John and the information I'd gleaned from him, my maternal family tree was as follows:

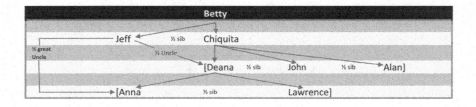

What a mess. It seemed that the "Chiquita apple" didn't fall far from the "Betty tree." Chiquita seemed to be even more promiscuous and wild than Betty in her early adulthood. Chiquita had three children, with three different men, all within a four-year period. Every person related in my small maternal family tree had half relationships because Betty, Chiquita, and Deana didn't have stable relationships with the men they were with. My adoptive family had its share of dysfunction, but nothing of this magnitude.

I asked John where Tom Brent lived, and he told me that he hadn't seen him in many years, but he guessed he still lived in California. I also asked him where his mother Chiquita was buried, and to my surprise, he told me she was buried right next to Betty's grave at Palm Mortuary. He told me that they didn't have enough money to formally bury his mother, or my birth mother, so the State of Nevada buried them with simple metal plaques listing their name, birth, and death dates. I had been standing right next to Chiquita's grave when visiting my birth mother's grave without knowing her grave was there. I went back to the graveyard a few weeks later and noticed the plaque on Chiquita's grave listed her as "Chiquita Jo Brent." She died with her second married and divorced name from eleven years earlier, in the same way that my birth mother kept the married name of Heady the rest of her life.

Dropping the "Twin" Bomb

Now it was time to get down to business with John and his wife. I told him how nice it was meeting them, how thankful I was for the information they'd provided, and just how desperate I was to find a least one picture of my birth mother. It was another dead end in my journey: there were no pictures to be had. John explained to me that after my birth mother died six years earlier, they had put all her possessions, including her pictures, in a storage facility. But since paying for their apartment, utilities, and groceries was their top priority, eventually they couldn't afford to continue paying for the storage unit. He told me that all the contents of her storage locker had been confiscated and discarded. Not only did John have no pictures of my birth mother, he didn't have a single picture of his own mother Chiquita. Not one! This was terrible news, another huge drop into greater frustration along this seemingly never-ending roller-coaster ride.

I asked John if he knew who my birth mother associated with or any of her close friends. If I could find them, they might have a few pictures. He thought about it for a few minutes and gave me the name of a woman who lived in the same apartment complex as my birth mother many years earlier. Her name was Kathy and he told me that his grandmother was a close friend to her, but he hadn't seen her in years, nor did he know where she currently lived.

Before I left John and his wife, I told them how thankful I was to have been able to meet with them. I also promised them that if I ever found any family pictures, I would make copies for them.

When I returned home, I knew I had two searches to make. One was for my birth mother's friend Kathy, and the other was for Tom Brent who married Chiquita a year and a half after I was born.

First, I searched the White Pages website for Tom Brent in California, and after numerous attempts I found the right one. He was in his mid-fifties by then, remarried, and living in the Palm Desert area of California. He was pretty shocked to hear from me, but he was not shocked to hear my story. He told me that my birth mother Betty and his ex-wife Chiquita were both completely nuts. They both liked to party, and Chiquita never provided a stable environment for his infant son Alan. He said he got out of that marriage as quickly as possible, and not much later took Alan from Chiquita. Tom didn't trust Chiquita with their son and drove from Los Angeles to Las Vegas to take him back. It turned out to be easier than he thought. Chiquita told Tom that if he would give her the new car they'd purchased before they decided to divorce, she would give him their son without a court fight. Tom boggled my mind with that story, and it further confirmed that my half-sister was even more unscrupulous than my birth mother appeared to be. What kind of mother would trade her son for a new car? Tom was very blunt about it. He said he made a huge mistake marrying Chiquita and there was no way he would have allowed her to raise their son, given the kind of relationship she had with alcohol, drugs, and partying.

I asked Tom if he had any pictures of either my birth mother Betty or Chiquita. He thought he might of Chiquita, but at best it would only be one. He was sure he didn't have any of my birth mother. I provided my address and phone number and asked him to mail it to me if he found it. It arrived the next week.

That was the first picture I had seen (Chiquita far left) of anyone very closely related to me and I stared at it for hours. I didn't really see a resemblance to me in an obvious way. If we had anything in common, maybe it was our brow line. That picture was taken in the summer of 1963, when Chiquita would have been about eighteen. It was taken outside of a church with Tom and his immediate family, and Chiquita was standing behind her daughter Deana. I had to admit, Chiquita was an attractive young woman. And with a mother who most likely wasn't modeling good moral values, I could see how she ended up pregnant so many times at such an early age. I called Tom to thank him for that picture and for the information he provided because he put the finishing touches on the understanding that had become so clear to me: I had been saved.

I called Tom from to time over the next year or so to clear up other questions I had. After that, it would be twenty years later before we would speak again, but this time, the information he would provide would help solve another mystery for someone else.

So, I was on to my next search for my birth mother's close friend Kathy (or Cathy). At first, it seemed to be a dead end. I narrowed the search to Las Vegas, hoping she still lived there, but nothing came up. John wasn't certain about the spelling of her last name, so I tried different iterations of both her first and last names. It wasn't until I removed Las Vegas from the search field that I found the person who I hoped was the right Kathy. It listed her phone number and that she lived in Mesquite, Nevada, only ninety miles north of Las Vegas.

I called this Kathy and left a brief message on an answering machine with my name, phone number, and that I was searching for some lost family. Within ten minutes, Kathy returned my call. I briefly told her my story and how John had referred me to her. She claimed to know my birth mother very well at one time, but said that it was many years ago. I asked her if it would be possible for us to meet, and she was open to the idea, but asked if her husband could tag along and if we could meet near the registration desk in the main lobby of a local Mesquite hotel. The day before I left to meet with them, I called Kathy and told her exactly what I'd be wearing so that they could easily identify me. That turned out to be an unnecessary piece of information.

As I walked into that lobby, I only saw one older couple standing next to the registration desk. The woman was staring at me as I approached them, and I could see the shock on her face and tears welling up in her eyes. She didn't even ask me if I was the Jeff she'd spoken to the day before. She just looked at me and said, "You look so much like your mother." Wow! There it was again. It was yet another confirmation that I came from somewhere that was identifiable to someone else, a somewhere that was recognizable to a stranger, even if I hadn't seen it yet myself.

Over lunch I peppered Kathy with countless questions. Of course, the first question was about photos. But it was another dead end. She explained to me that when she and my birth mother lived in that run-down apartment complex near old downtown Las Vegas, they were so poor, owning a camera or paying for rolls of film was never an option.

Kathy knew about Chiquita's death and how that event had destroyed my birth mother. Apparently, in the months after, Betty let herself go physically and Kathy was worried that she might consider taking her own life. According to Kathy, Chiquita was Betty's world, and after she died, Betty didn't care about anything anymore.

Looking for clues about my birth father, I asked her if Betty had ever mentioned anything to her about boyfriends or marriages. She knew about Betty's only marriage in 1956, and the separation and later divorce in LA, but all of that had occurred many years before she met her. I didn't ask her the exact years she knew my birth mother and just how long my birth mother had lived in Las Vegas. I later realized that information could have been used to help me figure out exactly where I may have been conceived—which, in turn, may have helped me determine where my birth father was living.

And then I asked her if my birth mother had ever mentioned anything about having other children besides Chiquita. I was curious if my birth mother was close enough to this woman to have ever mentioned that she gave me up for adoption. She rocked my socks off by what she told me next.

She said, "I can't be sure about this, but I thought your mother mentioned something to me about having twin boys in the early 1960s, many years before I knew her."

TWIN BOYS!!!!????

Holy God in heaven!

Blood rushed through my veins as I contemplated the fact that there could be a full brother out there somewhere, and if he was an identical twin, just how crazy that would be. I was already picturing the two of us walking out on some talk show stage and telling the story of how we reunited.

I'm sure Kathy could see I was astounded, and she seemed to decide to temper her words a bit. She told me she wasn't 100 per cent sure about what she had said, but it's what she thought she remembered. I thanked them for their time and willingness to meet with me. I was anxious to get back home and plan my next move. No pictures had come of this meeting, but I felt full of energy and hope again. I knew I needed to speak to Gail about this "twins" notion when I returned home.

Ignoring the Evidence

If you recall, the impetus for beginning this search was the potential of discovering siblings. And since my birth mother and half-sister were gone, and there was not nearly enough information available to identify my birth father, all I had left to hope for was finding another sibling and obtaining pictures of my birth mother.

I called Gail and had her start up the money meter again. I say that jokingly—she was always fair with me from a business standpoint, but it wasn't cheap. I reported to her what Kathy had conveyed to me. Gail may have been older, but she was on top of her game. She reminded me that the original birth records only reported one record for a "Baby Boy Heady." She also said that she had only looked on my exact birthdate of May 19, 1961, so I may have a twin out there, but that twin would have needed to have been born late at night the day before me, if I was born just after midnight, or minutes after me, if I was born right before midnight. That would mean me and my twin would only be separated by minutes, but legally have different birthdates.

Knowing it would be easy for her to check those records on her magic microfiche machine, it took her less than an hour to call me back and let me know there were no other Baby Boy Headys born either the day before or the day after I was born. She thought it was very unlikely that my birth mother would have used a different last name than Heady, or that she would have named one of the twins legitimately, or even kept one but given the other up.

I felt like I was at the lowest point on the tracks of the tallest roller coaster ride in the world. And with this latest news, which completely deflated my excitement about the potential of having a twin brother, it felt like the car of my roller coaster was dead stopped. I could look up and see tracks rising steeply in front of me, but there seemed to be no remaining steam to move forward. The puzzle pieces that could identify or display the pictures of my closest biological family seemed to be missing, or maybe they were never included in the box.

In some ways, I'm embarrassed about allowing myself to run off the rails with Kathy's mention of twins. How could I have let myself get so excited when the evidence against having twins was staring me in the face? The background document mentioned nothing about twins, and I was the only one my birth mother delivered that day. But I still wondered, if I had a twin and we were separated, would the adoption agency have been required to report it in my background document? It seemed like such a long shot that I decided to let that theory go. My hope got the best of me, and both Gail and I laughed about it later.

The dilemma for all adoptees who'd searched without the aid of today's DNA capabilities is the possibility that some leads could send you straight off the right trail. DNA won't lie, nor will it lead anyone in the wrong direction or provide false evidence. It's our false interpretations of evidence (DNA or paper records) that can lead us astray. It's not uncommon for people to allow their excitement or desires to override their ability to focus on the facts. We get locked into theories that distract us from other evidence that would keep us on the right track. Identifying people through paper trails or even trying to use resemblance as a marker for genealogical purposes can lead one to false conclusions, and the deep disappointments that may follow. I should have learned a big lesson from allowing myself to get so full of hopeful expectation regarding a twin brother. But apparently, before I learned my lesson, I needed to be hit much harder with the reality hammer, when I tried helping others solve their mysteries.

[7]

BY ANY MEANS NECESSARY

I HAVE A GOOD FRIEND AND HUNTING PARTNER NAMED GARY WHO attended the same church as me. He was a native of Las Vegas and owned a big accounting firm in town with many high-profile clients. He was connected to some of the movers and shakers in town, including a few congressmen and district court judges.

During one of our hunting trips, I told Gary about my search and just how desperate I was to find a picture of my birth mother. When I finished, he asked me to confirm that she worked as a waitress in the casinos. I said yes, because my half-nephew John told me she had worked in that industry for as long as he could remember. Gary informed me that anyone who worked in the Culinary Union in any Las Vegas hotel must have a Sheriff's ID card confirming they have been background checked. They take a front and side view just like a law enforcement mug shot, and then their pertinent identification information is listed below those pictures.

I began to wonder if that card with her photos still existed if she was no longer alive, and if so, how I could get my hands on it. Gary was a step ahead of me. He said he would make some phone calls when we got back to see if any of his connections could help me.

While waiting to hear back from Gary, I started my search for my newly identified aunt and two uncles. It was back to square one because I knew that none of them still lived in Lilbourn. But Mabel had told me that the last place she knew my uncle Loran and his wife Irene lived, back in 1980 when my grandmother died, was somewhere in Iowa. So, it was back to searching WhitePages.com. Lewis is a common name, but Loran isn't common like "Joe" or "Mark." It didn't take long to find him. His last known address was in Urbandale, Iowa. If they (Loran and Irene) were still living, it would be another round of trying to explain who I was and convincing them I was telling the truth. Cold-calling the elderly is not easy. After my own search, I went on to do this kind of research for others, and I can tell you that older people often have a deeper distrust toward a stranger calling them because they fear being scammed.

So, I made the call, and a pleasant older woman answered the phone. I asked if I could speak to Loran Lewis, and she replied that he wasn't available. She asked me what the call was regarding, and again I found myself in a defensive posture, pleading with her to not hang up on me. I told her it wasn't a scam, gave her my name and where I was calling from, and told her that I was looking for information about a "Betty Jo Lewis." It was only then that she identified herself as Loran's wife, and asked me what information I was looking for. So, I laid out my story, and to my surprise, she seemed interested, even compassionate. She opened up and shared that Loran actually was in the room, but the reason he could not come to the phone was because he was suffering from late-stage dementia. She told me he was unable to carry on a conversation with anyone. I didn't want to hear that. He was the first uncle I'd found, and if he had dementia, it wasn't really an option to ever fly to Iowa to meet him.

Irene told me what she knew about my birth mother, and in the kindest way she could, gave me a toned-down version of what Mabel had conveyed. She and my uncle Loran hadn't seen my birth mother in over thirty years. She told me that when my grandmother Ora Lee died in Iowa in 1980, Betty Jo didn't show up for her own mother's funeral. Irene described my birth mother as an extremely pretty young woman. She also told me that Loran had been ashamed of the lifestyle his sister had lived, which was the anthesis of every one of her minister husband's moral values. She wasn't surprised to hear that Betty Jo was unwed when I was given up for adoption. She didn't know anything about what Mabel had shared with me about self-aborting, at least she claimed not to, but that didn't seem to surprise her either. Irene knew about Chiquita's death in 1974, but she and Loran only knew Chiquita as a young child when she lived with my grandmother Ora in Missouri.

I asked her about my other uncle, Matt Lee Lewis, and she told me that he had passed away in 1989 in, of all places, Las Vegas. Irene and Loran hadn't heard from him in decades before his death, either. When I asked about my aunt Christine, Irene told me that she had passed away in 1991. Christine had married a man named Karl Latham, they had five children, and had moved from Missouri to Texas many years ago.

I was clearly late to the party. My maternal grandparents, half-sister, birth mother, and all her siblings were now gone. Even though Irene's husband, my uncle Loran, had not passed away yet, it was effectively the equivalent because he would never be able to understand that I was his nephew. The gateway to meeting them had been eternally locked shut.

Of course, during the entire conversation, I knew I needed to ask if Irene had any pictures of my birth mother. After hearing that she hadn't seen Betty in at least thirty years, it seemed that probability was very low. But when I asked, she said, "I do believe we have a few and they are mostly tucked away in boxes up in our attic. Your grandmother Ora Lee left behind a lot of pictures when she passed away." This was certainly welcome news. I didn't want to push her, but it crossed my mind that I could get on a plane and fly to Iowa to help her sort through the boxes and find those pictures.

Those pictures were worth way more than gold to me, and if I did that, I wouldn't worry about them getting lost in the mail. She told me she would see if one of her grandchildren would come over and take the boxes down from her attic, and when she finished sorting them, she would mail them to me. But I asked to her to call me when they were ready, and I would send FedEx with a preaddressed envelope to her home to pick them up.

I thanked Irene for her time and said I hoped to speak to again her soon. She gave me confidence that this time, I would finally have what I so desperately wanted.

About a week later, while I was still waiting for Irene to call, Gary called me with some great news. It was about two weeks since we had returned from our hunting trip, and he told me that he had contacted a district court judge friend of his, who had ordered my birth mother's sheriff's card from the court records, and they were able to locate it. The judge would have it in his office the next day. Gary gave me the address and told me to meet the judge there tomorrow at 10 a.m.

I was extremely excited. All my work, despite all those frustrating dead ends, was about to be rewarded. It seemed extremely unlikely the courts had anyone other than my birth mother's picture. There couldn't be more than one Betty Jo Heady working in the Las Vegas Culinary Union.

I had a terrible time trying to sleep that night and got up around 4 a.m. I was so anxious about what was about to go down. Would I be able to see any of my physical traits in those two pictures? Would her pictures display the striking features the adoption summary indicated, or that she was, as Mabel described her, the most beautiful woman on the planet? Just how was I going to react in front of that judge? Would I break down and cry?

The next morning, I drove to old downtown Las Vegas, arriving about fifteen minutes early. My heart was pounding, and I was sweating profusely. The judge's receptionist seated me in his chambers in front of his huge mahogany desk. The judge walked in about ten minutes later, introducing himself as we shook hands, and then sat down at his desk. He reached into the top drawer, pulled out a small manila envelope, and placed it on top of his desk. He then informed me that we needed to keep this between the two of us and his name should never be associated with the material he was about to give me. It was clear to me that this judge was circumventing the law to help me. I promised him I would keep it between us, and that I would honor my word and never mention his name to anyone. He then put his hand on top of the envelope and pushed it across the desk to the edge where I sat. I was shaking like a leaf, and I knew he could see the bottled-up emotions I was feeling.

I bent back the two little aluminum clasps and opened the envelope to pull out a sheet of paper that contained what looked like a mug shot with the front and side view of a woman.

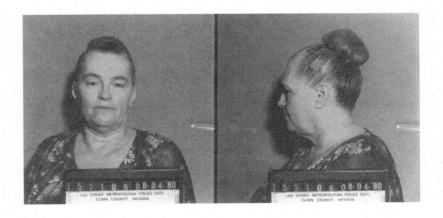

There had to be some mistake! The photographs were dated 1980, when my birth mother would have been fifty-four years old. But these could not be pictures of the woman that others had described to me. This woman was heavy in the face. She didn't appear to be wearing any makeup, and her hair was up in a bun. Not only was she not smiling, but it also looked like she was slightly scowling. The picture was cut off around her elbows, and she was wearing some sort of purple muumuu with a floral pattern. The only possible shared traits I could identify were the shape of her eyebrows and a few moles on her cheeks. That was it!

I immediately wondered, how could John and Kathy well up with tears and tell me they could see my birth mother in me? Were Mabel and Irene not being truthful when they claimed my birth mother was an extremely pretty woman? How could anyone ever compare us and see any resemblance? Perhaps their ingrained memories of my birth mother were from her younger years, and not when she was fifty-four.

I honestly don't know how long I sat there staring at those two pictures while the judge waited there patiently, never saying a word. It could have been as much as ten minutes. He must have noticed my countenance had changed from excitement to disappointment. When I finished perusing every pixel of those two pictures, I stood up and thanked him for what he had done for me. Even through my disappointment, I was still grateful he had been willing to cross a line to help me.

As I drove home, I had this feeling come over me that I didn't want to show those pictures to anyone. But that wasn't really an option because I had told everyone I knew about what was going to happen that day. As I thought more about it, I realized that I was basing my feeling of self-worth and maybe even my pride on the appearance of my birth mother. How ridiculous was that? I was only thirty-seven at the time and wondered what I would look like at fifty-four. (I know the answer to that now, but we don't need to get into any of that.) If no one had ever mentioned how beautiful she was, would I have felt that same disappointment? Were the words of my birth mother's friend Kathy true, had my birth mother really let herself go after Chiquita died? These pictures were taken about six years after Chiquita was killed. I needed a change of perspective and to get myself right with reality.

When I arrived home, I showed the pictures to Debbie, and she couldn't really see any resemblance either. I don't remember if I shared them with our kids. Over the next week, I showed the pictures to some friends and people in my office. I couldn't help but express my disappointment when sharing those pictures because I'd already told everyone what others had said about my birth mother's beauty. Perhaps I felt like I needed to quell their expectations.

I Can See Clearly Now

After coming to terms with my disappointment in those pictures, I settled in and waited for Irene to call. It had been over three weeks since I'd last spoken to her. She called me one morning when I was at my office and told me she had gone through all of my grandmother Ora's pictures and found five of my birth mother and six of my half-sister Chiquita. She also had found a group picture of my maternal side of the family that included my grandparents, she and her husband Loran, and my maternal great-grandmother. Most of the pictures she was about to send were in black and white because they were taken in the 1940s and early1950s.

I'm not sure if I even thanked her or if she just suddenly heard a dial tone coming from my end as I started speed-dialing FedEx to get to her house so I'd have those pictures in my hands the next day. Despite the disappointment I'd felt when I saw the first two pictures of my birth mother, my anticipation for what would be arriving the next day was like the feeling on Christmas Eve waiting for Santa Claus to show up, a hundred-fold.

But I needed to subdue my expectations to preserve my mental well-being. Throughout the day, I continually reminded myself that my feeling of self-worth could not be based on these forthcoming pictures, whether my birth mother was the most gorgeous woman on Earth, or as homely as a bulldog. What was driving me to want her to have been so beautiful? Did I want others to think I came from a genetic line of beautiful people and that somehow made me more special? I had to set myself straight. Physical appearance should have no bearing on one's character or sense of self-worth. At least that's the way I think it should be.

I arrived at my office at 6 a.m. the next day. I had already told my FedEx driver that I had a very important Priority Overnight envelope coming the next day and to please bring it to me before any of his other deliveries that had a 10:30 a.m. deadline. My receptionist Nancy, who'd been following my journey the entire time, anxiously waited with me. She had been very helpful to me during my search. We kicked around many different theories and hypotheses as each new piece of evidence became available, and she wrote general summary documents along the way to record the order of events as they occurred, in case I ever wanted to go back and review them.

I heard Nancy yell "He's here!" as the driver approached our front door. I came out of my office and waited in the lobby. My heart was pounding as the driver handed me the envelope. I sat down at Nancy's desk in the reception area as she stood behind me. She seemed as nervous as I was. I carefully slid all the photos out of the envelope and placed them on the desk. There was also a standard-sized white mailing envelope included in the FedEx envelope. That envelope had been postmarked 1965 and it was addressed to my grandparents (Matt and Ora Lee Lewis) in Missouri. The return address was from a "Betty *Roberts*," with a Las Vegas address. It contained a handwritten letter from my birth mother, but I didn't understand why she wrote her last name as Roberts. It would take twenty years to solve that mystery, and to learn the biological origins of three other people I didn't know existed at the time I received that FedEx envelope in 1998. Anyway, the letter didn't have any photos inside, so I didn't pay much attention to it until weeks later.

The first photo that caught my eye was a 5"x7" portrait of a beautiful woman with hair that barely reached the top of her ears and was longer, more stylish, and curlier on top. Nancy immediately blurted out, "Wow, she was beautiful!" My hands shook as I studied that photo. Even in black and white, I could see she was well-manicured, wearing makeup and lipstick and sporting stylish earrings. She had a beautiful smile as well. She must have been in her late thirties, probably four or five years after she gave birth to me. There wasn't a date listed on the back, but there was some handwriting. In cursive writing, it said, "My beautiful daughter Betty Jo Lewis" with my grandmother's signature below that. In that picture, I saw myself in her jawline, ears, eyes, and eyebrow line. She was stunning to me.

There was another beautiful large portrait of her from when she must have been in her late teens. Her hair was much longer and fluffier, and she had a flower on each side of her forehead, the stems probably tucked behind each ear. That photo rocked me a bit because, to me, she looked so much like my daughter, who was probably close to the same age as my birth mother when that picture had been taken.

There were a few other pictures of her from her teens that were nice to look at, but the first two portraits are the ones I will always cherish. It seemed I'd selectively forgotten everything I had been trying to convince myself of regarding appearance. That pep talk I gave myself about looks not mattering went straight out the window. For the next few weeks, if you were near me, had a temperature, and appeared to be breathing, even if you were a complete stranger, you were going to see those two pictures of my birth mother.

For adoptees, there's nothing like having someone tell you that you resemble one of your birth parents. When we finally have pictures of our birth parents, and we show them to others, we desperately want people to identify and acknowledge our resemblance to them. Since we've lived our entire lives never being able to identify any of our physicality with someone else and never hearing, "Oh, you look just like your mother, or, you have your father's jawline," we crave hearing that from others. Non-adoptees have lived their entire lives observing their resemblance to one or both of their parents, as well as hearing that frequently from other family members.

After feeling that sense of joy, I turned to the pictures of Chiquita. There were six in total and she ranged in age from eighteen months to thirteen years old. She was a cute little girl. The portrait picture of her at eighteen months had been "colorized." Another showed her standing in a street in a knee-length dress, with two very old buildings and what appeared to be a large dead tree in the background. The picture was dated 1950, when she would have been five years old. I assumed that it must have been taken in that rural town of Lilburn.

A picture dated 1958 showed her near a tent, holding up a small trout she must have caught while camping. And then it hit me. I know children grow up fast, but how was it possible for the thirteen-year-old girl in the camping picture to be married and pregnant within the next two years? What I discovered later through DNA technology was even more difficult to contemplate than being married and pregnant at that age.

I moved on to the last photo, which showed some family members standing in front of an old brick building in shin high weeds. My grandfather was wearing a cowboy hat, and had his right arm on one hip and his left arm around his son Loran. My uncle Loran was standing next to his mother Ora Lee, with his left arm draped over her shoulders. Standing in front of them was my half-sister Chiquita, who was about eight years old, and a young boy who was Loran and Irene's first child. Irene was off to the left, holding their infant daughter. On the far left of that photo stood my great grandmother Rosalie Allison (maiden name Stein). She was my grandmother Ora Lee's mother and was born in 1873 and died in 1954. She looked very old in that picture, and since Chiquita appeared to be about seven or eight, I deduced that this group picture must have been taken near 1953, a year or so before Rosalie died.

I wasn't interested in anything work-related that day. I sat in my office and combed through every detail of every picture. Pictures have a special appeal for adoptees who will never meet their birth parents because pictures might be the closest thing an adoptee will have to being with their birth parents. It might be the only identifying connection they will have, and for many, pictures can be a crucial element in finding closure.

None of these pictures were taken at the time of my existence. Adoptees like me often find themselves wondering what their birth parents' lives were like at the time these still shot photos were taken. And for most adoptees, the inevitable fantasizing begins. They ask themselves, what would my life have been like living with my birth mother or birth parents? How would they have treated me and how much love would they have provided? How much would they really have cared for me? Assuming my birth mother wasn't raped, two decisions made by both my birth parents on one particular night, and one decision made nine months later by my birth mother, altered and rearranged everything that could have been.

I had finally found a small piece of closure regarding my genetic lineage. I could see clearly now where half of me originated, backed up by concrete evidence. I came from somewhere now. I didn't come from nowhere.

My birth mother's death certificate had listed her last known residence. I decided to drive to that address to see where she lived, and it wasn't a great neighborhood. Her apartment was on the first floor in a small complex that had ten units, right behind where the Stratosphere Tower (a hotel, casino, and observation tower) currently stands. The contractors began construction of that 800-foot tower about four months before my birth mother died in 1992. When I got out of my car, I was worried my wheels might get stolen before I returned to it. The complex was run-down and had already been condemned by the city. It was clear my birth mother had lived in poverty.

Before I left my office that day, Nancy asked me a question, and to this day I have not been able to answer it. She asked, "Knowing how poor your birth mother was, if she would have been alive and you met her, would you have been willing to help her financially?" That has continued to be a perplexing question for me. I guess it would have depended on how she received me during our first encounter. Would she have been excited to meet me? Would she have desired to have a meaningful relationship or any kind of relationship at all? Would she have been the type of person I would have wanted to have a relationship with? Did I "owe" her? After all, irrespective of the conditions in which she was intimate with my birth father, she was responsible for giving me life. It can be an awkward position to be in for adoptees who've identified a living birth parent. I've imagined many times knocking on her door and observing her face as she opened the door, either recognizing our resemblance, or realizing who it was after I'd identified myself. I've played out a couple scenarios in my mind. The first being her immediate recognition of me and inviting me into her apartment. In another scenario, she doesn't recognize our resemblance, and slams the door in my face after I announce that I'm the son she gave up in 1961.

A few days later, I went to a local drug store that had a photocopying machine that could blow up the pictures to 8.5"x11". I took all the pictures I received and enlarged them, and made multiple copies of each to ensure I would have enough to give to others. It's funny to me now; I guess I unconsciously assumed there were dozens of people that would desire and value them as much as I did.

I was excited to call John Lewis because I had promised him I would give him any pictures I found. I called him during the afternoon to ensure he wasn't sleeping, and after speaking with him, I was on my way. Again, I sat down with him and his wife at their kitchen table, and I placed copies of all the pictures in front of them. His mother Chiquita had been gone for twenty-four years and he seemed as anxious to look at the pictures as I had been a few days earlier. Even with his rough and coarse demeanor, he started to tear up a bit, which induced his wife to do the same. He hadn't seen his mother's face in so long, and even though all those pictures were taken years before he was born, they were still very meaningful to him. He remembered seeing two of the pictures before in his youth, but the other four of his mother were new to him. I also gave him all the pictures of his grandmother (my birth mother) and selectively told him what I had learned about our maternal family history. I didn't share with him any of the negative details I'd learned. He didn't seem as interested in the family history as he was in the new pictures. I felt joy watching him go through those pictures. After a little while longer sitting with them, it was time for me to leave. He thanked me, and I told him I would update him if I found anything more.

Ironically, after waiting what felt like forever to receive all those pictures, my birth mother's friend Kathy called me a few weeks later to tell me she did find a picture of her friend Betty. She mailed it to me the next week. It was a photo that had been taken about two years before her death. Kathy and her husband had driven down from Mesquite to visit with Betty, and they all went to the grand opening of the Mirage Hotel in November 1989. In the picture, she was standing in a large atrium that had a wooden walk-over bridge surrounded by large tropical plants. The picture showed her pure white hair (although that may have been a wig), and she seemed very thin. She looked nothing like the photos from her identification card from nine years earlier.

Ironically, Debbie and I had been visiting Las Vegas that weekend to see how close our new house was to completion. Debbie and I, along with my friend Kevin and his wife, had also attended the same grand opening that night. There were mobs of people there because it was about to become one of the biggest and most luxurious hotels on the Strip, and everyone wanted to see it. I doubt we were there at the exact same time, but it is certainly possible I could have walked right past her and never known the difference.

Debbie and I scheduled a trip back to LA to see both of our parents a week or so later. I had been giving my parents updates about what I'd been discovering and the pictures I'd received. I was anxious to show them the pictures and kept trying to reassure myself that they would be okay with it. Debbie was against the idea because she thought it would hurt them. But my parents had told me multiple times growing up that they would help me search for my birth parents if or when I had the desire to do so. If they were being truthful back then, and I assumed they were, we would have come to a similar place much earlier.

A week later, I placed the pictures on my parents' kitchen table and both my mom and dad were examining them with a fine-tooth comb. I could see my mother looking at a picture of my birth mother and then tilt her head up multiple times to compare it to me. My dad didn't seem to care as much about any possible resemblance. I just remember him staring at the portrait of my birth mother when she in her late thirties and saying, "Damn, that's one good-looking woman!"

My parents seemed happy for me, and if they did feel any sense of hurt, I certainly couldn't detect it. They knew this had been an emotional roller coaster for me. My mother had heard the emotions in my voice the day I called her kneeling next to my birth mother's grave, and I'm sure she relayed that information to my dad. They both knew how grateful I was to them for loving me the way they did.

My sister Sharon came over during that visit. She seemed happy that I had solved half of my mystery. I proudly showed all the pictures (minus the sheriff's card photos) and told her that if she wanted me to help her, I would do whatever I could. But for some reason, when I put it all on the line and offered help, she didn't seem to want to go there.

When we returned to Las Vegas, I asked Debbie to take one of the copies of that blown-up portrait of my birth mother and have it framed. I wanted to have it sitting on the console table behind the sofa where we had other family pictures displayed. But Debbie was against that idea because she didn't want my parents to visit our house and see it displayed like that.

In her opinion, and I understood her reasoning, having my birth mother's picture sitting anywhere near my parents' portraits was in some way equating their value. Debbie thought it would never be possible to put my birth mother on an equal plane with my parents. She thought that was disrespectful to my parents. She also never wanted our children to ever consider my birth mother their grandmother. Debbie believed our children had exactly four grandparents. Her two parents and my two parents. Despite her reservations, she honored my request, had the portrait framed, and placed it on our sofa back table.

It wasn't until many years later that I fully understood why I wanted that picture displayed. In some way it was telling anyone who walked into our house that I came from somewhere. For the longest time, from a physical perspective, I came from nowhere. There was nothing to show anyone because there was no evidence available to me. I was never able to walk through any house I ever lived in and identify with anyone (other than my children) who looked anything like me. Now, when my children walked by that picture of my birth mother, maybe even subliminally on my part, I wanted them to see and know where I physically came from, as well as where they came from.

I felt that there were two separate, compartmentalized components to my life. There was the physical component that my birth parents provided, and there was a nurturing component that my parents provided. Both of those components carried weight, and both were of value to me. Displaying that picture was not an attempt to place a greater value on one, or even to equate them. It was a simple statement that said, if anyone wants to know what one of Jeff's biological parents looked like, the evidence is sitting in that frame on the table behind our sofa.

[8]

ACTING ON A HUNCH

I WAS STILL IN CONTACT WITH GAIL, WHO I CONSIDERED TO BE my search angel. I would call her from time to time, giving her updates on all my discoveries. She wasn't charging me for that, and I know she found pleasure in it because she was a fellow adoptee and knew what it felt like to find some sense of closure.

For the next couple of months after finding the photos of my birth mother, I just couldn't seem to let go of Kathy's "twins" comment that had ended in a huge letdown. I was probably still trying to bring those fanatical feelings about meeting a twin brother back down to reality. But then it occurred to me: what if Kathy's memory of what my birth mother told her was faulty? What if my birth mother mentioned something to Kathy about giving up "two boys," and Kathy mistakenly remembered it as "twin boys"?

There was only one way to find out, and I would need Gail to light up her magic microfiche machine again. When looking for twins, she only searched the day before and the day after my birth. Now, she would need to look for adoptees born some undetermined time before or after my birthday. But how many years on either side of my birthdate would she look? I was certain a search like that could take Gail a long time. She'd potentially

91

need to search through years of records. The other problem with a search like that was the possibility that my birth mother gave up another child in a different state, perhaps in Missouri or Nevada. Gail only had records for California.

Before I called Gail, I called Kathy in Mesquite again. I wanted to let her know the "twins" theory didn't work out and go over the subject one more time. After all, she had told me she wasn't positive my birth mother used the term, "twins." She reiterated that it was so long ago when she discussed the subject with my birth mother, she just couldn't be sure. I presented my "two boys" theory to her, and she agreed that it could be a possibility. And that was enough for me to get the ball rolling.

I also wanted to call Tom Brent again. I wanted to confirm the time he had met, married, and divorced Chiquita, and if he remembered ever seeing my birth mother pregnant. When I called him back, he said he was sure that he met Chiquita in early 1962, married her in November of 1962, and their divorce was finalized in December of 1963. He told me during the time he dated and was married to Chiquita, my birth mother had various boyfriends, but at no time did he ever see or hear that Betty was pregnant. He was also clear with me that he didn't have anything to do with my birth mother after he exited the family. It was useful information because it could help Gail narrow her search for a sibling that may have been born after me.

Gail seemed intrigued by my theory when I called her, and agreed that it appeared to be a work-ladened task. But she told me in such a witty way, "As long as your checkbook is alive and well, your wish is my command." I laughed at her comment and was confident she wasn't going to gouge me financially. We also agreed on a fact that we thought might help her minimize her search time, which, of course, was of interest to me.

If you recall, I was listed on the private birth index in 1961 as "Baby Boy Heady." My birth mother changed her maiden name from Lewis to

Heady when she married in 1956. They separated in 1957, and didn't divorce until late 1961, but the plaque on her grave listed her as Betty Jo Heady. This implied she never changed back her name, even after divorcing. It was likely that she lived the rest of her life with the last name of Heady. (Trust me, we'll get to the envelope with the "Betty Roberts" name a bit later.)

If she did have another child before she married John Heady, and she gave it up for adoption, the name she would have given that child would most likely have been Baby Boy Lewis. If she had a child, even with a man other than John Heady after she separated from him in 1957, but before my birth, that child would most likely have been another Baby Boy Heady. But based on what I learned about custody rights from my delayed adoption, she most likely would have had to initiate a divorce from John Heady to give up a child before me. And since she wasn't divorced from John Heady before my birth, it was unlikely that she had a child between 1957 and 1960.

If she had another child after me, it was likely to also have been named Baby Boy Heady on the original birth index. She used that name for me, so why wouldn't she use it again for another child? It seemed to me, if she gave up another child, it was more probable she did it after me, so that's the time period I asked Gail to search. And since Tom Brent confirmed that he never saw my birth mother pregnant as late as December of 1963, I asked Gail to begin searching no earlier than June of 1964 (six months after Tom left that family). In essence, we were able to eliminate the years 1957 through June 1964. Gail got back to work. If I was wrong about a child being born after me, Gail would need to start searching before my birth, and who could know how many years back she would need to go?

Debbie and I had planned a trip to Hawaii for our fifteenth wedding anniversary in May 1998. We were leaving only a day after I turned Gail loose again. I had a cellphone at the time, but I wasn't sure how good the coverage would be on the island. I knew that pagers had better reception than cellphones, so I gave Gail my pager number and an answering service phone number in case she came up with anything while I was away. If she paged me, a live operator could type the message, and it would appear on my pager in a way similar to how a text message is received on a cellphone today. I know. It must seem to anyone younger than thirty reading here that we lived during the Flintstone era.

Debbie and I were enjoying ourselves immensely in Hawaii. Lots of rest and relaxation mixed with a few snorkeling adventures and some great meals. But every time we snorkeled, and I needed to be away from my pager, a sense of panic engulfed me. I don't know exactly why, but I had higher hopes for finding a sibling than Debbie or Gail did. It was something about Kathy's facial expression when she said "twins" that convinced me she was genuinely trying recount something my birth mother said, even if it wasn't "twins." One would think I would have been a little more realistic and might have tried to protect myself rather than face more disappointment. But my elevator doesn't always go to the top floor.

It was our fourth day on the island with three days remaining. We were shopping, just walking around in the downtown shops in Kaanapali. I received a pager alert, and my heart performed its rapid pumping ritual that had become commonplace over the past few months. I looked at the screen and the message read:

"I've found your brother. Please call me ASAP. Gail"

I showed the message to Debbie and dialed Gail's number from my cellphone, but it wouldn't connect. We weren't far from our hotel, and I told Debbie that we needed to immediately return to our room because I needed to use a landline. No one has ever been on a longer seven floor elevator ride.

I called Gail immediately, and said, "Gail, are you serious?" She replied, "I normally don't tell my clients I'm certain about any search, unless I am certain. But this time, I'm sure I've found at least a half-brother to you."

She went on to tell me that not only did my theory turn out to be correct regarding my interpretation of Kathy's "twins" comment but that narrowing the search to the time periods after my birth and six months after Tom Brent left Chiquita also paid off. She found another Baby Boy Heady born September 5, 1964. She only needed to search through about four months of California birth records. Not an easy task, but at least she didn't start years before my birth to try to find a Baby Boy Lewis.

Of course, I immediately wanted to know his name. She told me his name was Luke, he was born three years and four months after me, and he was thirty-three years old. She had already searched for his last known address and phone number, and it appeared he was living in Ontario, California, only a twenty-minute drive from my parents' house. She also told me that she believed that his phone number belonged to his parents and that he may still be living with them. I grabbed the notepad and pen from the nightstand and wrote down the phone number she provided. She asked me to let her know if I was able to reach him, and I'm sure that's because she was as excited as I was about this discovery.

I felt an anxious pressure at that moment that quickly turned into an anxious fear. Now I needed to reach out and put it all on the line. What I was about to say, and how I said it, could affect any future opportunities to meet him. What if I reached him and he hung up on me? I'd come this far, and failure just couldn't be an option. I started this search because I saw two siblings get reunited and here I was in the middle of the Pacific Ocean, fumbling around trying to figure out what to say.

I called the number and a woman picked up immediately. I asked if Luke was available, and she told me he wouldn't be home for a few more hours. She had an accent that sounded Eastern European, but I couldn't completely place it. She asked me who I was and what this was regarding.

My heart sank because I didn't want to answer the second part of her question. Was I really going to try to explain the reason I was calling to this woman, especially if she was Luke's adoptive mother?

I introduced myself and asked her to please be patient with me. I explained that I was involved in some family research that had led me to Luke. But she didn't seem to want to have anything to do with me. She seemed extremely put out, as if I was a phone scammer. She told me she didn't think Luke would be interested in talking with me and it felt like she was about to hang up. Before she could do that, I asked her if I could leave my phone number, and to my surprise, she allowed me to do so. I gave her my answering service pager number to ensure I had a better chance of not missing Luke if he tried to reach me. And that was it. But I felt better after finishing that call because I clearly had the right phone number and a residence for him. I wondered if Luke would reach out, and if so, just how long I would need to wait.

Hour after hour I waited. Hawaii was three hours behind California and as it became later, the odds he would reach out that day became less likely. Sometime after the fourth hour he paged me. He left his name and phone number and wrote that he was available if I wanted to call him back. Whew!

I called him right back. I told him that my name was Jeff, that I lived in Las Vegas, and that I was adopted in Los Angeles in 1961. I immediately asked him if he was adopted, and without asking me anything else, he confirmed he was. I proceeded to tell him that my research led me to him because I believed we were half-brothers, sharing the same birth mother.

He seemed shocked and naturally wanted to know what evidence I had to back up my claim. I told him it would take a long time to explain it all over the phone, but if we could meet after I returned to Las Vegas, I'd be willing to drive to LA to explain it all to him. To entice him to consider meeting with me, I also told him that I had pictures of our birth mother, our deceased half-sister, and our grandparents.

But apparently, he wasn't done interrogating me. He asked me to tell him where my birth mother was born and the color of her hair and eyes. He was asking me as if he knew the answers to those questions, and I needed to have the correct responses or this would all be over in a hurry. I told him she was born and raised in Missouri and was reported to have brown hair and green eyes. He responded: "Okay. You've got me believing your story so far. When will you be back so we can meet?"

I was shocked that he already knew those facts about our birth mother. So, I asked him how he gathered that information, and he said his parents gave it to him after he graduated high school. He said some documents with general information about his birth mother were mailed to his parents only months after they brought him home from the adoption agency.

I told him I would call him when I returned to Las Vegas, and we could plan to meet soon after. I was so excited about this discovery, but when we finished our call, I was having a difficult time understanding how Luke's parents had some of his background information from the same agency I'd been adopted from, but apparently, my parents never received it for me. Or had they?

I called my parents the next day and asked my mother about those background documents and to my surprise, she nonchalantly told me she had them tucked away in a fireproof box. I was shocked. I asked her why she never told me about them or showed them to me, especially after she knew I started searching last year. She told me she just never thought about them after they received them a few months after they brought me home. I knew she wasn't purposefully trying to keep them from me. She didn't know that the background documents I requested the year before and waited nine months to receive would contain some of the same information she had all along in her fireproof box. When she did give them to me, it was clear not all the pertinent information I'd received from the adoption agency was included.

And then it all made sense to me regarding my sister Sharon's knowledge about her birth mother's circumstances and the name she had been given at birth. My parents must have given Sharon some of the information in her background documents, including her birth mother's age and that her birth mother's parents had forced her birth mother to give Sharon up. The name her birth mother provided her on her original birth certificate was Nikki Loraine Whitney. It wasn't a generalized name like the Baby Boy Heady name my birth mother had given me.

So there had been nine wasted months when I was waiting for my background documents to be mailed. But that didn't really matter—those nine months didn't make a difference in whether I had chance the meet any birth relative or not. But what if those nine wasted months had been the difference between meeting an unidentified biological relative just before they passed on, or not? But, if my mother would have given me those documents, I may never have found Gail and she was instrumental in helping me identify my birth mother. I just had to move on.

I called Gail to tell her the good news. She was so happy for me, and it felt like we were a good detective team that solved a case that could easily have snuck past us both. If I never asked my birth mother's friend Kathy, if my birth mother said anything about giving me up for adoption, I may never have found Luke. If I hadn't acted on a hunch about "two boys" rather than "twins," Luke may never have been discovered. It was very clear now: whatever my birth mother said to her friend Kathy many years ago had been incorrectly remembered as a reference to twins. My birth mother must have mentioned that she had given up to "two boys" for adoption.

Blood versus Water

I called Luke as soon as I returned home from Hawaii. We chatted briefly and planned to meet at his workplace a few days later. He was a waiter at a very nice restaurant in Ontario, California, and we agreed we would meet in the lobby at 4 p.m. when his shift ended. The day before our meeting, I drove down and stayed with my parents. I brought copies of the pictures of our maternal birth family and a few of me growing up to compare with his childhood pictures.

I sat on a bench in the lobby of the restaurant, about fifteen minutes early, waiting for him to appear. There was an older couple sitting on the same bench and the husband must have noticed the UNLV logo on my shirt. He asked me if I was a UNLV basketball fan and if I lived in Las Vegas. I confirmed both of his questions, but I was too excited to stop there. I added that I was an adoptee, and at the restaurant to meet with a half-brother for the first time who was also given up for adoption. They seemed to love hearing that. It felt good to say it, and I fantasized there were hidden news cameras about to record us meeting face to face.

Luke walked through the open doorway that led from the dining area into the lobby, straight toward me. I immediately knew it was him, although at first glance our resemblance wasn't overwhelming. As I stood up, he said, "Jeff?" and I said, "Luke?" and from there it was a nice strong handshake. We went out to the parking lot and leaned against his car and began to share of our life stories. He told me he had a seven-year-old son and was recently divorced. He was living with his parents to get back on his feet financially. He told me he had an adopted brother named Paul who had been killed in a car accident only five years earlier, and how hard that was for him. I shared the details of my family and some of my major life events as well.

I placed the pictures of our birth family on the hood of his car and identified all of our family members. He seemed very interested as he looked at the details. A parking lot wasn't the ideal place to be having this kind meeting, but that wasn't important. We talked about the reported circumstances that led our birth mother to giving me up, but he didn't seem to remember from his background documents what reasoning our birth mother provided for giving him up. I also provided the negative details I'd learned about our birth mother. I wanted him to know what I knew, and he could form his own opinion about her. With no suggestive leading on my part, he concluded she must have been a fast and loose woman.

He didn't seem as excited about our discovery as I was. Perhaps it was because he was the hunted, and I was pursuing him. Or maybe it was a lot of information to take in at one time, whereas I had been knee-deep in it for many months. After about two hours, we finished up and agreed to meet at his parents' house the next day.

When I arrived, I was greeted by his adoptive mother, who had answered my first call to Luke. She seemed much nicer this time because she knew why I was there and knew I wasn't there to scam anyone. But I had an uneasy feeling about what I was doing by revealing all this information to her son. In some way, I felt I may have been imposing on her territory with this information about Luke's birth mother, and it may not have been welcome. Perhaps she never wanted Luke to know anything about his birth mother. Maybe she wanted to be the sole focus of Luke's attention, his only mother. But I quickly got over that. It wasn't like our birth mother was alive to compete for Luke's attention.

Luke introduced me to his cute little seven-year-old son, Kyle. When Luke introduced me, he prefaced my first name with the term, "uncle." And I must admit that felt uncomfortable. Don't get me wrong, I appreciated Luke's efforts to use that term to not only to solidify our genealogical positions but also as a term of endearment to make his son feel closer to me, or me to feel closer to his son. And that seemed like a great thing to do. But I had other non-biologically related nieces and a nephew that I was very close to, and for me, that term of endearment didn't seem to fit for a child I'd just met. I thought, if it ended up that Luke and I developed a stronger relationship and I was around his son more often and got to know him better, I'd welcome it. It's just one of those awkward positions adoptees find themselves in when they meet blood relatives for the first time. To me, an uncle or a brother you just meet doesn't carry the same weight relationally as an uncle or brother you grew up with. Here's one of the pictures we took at his parents' house that day (Luke on the left).

We sat for hours in his parents' backyard comparing pictures from our youth. I think we looked a lot more like each other when we were younger than we did as adults. It was time for me to return home. As I was leaving, Luke mentioned that he came to Las Vegas every few months, and the next time, he would call ahead and see if we could meet. I thought that was a great idea and looked forward to it.

When I returned home, I gave Debbie all the details of my meeting with Luke. It was so strange and exciting to learn for the first time in my life that I had a "brother." She knew that was important to me, but I could also sense that she was leery about introducing new people into our family that neither of us knew all that well. I understood her concern, but I wanted to trust the process and see how my relationship with Luke would develop.

About three months later, Luke called and said he would be coming to Las Vegas for the weekend and wanted to see if we could meet. We agreed to meet at a restaurant near where I lived for lunch. Before he showed up, I asked Debbie if it was okay with her if I had him over to meet her and our kids. She seemed okay with the idea and was relying on my judgment that Luke wasn't an axe murderer.

We had lunch that day, and during our visit, it started to become clear there were some obvious differences between Luke's lifestyle and interests, and mine. He didn't seem that different than he was the first time we met, but that day, I hadn't really been paying attention to those kinds of things because my excited state had me overlooking any of that. He was single, and from what he told me, I gathered that he was still into the partying scene and liked to gamble when he came to Las Vegas. He certainly wasn't asking me to participate in any of that, and just because I couldn't control myself years before, didn't mean Luke had a problem with gambling. For all I knew, he was like most people who could have fun gambling without becoming addicted. But it still made me slightly uncomfortable.

I want to be clear here. I'm not trying to bash Luke, and initially I did want to try to further our relationship. I've already revealed that I've had my own wayward ways that certainly don't meet the standards I hold today. I had only been clean from my gambling addiction for five years, and I had committed my life to honoring God and my family. I had made changes in my life, and I tried to move away from any influences that could lead me down a path I didn't want to be on. I knew I wasn't perfect or better than Luke. My concern was associating with someone who lived a different type of lifestyle, and how that could possibly lead me down the wrong road.

After following me in his car to my house, I introduced him to Debbie and both of our kids. I did tell my kids before he arrived that Luke was their biological uncle as a way of differentiating between him and the family uncle they knew and loved. We all had a nice visit in our family room for about an hour. Although I felt a bit anxious, everything went well and then Luke and I went into my backyard and talked for another hour or so before he left. It troubled me knowing that now I wasn't so sure I wanted to further our relationship, and if or what I would do to minimize it. I certainly didn't want to hurt Luke. Luke and I also had completely different interests, and I just wasn't sure either of us would want to spend all that much time together. It hurts me to even think and write that today. It might have been completely different if we grew up together, but we'll never know.

I was beginning to learn something of great importance: for me, blood is not thicker than water. I'm not as close as I'd like to be with my sister Sharon, but it would be impossible for Luke and I to have a closer relationship than my sister and I share. Likewise, I doubt I could have ever become closer to Luke than he was with the adopted brother he grew up with. I'm not saying that only because Luke and I lived different lifestyles. Family is who you have or are in relationship with. It isn't solely because you're blood-related. I also know many people who are closer to some of their friends than they are with their own blood-related siblings. Blood can determine who you are raised with, but blood shouldn't and normally doesn't determine who you want to spend time with. Relationships are made by choice, and they are not necessarily nurtured out of obligation due to genetic ties. People desire and are drawn to spend time with others they enjoy and who they have interests and values in common with, independent of genetic commonality.

To be clear, I'm not saying that adoptees or people who later discover the identities of long-lost family members can't develop tight bonds over time. There are many examples of adoptees who have found one of more of their birthparents or siblings, who were not just simply accepted by their blood relative, but also developed loving long-term relationships with them. The opposite is also true and there are many instances of adoptees being completely rejected by their newly discovered birth family members.

Over the next couple of years, Luke would call me to see if we could meet and I always struggled by resisting his offers. I feel guilty about that to this day. I wished things could have been different and that we had more common ground that would have allowed us to be closer. Luke is a good person and I know his motives were pure. Although I resisted a closer relationship those first couple years, I did end up meeting with Luke again down the road, when I reached out to him to help him discover the identity of his birth father, hoping to jump-start a relationship with him.

[9]

MOVING THROUGH LIFE

THERE WAS SOMETHING BOTHERING ME AS I REFLECTED ON MY birth mother giving up two children and the reasoning she provided in my background document. I wondered what excuse she used for giving up Luke. Did she claim Chiquita was having to care for a three-and-a-half-year-old Deana now, and that she couldn't provide for Chiquita, Deana, and Luke, who was about to enter this world? By September of 1964, when Luke was born, Chiquita and Tom Brent were already divorced, and Chiquita was a single mother again. I asked Luke if he still had his background information, but he didn't know where it was and said he hadn't seen it in years. It seemed way more likely to me that our birth mother considered children an inconvenience, and that may have been her motivation for giving both Luke and I up. I'll never know if that's true, but I felt that was the most likely explanation, and I continue to believe it today.

There was something else that I couldn't explain—the letter that Irene sent me. If you recall, that letter was sent by my birth mother to her parents, and it was postmarked September 1, 1965. My birth mother wrote her name as Betty Roberts on the return address as well when signing her letter. I searched on Ancestry.com many years later, and I was never able to find a record of her marrying anyone with the surname of Roberts.

Furthermore, I knew she used Heady for her last name from the time she was first married in 1956 until the day she died in 1992. The letter she sent to her parents (my grandparents) was a small single sheet of paper, covered in cursive writing on both sides. This letter was written when Chiquita was twenty years old, and it's regarding a supposed illness that Chiquita had. But the letter never mentions that Chiquita was about six months pregnant with her son John Lewis, who was born on December 2, 1965. I've always wondered if my grandparents knew that Chiquita was having a third child. The letter read as follows:

August 31, 65

Dear Mom and Dad,

You don't know how much I thank you for sending the money. Chiquita was in the hospital for three days just having tests made. They are quite sure it is rheumatic fever, and a bad stage. She tells me sometimes it hurts when she breathes. She is at home now. Her ankles swell up and the big knots on her legs you can't even rub them. We don't have all the reports yet. They won't give her any medication until after they've found out about the tests. I don't think there is one good doctor in this town. All a bunch of thieves. I am going to take her to LA General hospital where they have the best doctors in the world. The county hospital if I can't find out anything.

It was nice to hear your voice on the phone. I wish I could have talked to daddy & Marceline.

I am in a hurry to get to work. I will repay the money as soon as I can.

I love all of you. Bye now.

Betty Roberts

414 A So. 2nd Street

Las Vegas Nevada

I didn't understand why she used the last name of Roberts and I'd stew on this mystery for nearly twenty years before making more sense of it.

By the fall of 1998, I seemed to be at the end of my search capabilities. I'd gathered a lot of information and enough pictures that I felt somewhat satisfied. If there was a sense of incompleteness, it had to do with there being no foreseeable path toward identifying my birth father. The background information I received described only a few of his physical characteristics and that he may have been of English descent. My birth mother was gone and couldn't provide any clues and I couldn't figure out a way to find anyone who knew who she was with in August of 1960, when I was conceived. At this point, I had nowhere to go.

So, I placed my thick folder with all my research documents, search lists, and pictures in a filing cabinet. I was convinced I would only be able to assemble half my genetic puzzle and that the pieces containing the information necessary to identifying my birth father were never included in the original box. Every so often, I would sort through that file and look at the pictures. As years passed, I seemed to retrieve them less and less often. Later, when cellphones added cameras as a feature, I added all those pictures to my phone. Even with them readily accessible in my phone, I looked at them infrequently. For all intents and purposes, I was finished searching, and as satisfied as I could be.

In March of 1999, I was at my office when I received a frantic call from Debbie, who had just received a distressed call from my sister Sharon. My seventy-year-old father had died in his sleep while taking an afternoon nap. I immediately drove home, packed up my family, and headed to California to be with my mom. I cried all the way there, feeling devastated. It was one of those life events where you'll never forget where you were, what you were doing, or how you felt when receiving the information. But in the end, I felt good knowing that my dad and I had a good relationship.

When he died, he knew just how much I loved him, and I knew the depth of love he had for me. He sacrificed a lot to take me in and adopt me as his son, and I will always be indebted to him for that. He wasn't a perfect father, nor was I a perfect son, but he was way more than enough for me.

In the spring of 2001, at the age of forty, my friend Gary and I went to the Mayo Clinic in Scottsdale, Arizona, to have extensive executive physicals. I'd never done anything like that before, and the testing was thorough. At the end of that day, I met with a general doctor who collected and reported the results from all the tests they performed on me. He proceeded to tell me that my platelet count was outside the normal range by about 50 per cent, and suggested I see an oncologist when I returned home. He said he thought it was unlikely to be something serious, but I should check it out to be safe.

When I returned home, I saw my family doctor. He told me he had noticed that my platelet count was high the last time I tested, and he'd planned to compare them with the next test I took. So, he referred me to an oncologist, who ran a lot of different blood tests but found nothing in my blood that might cause my counts to be so high. He informed me that I would need to have a bone marrow biopsy. He explained that the marrow is the factory that produced our blood cells, and that biopsy would help him understand just what was causing my counts to be so high. He told me not to worry, but that was the equivalent of telling me not to think about the gigantic purple elephant in the corner of the room.

I had that biopsy performed the next week, and it was just about as much fun as watching two old men fish without hooks on their lines. While I was still awake, but with some numbing agents, they effectively augured a long core of bone marrow, about the diameter of a pencil eraser, from the small of my back.

Then it was on to waiting. I did the unthinkable and searched various medical websites to see all the horrific possibilities I might have been facing. I was already a known hypochondriac, so of course, I was really freaking out waiting for the results. My oncologist had given me his cell-phone number, and one night, I went into our garage, away from Debbie and the kids and called him. I told him I knew he was looking to see if I had some form of leukemia. I was emotional, and he told me he wasn't sure what it was, but he didn't think it was anything immediately life-threating. Debbie came into the garage as I was finishing the call with the doctor. Tears were pouring down my cheeks as I told her, "I'll be crushed if he tells me it will be unlikely that I'll live long enough to walk our daughter down the aisle someday. What will I do if he tells me there's little chance I'll ever be able to meet our grandchildren?" After a long embrace, we went back into the house as if everything was normal.

Debbie and I walked into the oncologist's office a week later to receive the results. He diagnosed me with a rare form of blood cancer called Essential Thrombocythemia (ET). There were four different diseases in the category of myeloproliferative disorders, and ET was the least life-threatening. He thought we could control the disease if I took an oral form of chemotherapy that was developed in the 1960s.

I took that medication for the next three years, and then tried a medication that had been developed only ten years earlier by the Mayo Clinic. This newer medication was supposed to be a better, more efficient drug that would only help minimize my platelet counts and wouldn't affect the red or white cell counts like that older medication I'd been taking. That new medication was nasty, and I suffered from heart palpations and an irritable digestive tract for the next four years. It controlled my platelet counts well, but I was miserable. After four years of suffering from the side effects, my doctor recommended I go back to the old medication, and thankfully they disappeared.

In 2011, about three years after switching back to the older medication and ten years since my initial diagnoses of ET, I had an MRI of my ribs because I was having a lot of pain on my left side. When the radiologist read the scan, he remarked that my bone marrow wasn't "lighting up" correctly in the areas they scanned, which was indicative of another disease within the same spectrum of myeloproliferative disorders. They were concerned that my initial ET disease had migrated to a more dangerous disorder called Myelofibrosis (MF). Myelofibrosis causes fibers to build up in the bone marrow, restricting the marrow's capabilities to make all types of cells.

My oncologist ordered another bone marrow biopsy, and it confirmed the radiologist's findings. I flew to the Mayo Clinic in Rochester, Minnesota, to get the opinion of the top doctor specializing in that disease. He reviewed my biopsy slides and confirmed I had MF. That doctor laid out for me my prognosis: I had a 75 per cent chance of making it another ten years, and a 60 per cent chance of making it another fifteen years. At the time of this writing, I've made it exactly ten years.

I'd never throw a party to celebrate having cancer, but it has made me appreciate life in ways I never would have otherwise. I did get to see my kids graduate from high school and college and I did get to walk my daughter down the aisle and make a toast at her wedding. I watched my son get married and I have one grandchild I've held and another one that just entered this world. I've had a great life, and for the remainder of it, I plan to appreciate everything I can.

And, if my theory is correct, I'm not even supposed to be here. I'm probably just the product of a one-night sexual encounter. But I'm grateful to whoever my birth father was, and the birth mother who gave me up, and the parents who loved me dearly.

[10]

PEACEFUL GREETINGS, FATHER

IN 2017, ABOUT TWENTY YEARS SINCE I FIRST BEGAN MY SEARCH, I began to hear a barrage of radio and TV ads for genealogical websites that offered DNA testing to the public. To me it seemed those ads only focused on offering people the ability to determine their ethnicity. I remember listening to one ad where a wife was talking about her husband recently discovering he was 60 per cent Norwegian. The woman was saying that her husband bought a sword and helmet with horns after receiving his results and how he would run around the house as if he was some kind of Viking marauder. While she was speaking, you could hear her husband in the background, grunting and playing the part of an eighth-century Nordic sailor.

I thought those commercials were funny, but I did not consider that taking a test like that could help solve adoption mysteries. I don't remember any part of those ads claiming that their tests that could help lead someone to identifying others who were genetically related. It never occurred to me that a test like that could help me identify my birth father.

23andMe was the first major company to offer autosomal DNA testing to the public in 2007. Of course, there are others today like Ancestry,

Family Tree DNA (FTDNA) and My Heritage. When each of these testing sites was first launched, its database was very small, so looking for genetic connections to others was probably not very effective. But the database for each of the companies I've mentioned above has grown exponentially over time. Today, Ancestry has the largest database, with 23andMe coming in second, followed by the much smaller databases of FTDNA and MyHeritage. Ancestry.com, Ancestry's website, also has the best and most extensive genealogical record database. The search engine on Ancestry.com contains billions of records, and if you have never used it, you would be shocked at what you can find. With the world going digital many years ago, it now seems as if nearly every surviving paper record for every person who's lived in the last four centuries is available at the touch of one's keypad.

In 2012, I signed up with Ancesty.com, and paid a monthly service fee to use their search engine to try to build a family tree, even though at that time, I could only build a small family tree for the part of my biological maternal family that I had discovered years before. If I recall, I may have also been trying to build another tree for my adoptive family, for historical reference. Ironically, 2012 was the first year Ancestry offered DNA testing, but I was unaware of that. Even so, taking their test at that time, or even three to four years later, would probably have resulted in minimal genetic matches for me. Their database of people who'd tested just hadn't grown anywhere near what it has today. After I first built my biological maternal family tree, I stopped paying for their search engine and their family tree builder, and didn't check their website for another six years.

Sometime late in the spring of 2017, my daughter and I were talking on the phone, and she mentioned in passing that she and her husband were taking a DNA test from Ancestry.com. They had just put their tests in the mail that day. She told me about how simple it was—all one needed to do was spit into a tube and Ancestry would post their results online for them to view. Out of complete ignorance, I replied, "Why would you care about any of that stuff?"

I was thinking, "What is she going to really find out? That she's 35 per cent German, 30 per cent English, 13 per cent French and a host of other ethnicities? Does she really need a test to determine she's Caucasian? It's not a big deal!" I didn't care about any of that, and I didn't consider the implications of her results for her mother and me. As I've said, sometimes I'm no sharper than a bowling ball. She told me it would take six to eight weeks to get her results and that was it. We moved on to discuss other things of greater importance. By my standards, that was almost any other subject besides DNA ethnicity testing.

I spoke with my daughter a few times during her test waiting period, and not once did I think about the test—until she texted me.

She texted, "Whatcha doing?" and I replied, "Just hanging out watching a little TV." Her next text read, "I received my test results back." Not remembering anything about the DNA test she'd taken, I asked, "What results?" And she wrote, "You know, that DNA test I told you about a couple of months ago." I wrote back, "Oh yeah. What did it say?"

Her next text sent me reeling. She replied, "*SHALOM ABBA!*"

Not understanding what she meant, I wrote back: "Shalom Abba? What are you talking about?" I knew the term "shalom" was used as a peaceful greeting, and "abba" meant father in Hebrew, but what did that have to do with her DNA results?

She quickly replied, "Dad, that test says I'm **25 per cent Ashkenazi Jewish!**"

Jewish!? I was in shock. My daughter had that much Jewish blood? Before I could think too deeply about it, I wondered where it could have come from. I thought I knew about Debbie's genealogical background and was pretty sure her maternal side was loaded with nothing but full-blooded

Germans. Her paternal side seemed to be filled with almost exclusively English ancestors, with maybe some French lineage sprinkled in. Was there some Jewish blood in her upline that no one was aware of? Debbie's side of the family had to be the explanation for our daughter's results; surely they couldn't be coming from me. I was pretty sure no one in my birth mother's lineage was Jewish, unless my birth mother was wrong about the ethnicity information she provided—she claimed she was of English, German, Scotch, and Irish descent. I had read and reread her ethnicity statements from my background information numerous times, and "Jewish" was not one of the four ethnicities she listed. But just how much did my birth mother really know about her ethnicity?

What the hell did all this mean? Of course, I knew what Jewish meant, but what was Ashkenazi? I'm a firm believer in science, but I didn't really know how these DNA companies made their measurements or how accurate they were. Maybe it was all junk science, a gimmick to get people to pay for these tests. But even as I thought that, I knew my theory was a long shot. If my daughter's results had indicated that she was 2 or 3 per cent Jewish, then that could be attributed to some small statistical error. But 25 per cent was way too high to consider her results a statistical aberration.

I wasn't as well versed in the genetic components of ethnicity or interpreting autosomal DNA test results as I am today, but I did take a few biology courses during my high school and college days. I knew that my daughter's ethnicity results should comprise roughly 50 per cent of my ethnicity and 50 per cent of Debbie's. If I was right, and Debbie had no Jewish lineage, my daughter's results could only mean that I had to be at least 50 per cent Ashkenazi Jewish. And if I was 50 per cent Jewish, and my birth mother had no Jewish ethnicity, that could only mean that my birth father was 100 per cent Jewish. If my birth father was less than 100 per cent Jewish, the only other possibility to explain my daughters' results would be such that either my birth mother or Debbie, or both, were carrying some percentage of Jewish lineage.

But there was no way I could be 50 per cent Jewish. At the time, I didn't know where our daughter's Jewish ethnicity originated, but I felt pretty sure Debbie had a big surprise coming regarding her lineage, and I was anxious to tell her about it.

But what if all our daughter's Jewish lineage was coming from me? It seemed impossible that I'd been walking around as an ethnically Jewish person for the last fifty-seven years and never known it. And no one had suspected it by my appearance! But what was I thinking? If I had never suspected it, why did I think others would? I have many Jewish friends and some Jewish business partners. If it was true I was genetically Jewish, I couldn't wait to tell them. I knew just how funny the news would be to them.

I Googled the term "Ashkenazi Jewish" and discovered that they represent nearly 80 per cent of all ethnic Jews. They are of central or eastern European decent and they preserve Palestinian, rather than Babylonian, Jewish traditions. Then I began to consider my physical characteristics.

I first considered my nearly bridgeless nose, which runs between my eyes and straight into my forehead. I've always had a terrible time keeping my sunglasses from sliding down my nose. My birth mother's pictures didn't reflect a nose like that. Over the years, a few people had told me that I have a nose like a Roman statue. Did my daughter's results explain that?

I stopped texting my daughter and called her. She mentioned that her results listed people that she was genetically linked to, but she didn't immediately recognize any of the names. She had a huge list of cousins and other biological relatives but most of them appeared to be distant. Obviously, there would be matches to both Debbie's genetic line and mine. It was only then that the light bulb went on for me: I finally realized this type of DNA of testing could possibly lead to identifying my birth father. It had been almost eighteen years since I had tried to let go of the notion that I could discover his identity. My daughter's genetic discovery was big news, and just as the passion had boiled in me all those years ago, again I was on fire to find answers and discover the identity of my birth father.

There was only one way to get to the bottom of this, and that would be to test. The instant I got off the phone with my daughter, I went to Ancestry.com's website and ordered their DNA kit. I almost considered camping out near our mailbox for the next few days to intercept the mailman before he could put it in our mailbox. I wanted my results and I didn't want to waste any time.

Getting Another Education

I received my Ancestry test kit about a week later, and within ten minutes I had spit in the tube they provided, placed it in the small pre-addressed box, and taken it to the post office to make sure it was sent the same day. Ancestry's website was clear: depending on their workload, it could take between six to eight weeks to receive test results. That seemed like an eternity.

It was during the beginning of my wait that I remembered something a friend had told me about five years earlier that seemed so ironic and very funny to me. My friend Rich had been visiting Las Vegas, and we'd gone to lunch together to catch up. At lunch, he told me a fascinating story. He had also grown up in West Covina, but went to a rival high school. He told me that a few months before, his cousin Joey from New York had contacted him about a family discovery he'd just made. Joey's mother and Rich's mother were sisters and when Joey's mother died, a long-lost cousin named Albert showed up to the funeral, but nobody recognized him. When Joey asked him about his identity, Albert told Joey he was related to his mother, and had escaped from Holland just before the Nazis invaded. A few years later, when Albert died, Joey was shocked to discover that Albert's funeral was being held at a Jewish synagogue, where all the men were wearing their traditional head coverings known as Kippahs in Hebrew, or yarmulkes in Yiddish.

Joey couldn't put the pieces together until another cousin attending Albert's funeral gave him a shocking dose of reality. When Joey asked why Albert's funeral was in a synagogue, he was told that Albert, and his own mother, were 100 per cent Jewish. That meant that my friend Rich's mother was too. Joey phoned Rich in Idaho to tell him about this discovery and Rich was completely floored. That was Rich's "Shalom Abba" moment.

It turned out that Rich's maternal family escaped from Holland before the Germans invaded in 1940. When they arrived in the US, they changed their names from something that easily could have been recognized as a Jewish surname to something that appeared to be more of an Anglo-Saxon surname. Many Jews who had fled Europe at that time did the same, so it would be less likely that they would face persecution in their new homeland. Rich's mother and father raised him in a Catholic church, and his mother never told him about her Jewish lineage, taking it to her grave.

As we sat there, finishing up lunch, I started to laugh because it seemed so funny to me. How crazy was it that he walked around until he was in his mid-fifties, never knowing he was half Jewish? As I waited for my results, I knew that if they indicated that I carried any Jewish lineage, I would need to call Rich immediately and tell him my story. Not only would he be able to relate but it would also now be his turn to chuckle over my newly discovered genetic origins.

During that waiting period, I decided that I needed to understand a little more about how to interpret the results after receiving them. I did a few Google searches looking for "How to interpret DNA test results," and found some websites that provided information helping people understand and interpret their matches on their testing sites. I then searched on Facebook for "DNA groups for adoptees" and stumbled across a group called DNA Detectives. It was a private group, but I only needed to answer a few general questions to be granted access by an administrator.

After gaining access to that group, I started to read some of the past and current posts from group members. It was fascinating. There were questions posed by people searching for their birth parents, and from people who had recently determined from their results that the father they'd been raised by was not their biological father. There were other people who had recently discovered they had a full or half sibling they never knew anything about, and were figuring out how to approach their parents with that news. I even saw questions posed by a few birth mothers who were searching for the children they'd given up. There were adoptees posting devastating, disheartening news about contacting one or more of their birth parents, only to be rejected for the second time. Others posted pictures of the first time meeting their biological parents or siblings and writing about how great their experiences had been. It was becoming clear to me that this new technology could reveal a lot of family secrets, secrets that some would never want revealed.

The group focused on helping each other make scientific sense of their DNA results, and offered ideas, suggestions, opinions, and instructions for the future steps required to find answers. It was founded by a now famous genetic genealogist named CeCe Moore—you may have seen her on some mystery TV shows, helping solve cold case murders or other violent crimes. CeCe started out as a hobbyist, helping adoptees find their birth families using DNA. But that hobby turned into an overwhelming workload, and that's when she decided to start her DNA Detectives Facebook group. Shortly after I joined the group in 2017, it reached 80,000 members. As of today, the group has doubled to over 160,000 members.

While waiting for my results, I read every post that showed up on my feed. The answers to the questions posed were being answered in scientific terms, and I loved that. They also have a sister Facebook group called "DNA Detectives Social." That group deals with the emotional aspects of people's searches, rather than the scientific aspects of DNA. After joining the group, I felt I needed to take a crash course on reproductive biology to refine my understanding of how DNA combined after conception and how my DNA results would be presented.

Early on, some of the answers that people were providing in the group went way over my head. But the more I read those posts, day after day, the more I was becoming comfortable understanding the details they provided. I remembered from my earlier studies that a male receives a Y chromosome from his father and an X chromosome from his mother. A female receives an X chromosome from her father and a different X from her mother. Even before my results came back, I'd learned how I would be able to separate my maternal and paternal matches.

I saw people writing about shared match levels and they continued to use the term "centimorgans" (cMs) in reference to their genetic matches. It became clear that my Ancestry results would show each of my DNA matches and our associated match level measured in cMs. So, I researched that too, and quickly learned that the higher the cM value, the closer the familial relationship would be. Ancestry, like every other DNA testing site, would sum up the total amount of shared common DNA on each chromosome between two different people and that's how they determined their respective biological relationship.

People in the group also continued to post about what they termed "the green chart," which was a small green chart listing all the DNA match range levels measured in cMs and their corresponding relationship possibilities to other matches.

For example, if someone had a DNA match to someone else between 575 and 1,330 cMs, that could mean they were related as one of the following:

First cousin

Half aunt/uncle/niece/ nephew

Great-grandparent/great-grandchild

Great-aunt/uncle/niece/nephew

A larger match, of between 1,300 and 2,300 cMs, could have the following closer familial relationship possibilities:

Half-sibling

Aunt/uncle/niece/nephew

Double First cousin

Grandparent/grandchild

A third cousin, on the other hand, might only share an average of 55 cMs.

Based on the range measured in cMs, the DNA testing sites make their best guess regarding the relationship from the four possibilities listed within those ranges. The testing sites' algorithms cannot know which of the four possibilities is the correct relationship. It was up to the tester to try to determine which of the four was correct. For example, if two people shared 900 centimorgans, Ancestry may label their match as a First cousin. But there are three other possibilities in that range between 575 and 1,330 centimorgans. The DNA Detectives Facebook group offered help with sorting and comparing matches, providing techniques that involved interpreting DNA alone, or DNA in combination with known genealogical relationships.

One warning post, that kept arising continually, regarded how important it was to do extensive research before even considering reaching out and contacting matches. They advised for all those searching to take screen shots of every piece of data available for a match they'd found on the testing website they'd used. They also advised searching on social media websites such as Facebook or Instagram to learn more about their match and to see if they could determine who their match's relatives were. Too many people were discovering matches and immediately messaging them through the testing website. And if that message was unwelcome news for the recipient, they could immediately block the searching person from their DNA page on that testing website, or from their social media page. If the searching person did not take screenshots or capture other pertinent information beforehand, it was possible they'd never have access to it again.

There's another DNA website named Gedmatch.com. That site doesn't provide testing, but does allow anyone to upload their DNA results from the other testing websites like Ancestry, 23AndMe, My Heritage, and FTDNA. Ancestry and 23andMe do not allow anyone to upload their DNA results from any other testing sites, and I'm sure that's for financial reasons. To compare your DNA to others on those two huge testing databases, you must pay to play.

Gedmatch.com is also useful, because unlike Ancestry, it has a chromosome comparison tool, which allows the user to compare specific chromosomes between two different public users. As I previously mentioned, women receive an X chromosome from their father and one from their mother. If two women share the same father but have different mothers, those two women will have a complete full match on their X chromosomes, which they both received from that same father. Gedmatch.com allows a person to run that report online. I recently used that tool to solve a case for two elderly women. One of the women was searching for her biological father. Since the women had a complete match on their X chromosome, it was clear they were half-sisters sharing the same father.

One more note about Gedmatch.com. Most public DNA websites do not allow law enforcement to access their database to solve violent crime cold cases. But Gedmatch.com does, and each user can opt in or out of that feature to decide if they will allow their DNA to be used for that purpose. CeCe Moore has used that website to help law enforcement solve many cold cases. I encourage people to opt in to allow law enforcement access. I've decided that if one of my biological relatives has committed murder or rape, I'm more than willing to allow the authorities to have access to my DNA results to help incarcerate them. Love of "family" has its limits.

There are so many techniques provided in the DNA Detectives group to help steer people in the right direction, and everyone seems to want to help each other. And because the group is so large, when someone posts a question, there might be a hundred suggestions or answers within the first ten minutes. This group was instrumental in helping me navigate my way during my journey toward finding my birth father, and when I began to help others. I will always feel indebted to CeCe Moore for creating it, and to all the people who were willing to answer any question I asked.

Although I will be introducing and applying a few examples of these genetic genealogy techniques in the coming chapters, I don't want to make this book too scientific. There will be references to the DNA terms I just mentioned, but they are not crucial to your understanding of solving the mysteries of the relationships that I will describe. If you become disinterested in the genetic genealogy terms going forward, and want to skim the scientific explanations, you should still be able to understand how I used these techniques to help others.

[11]

REVELATION DAY

ANCESTRY'S APP ALLOWS USERS TO MONITOR THE PROGRESS OF their test as it makes its way through the process before they post the results in its public database. I watched that progress like a hawk until one day, nearly six weeks after they received my test, I received an update that my results were ready to view. I was at work that day and used the app on my phone. Here's what it listed for my ethnicity:

> Ashkenazi Jewish.................................…............. 50%
>
> England and Northwestern Europe..…................... 36%
>
> Scotland.....................................…................... 10%
>
> France...................................…....................... 4%

There it was in all its glory. Ethnically, I was 50 per cent Jewish, and not a person in this world had ever suspected it. Or if they did, I never heard a thing about it. The simple calculation I'd made after speaking with my daughter had been correct. Out of pure excitement and a desire to blow the doors off people's minds, I started telling everyone about my new revelation. I took a screenshot of my ethnicity results and texted it to friends and family.

My two married Jewish friends and business partners (Mark and Stacy), who live in Maryland, had me breaking out in laughter after I told them about my discovery and how shocked I was that nobody ever suspected it. Stacy said to me, "Mark and I always knew it. We just didn't think you were ready to hear it yet!"

My mother was very surprised as well. I jokingly told her that it wasn't fair that we'd only celebrated Christmas when I was younger. We should have spent half the time with a Christmas tree and the other half with a Menorah. I reminded her how from time to time, my dad would come home from work and tell Jewish jokes because the owner of the plant he worked for (a tyrannical boss, according to him) was Jewish. Jews weren't his only target, and he had a little Archie Bunker streak in him as well. I wished he was alive so I could see his face after blindsiding him with my discovery.

I called my friend and former receptionist Nancy, who'd left the company over fifteen years before, to give her the surprising news. She thought my discovery was the funniest thing, and then said, "It's all starting to make sense to me now." Another friend of mine mailed me a yarmulke (the head covering used by Jews) and I thought that was funny too.

That result confirmed that Debbie had no Jewish roots, since my daughter's results were 25 per cent Jewish, and she had to have received all of that from my 50 per cent. But that didn't rule out my birth mother having some percentage of Jewish ethnicity, coupled with whatever my birth father carried. But I didn't put much merit in her having any Jewish roots. Her and her upline most likely had been in the rural part of the Midwest for multiple generations, absent of any Jewish genetic influence.

I can't really explain why this discovery made me so over-the-top excited, but it did. I know it wasn't because I was any closer to identifying my birth father. Perhaps it was solely about discovering my ethnic heritage; the ethnicity I had told my daughter I never cared to learn anything about.

I knew there was a lot more digging to do, and with no way of knowing if I'd be successful.

It was time to get started with identifying the matches I had. And even though I'd been following that DNA Detectives group, I was intimidated to say the least.

Maternal versus Paternal

My position as a searching adoptee seemed to be somewhat favorable. At least that's what I thought early on. It wasn't unique, as many other people have a birth parent that carries no similar ethnicity to their other birth parent. For example, if a mother is 50 per cent Asian and 50 per cent Caucasian, and the father is 100 per cent African American, a child of those parents would be able to easily identify their DNA matches to their father, and separate their maternal matches from their paternal matches. Any matches with anyone of African American ethnicity of any percentage would come from that child's father's lineage. Similarly, if I was correct that my birth mother had no Jewish roots, and my birth father was 100 per cent Jewish, then any Jewish matches I found on my Ancestry match list would be connected to my birth father's lineage. I just needed to identify my Jewish matches because they would all be linked to my birth father.

But how would I be able to separate the people who were in my maternal line from my Jewish paternal line? I didn't recognize anyone in that huge match list. Ancestry and the other DNA testing sites have a simple report that allows someone to compare their ethnicity to any of their matches. The highest match I had was only 470 centimorgans (cMs), which Ancestry labeled as a half-first cousin, or first cousin once removed. What I found most interesting about that match was that her last name was "Lewis." Bingo! Since my birth mother's maiden name was Lewis, I made what I considered a highly probable assumption that she was connected in some way to my maternal line.

I then compared our ethnicities, and she didn't have an ounce of Jewish blood, which made me confident that she was from my maternal side. And one of the beauties of these testing websites is that you can run a quick report and see all the matches that you have in common with that one match. All the people that this "Lewis" girl and I had in common would be from my birth mother's lineage. Which meant all the matches that I didn't have in common with that "Lewis" girl would have to be from my birth father's family. Ancestry provided a place to click on a star-shaped icon that would highlight to yellow for each selected match, and I used that to highlight my paternal matches, so that going forward, I could quickly identify them. I had over 120,000 DNA matches and spent a few hours highlighting the ones I knew must be from my paternal line, but I only got through about the first 1,000 of my matches. I stopped there because there was no reason to keep going with more distant matches that were past fifth or sixth cousins.

But when I finished separating, I realized there really wasn't much to go on. I had no close Jewish matches, and to my dismay, my closest Jewish linked match was a fourth cousin at a whopping 73 cMs. That is just too distant of a match to make any sense of. Obviously if I had had a half-sibling match of about 1,800 cMs in my list, I could look to see if he or she had a family tree, or just reached out and asked them about their parents. Trying to put the pieces together by contacting a fourth, fifth, sixth, or more distant cousin is extremely difficult. I had as good a chance of identifying my birthfather by visiting every gravesite in the US and randomly guessing which one belonged to him.

Endogamy

Not only was I reading the hundreds of daily posts from the DNA Detectives Facebook group, but I also subscribed to another Jewish DNA genealogy group. On both of those group sites, many people were using the term "endogamy." They stated that if endogamy was present in any lineage of ethnicity, it can make it very difficult to trust the match levels measured in cMs. At the time, I didn't really understand what that term meant.

Endogamy is best understood as intermarrying over generations within people who carry traces of similar DNA. When people of a certain tribe or close-knit clan continually have children within that group, the DNA becomes skewed, and makes it difficult to differentiate between match comparisons within that group. There's a "stacking" process of similar DNA, which can inflate people's autosomal DNA matches to each other. People who are actually no closer than fourth cousins might share enough DNA to be predicted as third cousins using the standard autosomal tests. This occurs because they're picking up or carrying "extra" shared DNA through their similar connected familial relationships. The overall effect of endogamy is to make many DNA matches appear to be more closely related than they really are.

The problem? Jews had been practicing endogamy for thousands of years. This occurred because of the centuries-long religious requirement to marry only fellow Jews. Adding to that, Jews have been persecuted and held in captivity many times over thousands of years. When in captivity, marrying someone closely related may have been the only option.

So, I concluded that unless I received a very close match, such as a sibling, aunt, uncle or first or second cousin, I was almost dead in the water. Since my highest Jewish match was listed as a fourth cousin, and probably skewed by endogamy, that prediction couldn't be trusted: the "fourth cousin" was more likely to be a fifth or sixth cousin at best.

It was disheartening news. I couldn't really trust the DNA numbers being provided on Ancestry for my Jewish matches. And if I couldn't trust those numbers, what good would any of this DNA technology do to help me identify my birth father? I knew my birth father would have been 92 years old at the time I received my DNA test results. At the time, although

I knew it was technically possible, I had no confidence he would still be alive. It wasn't a rescue mission to find him alive. I knew that was a long shot. Rather, it was a recovery effort to identify him, find as many pictures of him as I could, and possibly connect with his other children if he had any, or closer relatives who knew him.

Fishing in Multiple Ponds

I read a post from a fellow searcher wanting to know what else they could do, given they didn't have close enough matches to make any determinations. A flood of people provided virtually the same advice. First, they said that since Ancestry had the largest database of testers, that should always be the place to test first. But if that didn't provide enough close matches, they recommended the searcher also pay to test on 23andMe, which had the second biggest database. They also suggested that anyone searching should download the raw DNA files they received from the site where they tested, and upload them to databases that provided matching comparisons free of charge. Those other DNA websites were, as I previously mentioned, Family Tree DNA (FTDNA), MyHeritage.com, and Gedmatch.com. These three websites contained smaller pools of testers, but the recommendation from group members was that anyone searching should fish in as many "ponds" as possible. As desperate as I felt, I was willing to dangle my DNA like fishing bait in any sized pool I could find.

In many of the other posts I read, group members encouraged those searching to find their closest match, and see if they had posted a public family tree. If they did have a tree assembled, they recommended that searchers use that tree to build their own tree and see where they may fit in. But there were many other group members cautioning people that family trees were only as trustworthy as the sound genealogical research put into them. Humans were certainly fallible. That wasn't a problem for me. In my case, my "fourth?" cousin match didn't have a tree built on Ancestry, so there was nothing for me to go on.

So, without a close enough Jewish match on Ancestry, I decided to take the 23andMe test. I mailed it off and waited. I also uploaded my raw DNA files to the three smaller free companies I mentioned, but after two days of looking for close Jewish matches on those sites, I ended up empty-handed again.

Pay for Play

As I was waiting for my 23andMe results, I received an email from Ancestry's website. They were advertising for a service where their professional genealogists would do research on behalf of those searching. It had been about three months since I'd received my Ancestry results, and found out those results didn't provide a close match. To add to that, in those days, I wasn't as advanced in search techniques on their website as I later became. I called Ancestry and spoke to someone who informed me that their service required a $2,500 retainer fee, and that their professional genealogists would charge $150 per hour. I thought that was pretty steep, but I was becoming frustrated riding what seemed to be the same roller coaster I'd been on so many years earlier. I scheduled a conference call with two of their genealogists for the next week, hoping I could pay my way out of this minimal close match blackhole.

The genealogists called me together on speaker phone. They asked me if I would allow them access to my DNA results and I agreed. I told them I was looking for what I had determined to be a full-blooded Jewish birth father, and that my closest Jewish match was listed as a fourth cousin.

We didn't spend that much time on the phone that morning. After reviewing my match list, they came to the same conclusion I had. They told me that with such a distant closest match and endogamy in play, there really wasn't anything they could do for me. They explained I would need to wait for a closer match to show up in the future. That was devastating news. I thought, "These people do this for a living, and they aren't willing to try to help because even they know they'd be wasting their time and my money." If they couldn't do it, what would ever make me think I could?

Free Fish

Every day that I waited for my 23andMe results, I checked my Ancestry app about every three hours, looking to see if any newer, closer matches were posted. I was constantly checking the three smaller websites as well. I've jokingly likened my frantic swiping of the touchscreen on my phone to hand-milking a cow. I was so desperate to find a close match, I found myself "squeezing," or scrolling through my phone, like a madman. I felt a sense of excitement each time I opened those testing site apps. Every day it seemed there was the possibility I'd hit the DNA lottery, and a new, closer Jewish match would show up.

At that time, both Ancestry and 23andMe had aggressive advertising campaigns. And the more they advertised, the more people tested, which was exactly what adoptees like me needed. Again, most people who were not adopted were testing merely to discover their ethnicity. But adoptees, or people who suspected the father that raised them was not their birth father, never cared why other people tested as long as they did and were willing to make their results public. I saw so many people posting in my Facebook groups about just how excited they were to receive new matches a couple of months after the Christmas holidays, or when those companies discounted their kits. At that time, DNA tests were popular gifts, and us searching adoptees were anxiously awaiting new fish to enter the pond and at no cost to us.

I've always wondered how many of those "gifts" were tossed in the trash by men who would never take them because they knew it was likely they'd left some unknown deposit, or deposits, at some point in their past.

Or perhaps there are mothers who'd discard it and make up an excuse to her children for not taking it because they'd given a child up for adoption many years before. I'm sure there's been a fair share of fear generated by those DNA kit gifts.

[12]

A WHOPPER!

FINALLY, MY 23ANDME RESULTS SHOWED UP, AND I WAS VERY excited by what I first saw. There was a closer match listed, a person with the screen name "Tommy." Like Ancestry, 23andMe also labels matches, and does their best at predicting the actual relationship between two testers. He and I shared 13 per cent of our DNA, which translated to 969 cMs. 23andMe suggested we were first cousins; that was a great match. But initially, I didn't know if we matched on my paternal side or my maternal side. He'd posted a note on his page that said he was born in 1959, but knew nothing about his family. That meant that if he was on my Jewish side, he was likely a fellow adoptee and wouldn't be able to help me.

Again, at 969 cMs, the four possibilities for our actual relationship were first cousin, half uncle/nephew, great-grandparent/great-grand-child, or great-uncle/great-nephew. Our proximity in age (only two years apart) would most likely eliminate the last two. I leaned more toward first cousins as our actual relationship, while not eliminating the half uncle/nephew possibility.

I wasn't yet familiar with 23andMe's website, but I quickly found the area that compared ethnicities. Tommy's ethnicity showed as zero per cent Ashkenazi Jewish. Another dead end. The next closest match I had was with a woman named Alice at 500 cMs, which is also a sizable match. Before I checked her ethnicity, I ran a report showing our common matches, and Tommy was the first one on the list. That meant Alice was also not Jewish, and had to be connected to my birth mother's lineage. As I continued to look through the other close matches, it became clear that I didn't have anyone Jewish on 23andMe closer to me than I had on Ancestry.

My match to Tommy intrigued me though. Since he claimed on his 23andMe page that he knew nothing about his family, I wanted to reach out to him and let him know what I had discovered through my paper trail search many years earlier. I sent him the following message through 23andMe's messaging portal:

"Hi Tommy, my name is Jeff Eddins and I live in Las Vegas. I just received my 23andme ancestry report and it suggests that we are first cousins. I just discovered that I am half Jewish a few months ago after taking the Ancestry.com test and I'm trying to identify my Jewish birth father. I was adopted at birth and know almost everything there is to know about my birth mother's (non-Jewish side). Unfortunately for me, we seem to share DNA from my birth mother's side of the family. However, perhaps I can help you understand something about that side of our family."

I provided both my cell number and my email address if he wanted to contact me. Little did I know at the time I offered to help Tommy just how many others would later ask for/accept my help in their searches. The times spent researching for others turned out to be some of the most rewarding of my life.

A few hours later, I received an email, but it wasn't from Tommy. It was from his sister Liz, who lived in LA. She purchased and managed Tommy's 23andMe profile after their father passed away. In her email, she told me that her brother was adopted into their family in late 1959. Liz's father had always wanted to have a boy, and after having three daughters with his wife, they decided to adopt. They adopted him from a Catholic charities adoption facility in LA and brought him back to Las Vegas. And that's where Liz, her two sisters, and Tommy grew up. She added that Tommy still lived in Las Vegas. I thought, "Talk about a small world!" Tommy had lived in my backyard for the nearly thirty years I'd lived in Las Vegas, and neither of us had known anything about it.

Liz seemed excited in her response; she wanted Tommy to identify his birth parents and find some sort of closure. I replied, asking her if it was okay to have a phone discussion, and she called me immediately. I reminded her that I had identified my maternal lineage and that Tommy was clearly related to that side of my family. I wasn't sure Tommy and I were actually first cousins, but I'd narrowed down our DNA match to one of two possibilities. I told her that I'd be open to meeting with Tommy if he wanted, and asked her to see if we could make that happen.

Tommy called and we agreed to meet at a local casino for dinner. When we met, I didn't see much resemblance between us. Tommy had strawberry blonde hair that had been a darker red in his youth. He showed me a few pictures of himself when he was younger. We talked about our lives, and what it was like for him to grow up in Las Vegas. Tommy had waited until his adoptive father passed away before taking his DNA test because, like many adoptees, he didn't want to do anything to hurt his father's feelings. Tommy was suffering from some sort of bone disease that affected his spine, and it caused him to lean forward a bit. He told me he was in constant pain. I shared with him some of the details of my disease as well.

When the waitress approached us to take our order, he told her that we were meeting as first cousins for the first time, and we'd used DNA testing to find each other. She seemed intrigued, like most people are when they hear stories like that. It was the same reaction I saw on the faces of the older couple I'd spoken with in the restaurant lobby minutes before meeting Luke.

I explained to him that if we were first cousins, that would mean that one of my birth mother's now deceased brothers, Matt Lee Lewis or Loran Lewis, was his birth father, or that my mother's sister, Christine Lewis, was his mother. Tommy didn't have any closer matches than ours on 23andMe, and certainly not a sibling. If he'd had a full or half-sibling match, it would have been easy to figure out the identity of at least one of his birth parents. As we finished up, I told him what I'd learned about analyzing DNA, and that if he wanted help in his search, albeit not from an expert, I would love to see if I could figure it out. He was up for that.

So, I got to work immediately, this time using genealogical research and DNA to do it. I first asked Tommy to allow me access to his DNA page on 23andMe, so I could review his matches. I had also recently started building my family tree on Ancestry's website, and it was a thrilling experience. Each time I added a relative, Ancestry's algorithm would search other people's family trees and make suggestions of people who might be related to the person I had just added. They also offered leads to any recorded documents in their system related to the persons I added. They offered military, birth, death, and baptism records, shipping manifests, social security applications, death notices, public records of where people lived, and even census records dating back to the 1800s. It was up to the end user building the tree to look at the record hints to determine if that was a correct record for their family tree entry. And to my surprise, most of their hints were connected to the person I'd just added to my tree.

Who Needs Credible Evidence?

After I entered my maternal grandmother's name, Ora Lee Lewis, in my tree, a flood of hints populated on my screen. I noticed she had two marriage records and the first marriage was not to my grandfather Matt Lewis. Her maiden name was Allison, and the first record showed she was married to a man named William Samuel O'Bannon and they had had two sons, all before she was married to my grandfather Matt Lewis. The first was named Samuel R. O'Bannon, and the second Welton L. O'Bannon. The two brothers would have been older half-brothers to my birth mother Betty.

Here's just how sharp I thought I was back then: Tommy had red hair, and you can't get more Irish than the last name of O'Bannon. And just how much is red hair associated with Irish people? Yep. I was thinking that one of the two O'Bannon boys, (because of age) Samuel or Welton, could be Tommy's birth father. I was willing to run with a far-fetched, anecdotal, nonscientific theory and not pay attention to what the DNA possibilities would mean for my theory. I didn't construct a simple family tree with all the players (Ora Lee, Betty, Tommy and Samuel O'Bannon, and me) and compare my cM match value to Tommy.

I looked for birth and death records for those two O'Bannon boys on Ancestry's search engine. They had passed away in the 1980s in California, which was where Tommy was born. That proximity seemed to add even more credibility to my theory. I started paying to use a people search engine called Truthfinder.com. It was a thousand times better than the old WhitePages.com I'd used eighteen years earlier. There isn't much you can't find out about anyone who's lived in the US for the last hundred years on a site like that. I searched both of the O'Bannon brothers' names on TruthFinder.com and they listed names of friends and family members. I was certain I'd found one of Samuel's sons, and then located him on Facebook. I reached out to him to see what he could tell me about his father. We finally spoke by phone, and as much as I didn't want to tell him my theory, there was no way to get around it. I told him I suspected that his father had another son born in 1959, and his name was Tommy. Samuel's son was a little bit shocked by that news and didn't see how it could be possible. He explained his father and mother were married long before that, and they really loved each other. I thought, "Love hasn't always stopped people from having affairs." Since his father would have been a half-uncle to me (my birth mother's half-brother), I asked if he'd send me a few pictures of his father, and to my surprise, he texted them to me. I couldn't see his hair color because the pictures were black and white, but his son told me that his dad did have reddish hair. But I had to admit, I didn't see any resemblance to Tommy.

Thankfully, before I sent those pictures to Tommy, I sat down and penciled out what I should expect from the DNA evidence and genealogical records to validate my theory. That's exactly what I should have done in the first place, rather than going down a speculative rabbit hole. Since Samuel was a half sibling to my birth mother, if Samuel was Tommy's father, then Tommy would be a half-first cousin to me. I referenced the green chart, and that's when I realized that a half-first cousin would only share and average of 450 cMs, which was approximately half of the value of 969 cMs that Tommy and I shared. My foolish theory was wrong, and I couldn't believe I'd let myself go there. I called Samuel's son in California as soon as I realized my error and begged him to forgive me for suggesting that his father may have stepped out on his mother. I was embarrassed and felt horrible. My only consolation was that I hadn't informed Tommy and Liz about any of it.

Tommy and I talked a few more times on the phone, and it seemed our relationship was ending up where my half-brother Luke and my relationship ended. We were different people with different interests. Finally, I told him he needed to test on Ancestry to see if he could find closer matches there. He eventually took that test, but it was many months later. When we eventually talked again, it would be regarding more definitive results.

Expanding the search

Around this time, out of the blue, I decided to look for the two children of Deana Jacques (my half-niece) that John had told me about so many years ago. If you recall, their names were Ana Jacques and Lawrence Jacques (named after his grandfather who was killed in 1960). I decided to search on Facebook for Ana Jacques and narrow that search to only Las Vegas. I looked at the friends list of one of the Ana's and saw that she was friends with Lawrence Jacques, confirming I almost certainly had the correct Ana Jacques. I messaged her and told her I was doing some family research that led me to her. I gave her information I knew about our maternal family, including my birth mother's name, Chiquita's name, and her mother Deana's name, and asked if she had any pictures of her mother Deana. At the end of my message, I promised her that this wasn't a hoax, and said that hopefully she would be able to tell that by all the information I'd provided.

She wrote back immediately, "Yes, I believe you!" I asked her if she'd be willing to chat by phone, and she called me within ten seconds. Ana was already crying when she called because she thought that there were no biological family remaining in her maternal upline. Her mother Deana had passed away in 2009, nine years before I contacted Ana. Immediately I could tell she felt a connection to me, and that made me feel good. She said she only had three pictures of her mother Deana and none of her grandmother Chiquita or her great-grandmother Betty. She sent me those three pictures and ironically, Deana had reddish hair and lots of freckles, just like Tommy. But I wasn't falling for that again.

She told me nearly the same story her uncle John Lewis had conveyed to me so many years ago. She said in her early years, her mother Deana was a heavy drug user, not a good mother, and did very little to take care of her and her brother Lawrence. For many nights during their youth, she left them to fend for themselves, often without anything to eat. Ana was born in 1978, four years after her grandmother Chiquita was killed on that mountain, so she never knew her. With a wayward mother and no grandmother, Ana's great-grandmother Betty (my birth mother) took both Ana and her brother Lawrence into her care up until Betty passed away in 1992.

Ana described Betty as her everything, and how close they were to each other. According to Ana, Betty was the most loving person, and she claimed she would never have survived without her. Ana also claimed that after Betty passed away when Ana was just fourteen, her world was never the same.

And here's what's interesting to me: Ana's description of my birth mother was completely at odds with the character of the woman I'd formed in my mind. Perhaps Ana's take on my birth mother was completely colored by feeling rescued and being grateful to her for how she provided for Ana and her brother Lawrence. But she seemed so sincere about it—enough to cry over the loss of Betty while we talked, which had occurred over twenty-six years before.

Perhaps I'd been wrong about my birth mother's character. Or she had changed from who she was in her younger years to someone more caring and nurturing in her later years. I doubt Ana was making up her story, the way she was sobbing on the phone with me that day. But Ana's description of my birth mother was not what I had been expecting.

Ana and I scheduled a lunch with her family, which included her husband, two of her four children, and her half-brother Lawrence Jacques (named after his grandfather) and his daughter. We met at a barbeque house in Las Vegas, and we had a great time. I learned a lot about my birth mother and about their families, too. We took some pictures, and it was so nice to make those connections. I also shared a lot of information with Ana about her great-grandmother Betty that she didn't know. And a lot of that information was not in line with the character of the great-grandmother she'd known, or what she'd been privy to about Betty's earlier life.

Another thing I wanted to accomplish was to have Ana tested, so I could solidify my understanding of our biological relationship. So, she tested, and her results came back in about six weeks. She didn't understand how to use Ancestry's system, so I asked her if she would allow me to manage her account, giving me access to all her DNA matches.

We were related exactly as I expected. We matched at 421 cMs, which was perfectly in range for Ana to be my half-great niece (my half-sister Chiquita's granddaughter). But there was another match in her results that startled me. I expected her to match Tommy because we were connected on my maternal side. But her match to Tommy was substantial. She matched Tommy at 831 cMs, which was in the same range as I matched Tommy at 969 cMs. From the four possibilities in the range of 575–1330 cMs, and because of their age differentials, it was likely that Tommy was either Ana's first cousin or half uncle.

So, like so many times when researching, I sketched out a simple family tree that included, Betty, Chiquita, me, Deana, Tommy, and Ana. Knowing Tommy was Ana's first cousin or half uncle, and also either my first cousin or one of us was a half uncle to the other, I tried different places for Tommy to fit in. When I placed Tommy as a half nephew to me and Ana as a half niece to Tommy, the bells went off. I quickly discovered the identity of Tommy's birth mother and at first it seemed preposterous.

If Chiquita was my half-sister, then I would be a half uncle to her daughter Deana. That would also make me a half great uncle to Deana's daughter Ana, and again, our DNA match confirmed that as one of the possibilities. I speculated that if Tommy, born two years before me in 1959, wasn't my first cousin and was actually my half-sister Chiquita's son, then that would make me Tommy's half uncle. And placing Tommy in that position as Chiquita's son made Tommy Ana's half uncle, which is how the DNA match values in cMs were listed on Ancestry's website. Tommy wasn't my first cousin. Even though I was nearly two years younger than

Tommy, he had to be Chiquita's first-born son and my half nephew! The maternal side of my family tree was finally coming together.

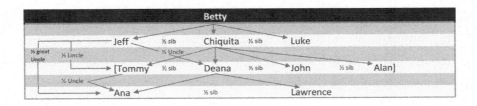

If the DNA evidence was true, and I had no reason to doubt it, that meant that Chiquita was pregnant with Tommy before she was pregnant with Deana in 1960. Remember, Deana was the baby born two months before me, and the main reason my birth mother claimed she had given me up. I'd always assumed Deana was Chiquita's first child, who she had just as she was turning sixteen. So how old would Chiquita have been when she was impregnated to have delivered Tommy on November 29, 1959? I counted back nine months from Tommy's birth date— assuming that she carried Tommy to full term, Chiquita was impregnated in the latter part of February of 1959, only a month before her fourteenth birthday. This was shocking and yet there was no way I could have been wrong about this. I'd screwed up a couple of things already, but DNA doesn't lie.

There was also the correlation of red hair. Both Tommy and Deana (Ana's mother) had red hair and a mass of freckles. Although described as having blonde hair in my background document, Chiquita must have been carrying some red-haired gene from her unknown birth father, unless both Tommy's father and Deana's father carried that gene. Or what if they shared the same father? I'd tackle that question later.

As I further researched Ana's match list, I saw she had a relatively high match to a woman named Cheryl. I ran a "shared matches" report and noted that this woman was not related to me, which meant Cheryl must be from Ana's paternal side, and I assumed it came from her Jacques lineage. The Lawrence Jacques who was married to Chiquita and was killed in November of 1960 would have been Ana's grandfather, and I wondered if this woman named Cheryl knew anything about that Lawrence. I messaged her through Ancestry's portal, told her I was doing family research, and wanted to know if she knew anything about Chiquita or Lawrence Jacques. I also told her that I managed Ana's Ancestry account, and was doing research for her.

The next day, I received a phone call, but it wasn't from Cheryl. It was from a man named Ken who didn't immediately provide his last name. He told me his half-sister Cheryl received a message from me through Ancestry, and he wanted to know the reason for my inquiry. Like others before, Ken seemed leery of me, as if I might have some ulterior motive for reaching out to Cheryl. He started quizzing me, wanting to know what evidence I had that connected me to Chiquita and Betty. It wasn't until I provided my backstory that he finally identified himself as Ken Jacques, the younger brother of Lawrence Jacques.

Ken was in his early seventies, and told me how his brother and uncle were driving near the Rose Bowl in Pasadena, California, on November 25, 1960. His brother Lawrence had been drinking, and lost control of the car and hit a light pole. Lawrence was decapitated, and his uncle was seriously hurt. Ken also told me that if he hadn't had a hot date that night, he would have been in the car with his brother and uncle.

It wasn't until later that I reflected on the random, chaotic world we live in, and the cascading ramifications that come from that chaos. What if Lawrence hadn't been drinking that night, or even just drank less and never lost control of his car? What if his car had missed that light pole and he was only injured, not killed? What if Lawrence had a thirty-second conversation with someone before he left his house that night? Perhaps that delay would have caused him to be behind other cars, and he would have been forced to go at a slower speed, and thus may not have collided with that pole at such a high speed? If my birth mother was telling the truth regarding why she gave me up, and any of the speculative conditions I just mentioned would have come to fruition, I may never have ended up with the parents that raised and loved me. If my birth mother was being truthful, I was potentially rescued at birth because of the actions of a drunk-driving seventeen-year-old boy. Of course, there were many other random events that led to my birth parents meeting and my existence. The most prominent of all was being declared the winner of a race against 250 million other sperm cell competitors to one of my birth mother's eggs.

[13]

DISTURBING EVIDENCE

THE NEXT TIME KEN AND I SPOKE, HE TOLD ME A STORY THAT WAS incredibly disturbing to me, and seemed to reconfirm that Chiquita was a chip off the ol' Betty block. He told me that after his mother and father divorced, both he and his brother Lawrence moved from LA to Las Vegas in late 1958 with their father. Ken was not quite fourteen and Lawrence was sixteen. They moved into the same neighborhood where my birth mother and Chiquita lived, and that's how they met Chiquita. Both brothers became good friends with Chiquita, and Ken knew that his brother and Chiquita (only thirteen at the time) were sexually involved.

Ken told me that one day, while Ken, Lawrence, and Chiquita were all at my birth mother's house while Betty was at work, he and Lawrence heard blood-curdling screaming coming from the bathroom. The two brothers rushed into that bathroom to discover Chiquita sitting in a pool of blood in the bathtub, naked from the waist down, holding a coat hanger in one of her hands. The boys ran out of the house to get their father just a couple of blocks away. After arriving, their father pulled Chiquita from the bathtub and rushed her to the hospital. Apparently, Chiquita wasn't successful in her attempt to take her baby's life and made a full recovery.

According to Ken, no one, including Chiquita's mother Betty, had known she was pregnant, and she'd showed no outward signs of being pregnant.

There was no way Betty could monitor her while working in a casino, so after Chiquita recovered, Betty drove Chiquita to LA and placed her in a Catholic Charities home for unwed mothers to ensure that she wouldn't try that again. That organization would also provide adoption services for her baby. Ken told me that when he and his brother Lawrence would drive back to LA to see their mother, they'd visited Chiquita at that Catholic Charities facility through a large fence that guarded the perimeter.

Are we ringing any bells yet? Bathtubs, coat hangers, hemorrhaging, and rushing to a hospital? A fourteen-year-old girl giving her child up for adoption in a Catholic Charities facility in 1959? There was only one conclusion here: the child that my half-sister Chiquita tried to abort was my red-headed half-nephew Tommy. DNA had already confirmed Tommy was my half-sister's son, and now I had an eyewitness telling me what had happened in 1959 in a small Las Vegas home and later at that Catholic Charities adoption facility. And Tommy's sister Liz had already revealed to me that Tommy was adopted from a Catholic Charities facility in LA before being brought to Las Vegas. These weren't coincidences. They were facts.

I began to wonder if Lawrence Jacques was not only Deana's father but maybe also Tommy's father. After all, Ken was pretty sure Lawrence was intimate with Chiquita long before they were married. But simply reviewing the DNA results eliminated that possibility. If Lawrence Jacques was Tommy and Deana's father, that would make them full siblings and Tommy a full uncle to Ana. But I'd already established that Tommy and Ana were a half- uncle/niece relationship at 831 cMs. Tommy and Ana would need to share twice that amount (about 1,800 CMs) to be a full uncle/niece. So, whether or not Lawrence was sexually active with Chiquita before they married in 1960, Tommy was not his son. Chiquita must have been impregnated by another person when she was a month shy of her fourteenth birthday.

I provided the DNA evidence to Tommy that indicated that Chiquita was his birth mother, as well as all the pictures I had of Chiquita, and the three pictures Ana had provided me of Tommy's half-sister Deana. Neither Tommy nor his sister Liz seemed to want to communicate with me after that, and I never heard back from either of them again. To date, I haven't been able to figure out who Chiquita's father was, nor who Tommy's father was. There just aren't enough close matches to connect the dots for Tommy.

More Rabbit Holes

Ken and I spoke on the phone a few more times before finally meeting for dinner in Las Vegas about six months later, along with Ana and her half-brother Lawrence. Ken wanted to see Ana and Lawrence because he was their great uncle, and hadn't seen either of them in over thirty-five years. We had a nice dinner at my favorite hole-in-the-wall Italian restaurant and shared a lot of stories. We all seemed to have a great time, and that meeting was only possible because of DNA technology.

When I spoke with Ken about six months later, he told me that when his father lived in Las Vegas near Betty and Chiquita's house, while he wasn't sure, he believed that his father could have been intimate with my birth mother. Since his father had moved there by 1958 and I was conceived in 1960, he wondered if his father could be my birth father. But since I'd already compared his half-sister's (Cheryl's) DNA match results to Ana's, it was clear that his sister Cheryl, and therefore Ken, didn't have a Jewish bone in their bodies. Ken and his half-sister shared the same father.

In an effort to help, Ken continued with another possibility. He told me that in LA, his father grew up and was best friends with a man by the name of Lawrence Roth. Ironically, Ken's brother Lawrence was named after his father's closest friend. Ken wasn't certain about his father being intimate with my birth mother, but he was sure that Lawrence Roth had been with her in that way. In fact, his father told him that the reason that my birth mother eventually stopped seeing Lawrence Roth was because Lawrence's libido was nowhere near that of my birth mother's. At that point, I was willing to chase down any leads I had. I researched Lawrence Roth—he had died at the age of ninety-seven in 2017, about six months before I began searching again. Through tireless research, I found the phone number of his living ninety-four-year-old younger brother. I called and tried to have a conversation with him, but he was dealing with some form of Alzheimer's or dementia, and I could tell he wouldn't be able to help me. So, I used my Truthfinder app to find the phone number of his next-door neighbor, to see if they knew any of that man's relatives. When I found one of his neighbors and told her my story, she told me that she looked in on Mr. Roth from time to time for his daughter Gail, who lived out of state. I asked her to give Gail my phone number and she did.

Gail called me, and after hearing my story agreed to test for me. I told her that if her deceased uncle Lawrence Roth was my birth father, then she and I would be first cousins. I asked her if she knew if she had any Jewish roots, but she wasn't aware of any. I also checked to see how many "Roths" were in my Ancestry DNA match list, and there were a lot more than I expected, but all of them were distant cousins. And even more surprisingly, at least half of the Roths in my match list were Jewish, and therefore related to my birth father's heritage.

Yet another six to eight weeks later, and her results were in. I had purchased her test kit, and she agreed to allow me to manage it, but we were not a match to each other. This was turning out to be another wild goose chase that left me in pretty much the same place I began.

I called Ken to tell him that his father's childhood friend Lawrence could not have been my birth father. Later in that conversation, he mentioned something about my birth mother being a waitress at a famous

Jewish deli in Los Angeles. Jewish! It took him a while to remember, but finally he remembered it was Canter's deli. But Ken had no idea what years she had worked there. If he was right, I was hoping that's where she was working in August of 1960 when I was conceived. But there was a conflict between Ken's memory and what my background information stated, which was that she worked as a power sewing operator up until a month before I was born, and it wasn't until after she delivered me that she became a waitress. But I still needed to check out this new lead in case the background info was wrong.

I was 50 per cent Jewish, and my birth mother was said to be a waitress at a Jewish deli. It seemed like simple math. I was picturing my birth mother hooking up with a Jewish customer she'd waited on, or a Jewish coworker or boss. I know this sounds nuts, but I was grasping for any available straw that might help me identify my birth father.

My conversations with Ken were occurring in 2018, and if he was right, my birth mother would have worked there fifty-eight years ago. I decided to contact Canter's deli to see how far back they kept records for their employees. Fifty-eight years seemed unlikely, but I called them anyway.

When the receptionist answered the phone, I asked her if she had time to hear a crazy story, and when she agreed, I launched in. I could tell that she was interested in helping me, but she was also pretty sure they didn't keep records from fifty-eight years ago. But she told me something that got my juices flowing: there was a woman in her eighties who had worked at the deli as a greeter for over fifty years, and might recognize my birth mother's name. She asked me to email her a photo of my birth mother, so she could show it to that elderly employee to see if she recognized her. I emailed the picture that was most likely to convey what my birth mother looked like in 1960. That receptionist called me the next day to tell me the woman didn't recognize my birth mother's picture, and that she hadn't started working at that deli until 1966. I'd just went down another rabbit hole that led to nowhere. This possibly crazy theory could still have been correct, but there was no way to know if my birth mother was working there in August of 1960.

Nowhere to Go

It seemed I had run out of options for finding my Jewish birth father. I had no choice but to sit, wait, and check my results on all five of the databases containing my DNA information. I did take what is termed a "Y" DNA test from FTDNA, which was the only company offering it at the time. That special separate test compares only the Y chromosome of other males in the smaller FTDNA database and tries to find matches through each person's paternal lineage. Since the Y chromosome is continually passed down from male to male, with only slight variances between each generation, the similarities in that chromosome allow for comparison. But just as with the standard autosomal testing, I had no match close enough to make sense of anything. The results indicated that the closest "Y" DNA match I had to other Jewish males was five to six generations way.

I started to wonder about something that I hadn't considered yet. Since, according to the background document, my birth father was born about 1926, he would have been in his mid- to late teens during World War II. What if he had lived in Europe and had survived a concentration camp because he was young, strong, and able to work, but all his other family had been exterminated? If there were no siblings, parents, uncles and aunts, or cousins, I'd never receive a close DNA match. And what if the only child he fathered was me? These scenarios were certainly possibilities. And the longer I waited for a close Jewish match, the more these scenarios seemed plausible to me.

It wasn't until sometime in 2018 that I received what Ancestry labeled a third cousin Jewish match. His name was Michael, and suspecting endogamy, I placed little importance in that match. Ancestry had us sharing a meager 133 cMs of like DNA, but it was still nearly double that of my former highest (fourth? cousin) Jewish match.

I messaged Michael and provided my story and contact information for the billionth time, and he was gracious enough to call me. He told me he had grown up in LA, which intrigued me, and that he was retired and living in Tennessee. He gave me his parents' full names and said that he was certain his lineage (all Jewish) originated in Lithuania, which coincided with one of the European regions that Ancestry listed for me.

With the information he provided, I started to build a family tree to see if I could find a way to place myself as a third or fourth cousin to him, using all his family members that I'd collected from Ancestry's suggestions. I took his family tree back to the late 1800s using shipping manifests and naturalization papers from when his grandparents migrated to the US. But it was just another exercise in futility. No matter how hard I tried, I could not make the DNA fit in such a way that allowed for the relationship that Ancestry reported between Michael and me. It was another strike out and I was pretty sure endogamy had distorted our DNA match levels.

Helping others

As I kept reading my Facebook DNA group posts, I saw there were always people looking for help. It seemed that unless I caught a request for help within the first ten minutes it was placed online, there were many others already offering to help. I loved helping solve these mysteries, using methods that went beyond interpreting DNA results. When others had matches that were only at third or even fourth cousin levels, and weren't dealing with endogamy, I enjoyed using Ancestry's search engine to build a tree for that person. It was detective work that involved contacting complete strangers through either Ancestry's system, Facebook messenger, or cold-calling using information from the Truthfinder app. Putting the pieces of a large genealogical puzzle together involved learning historical information about other people's family members during different generations. I helped a few people and found success nearly every time. Finding pictures of deceased birth parents for a stranger or solving a mystery for someone else was very rewarding, and I never charged anything for my services. Hearing joy in others' voices turned out to be the best paycheck because I knew what it felt like to be completely ignorant about where you came from and finally discover something. I knew just how important discovery was to those who felt they were living in an identity desert, with seemingly no oasis in sight. I had become a search angel to others, just as Gail had been to me over twenty years earlier.

Over the next two years, since there was nothing I could do to better my seemingly impossible birth father situation, I helped as many people as time permitted. I'm going to tell the stories of two of my most interesting and rewarding searches in the following two chapters.

[14]

UNVEILING SECRETS

I'VE INCLUDED THE CARTOON ABOVE TO PREPARE YOU FOR THE following two chapters. I am writing about these searches mostly for fellow adoptees who want to learn more about genetic genealogy, or anyone who loves solving mysteries. Admittedly, the following two searches are complicated because they involve many names, places, and relationships, and it can be difficult to keep them straight with just one pass through read. I'm hoping the familial descriptions and family trees provided will help keep things straight. But, even if you have difficulty keeping all the relationships or the DNA match levels in order, I'm encouraging you to give it a try. You'll certainly discover the potential risks and devastating consequences that DNA evidence can cause. You will also learn more about how ignoring sound DNA evidence and trustworthy genealogical records can lead to false conclusions and wrongly hurt others.

Neither of these stories are critical to understanding my journey, but if you're interested in discovering the answer to the mystery behind the letter my birth mother wrote in 1965, that can be found in Luke's story. I gave you a taste of how genetic genealogy works with Tommy's story. If Tommy's search using DNA/genetic genealogy was difficult to follow or didn't interest you, please feel free to skip this chapter and the next and continue to chapter 16 with the remainder of my journey.

Sharon's' Journey

I contacted my sister Sharon in 2018 and offered to help her identify her birth parents. She seemed reluctant, just like she had many years ago when I offered to help her, before we had the tools of DNA technology. It seemed so strange to me that all her life she had felt abandoned and struggled with the fact that she was adopted and yet, she also seemed afraid of what she might discover in searching for her birthparents. It took Sharon at least two months to pull the trigger and she told me she was sure I would uncover something she wouldn't want to know. She already knew that her birth mother's parents (her grandparents) forced her birth mother to give her up. She also knew that her birth mother named her Nikky Loraine Whitney.

I ordered her an Ancestry kit, and we began. As we waited for her results, "Jeff the Super Detective" thought he could do a little research on the side and see what he could find using the name her birth mother gave her on her original birth certificate, which was supposedly provided in her background information. I don't know why, but I didn't ask our mother if she had Sharon's nonidentifying background document before I moved forward.

I did a simple inquiry on Ancestry's search engine for "Nikky Loraine Whitney," with my sister's birthdate of July 9, 1966. I knew this would be a long shot because, as I mentioned previously, no matter what a birth mother names a child to be adopted, that name is never to be available as a public record. But there it was in all its glory. That record shouldn't have been available on Ancestry's record system, but it did confirm one thing: it listed Sharon's birth mother's maiden name as Whitney.

So, with a lot of idle time on my hands as we waited for her results and closer Jewish matches for me, I decided to search for any women with the last name of Whitney on Ancestry who would have been born sixteen years before my sister in 1966 (about 1950), and at one point lived in the LA area. The first item in the long list of results was the profile of someone who had constructed a family tree that included a woman named Elaine Whitney. She was born in 1949 in Santa Barbara. This woman had passed away only two years before, in 2016. I was hoping I didn't have the correct person because I didn't want to deliver the news to Sharon that she had missed a chance to meet her birth mother by only two years. There were some photos of Elaine Whitney from her high school days displayed on her profile in that tree. Elaine had very blonde hair, exactly the color of my sister Sharon's hair. Her cheekbones seemed to match those of my sister's and even her nose was shaped similarly. I could easily see a resemblance to Sharon in her younger years.

Back off the Rails

So, I started down a road I'd been on before, and it wasn't the path I should have been on. I reached out and contacted the person who owned that tree, who turned out to be one of Elaine's daughters. We spoke over the phone, and I told her I was trying to help my adopted sister identify her birth mother. And in a similar way to the red-haired, Irish, O'Bannon debacle, she explained that she didn't think that her mother could have given up any children for adoption before she married her father. I told her I was only speculating, and I had no evidence I was right. She was willing to keep our line of communication open, and I guess it was because if she had a half-sister out there (Sharon), she'd want to know more about her. After we finished our call, I located Elaine's daughter's Facebook page and began perusing her photos. There were about six of her mother that she had posted not long after her mother passed away. When I saw those pictures, my jaw dropped to the floor. I couldn't believe how much her mother looked like Sharon in those pictures. I took screenshots of them and texted them to my mother. And when she saw them, she was shocked by the resemblance too.

I already had a visit planned to see my mother and sister in LA about two weeks later, and I decided not to say anything to Sharon about my discovery. I needed to think about it more, and if I was going show her those pictures, and how to let her know I may have found her birth mother, and she had passed away. Anyone who has any experience in doing either paper trail genealogical or DNA research knows that what I was doing was foolish. I admit I was less experienced at doing these kinds of searches at the time, and I didn't have enough failures under my belt to realize I was making a huge mistake. Unfortunately, it took something like this for me to figure out that good research required hard evidence, absent desired speculation. It's okay to speculate and then use evidence to support theories, but it's not okay to make final judgments without irrefutable supporting evidence. I went on to solve thirteen more cases for others and not once did I base any of the results on speculation.

When I arrived at my mom's house, we discussed my findings. My mom was certain that the women I identified as Sharon's birth mother had to be correct. There were two pictures that had been taken at around the age Sharon was at that time, and all their facial features were almost identical. My mom and I agreed I should show them to Sharon, and I called her and asked her to come over to our mother's house. She knew her DNA results weren't ready yet, but I did tell her I'd found some interesting information regarding that matter.

As my sister sat on the couch next to me, I told her I didn't have any scientific evidence that I was right about what I was about to tell her, but there were signs that, to me, seemed overwhelming. I explained to Sharon how I searched and found a woman named Elaine Whitney with a birth year putting her at sixteen at the time Sharon was born. And that that woman was born in Santa Barbara, which used the LA County Social Services department for adoptions. I told her there seemed to be so much resemblance between her and Elaine, and I explained, if I was correct about Elaine being her birth mother, that the sad news was that Elaine had passed away about two years earlier.

I showed Sharon the pictures, and I could see she was looking for traits she could identify with in Elaine's pictures. As she looked at them, both my mother and I reinforced how clear it was to us that Elaine had so many facial similarities to her. I also informed Sharon that if it panned out, she had two younger half-sisters and one younger half-brother, and they all lived in the Northwest.

Although I did preface my findings by warning Sharon that I wasn't 100 per cent sure about my findings, it was a stupid path for me to follow. I had Sharon believing her birth mother was dead with no confirming evidentiary facts. I didn't know if my theory about Elaine being Sharon's birth mother was correct, but I hoped it was. If I was wrong, I'd feel horrible for hurting my sister.

I didn't have any further discussions with Elaine's daughter until a later date. If I was wrong about my speculations and Sharon's DNA pointed to someone else, I'd have a lot of crow to eat, and would need to call her back and apologize for my stupidity.

Sound Evidence

Sharon's results finally came in and things went very fast from there. I wanted so badly for those results to lead to Elaine being her birth mother so I wouldn't need to retract what I'd said to Elaine's daughter and, more importantly, to Sharon. Sharon's highest match was to a thirty-year-old woman named Gina and they shared 929 cMs of DNA. There were those same four possibilities where it was most likely that Sharon and Gina were either first cousins or they had a half aunt/nice relationship. Their age difference was about twenty-five years, so it seemed as if the half-aunt/niece relationship could be in play, and unlikely there was a great-aunt or great grandparent relationship. I immediately messaged Gina and told her about her match to Sharon, and asked if she could help us solve this mystery. Gina and I eventually communicated by phone, and early on, it was clear she knew who Sharon's birth mother was.

Gina explained that her mother had three older sisters (Gina's aunts) all with the maiden name of Whitney, and they all grew up in LA. The oldest became impregnated at the age of sixteen and married her boyfriend, but the marriage didn't last. Gina's grandparents had to help their daughter financially and were effectively their eldest daughter's baby's caregivers. A few years later, the next daughter in line, Alice, was also impregnated at sixteen, and apparently her parents weren't going to watch a rerun of the movie they'd just seen with their eldest daughter. Alice's parents told her there was only one option, and that she needed to give her baby up for adoption. And if you recall, that is what Sharon knew was her birth mother's reason for giving her up.

Gina added that many years ago, her mother had told her about her aunt Alice giving up a baby girl sometime in the mid-1960s. Gina even remembered seeing a picture of that baby girl the day she was born. Her aunt Alice had kept it all those years. But it wasn't a subject anyone in the family discussed. She added that Alice was still alive, living in the Midwest, and that although she'd been married three times, she'd never had any other children. According to Gina, Alice was traumatized by the experience of giving up her baby. Gina was almost certain that her aunt Alice was Sharon's birth mother, and confirmed that Alice was sixteen years old when she became pregnant.

That information, if true, meant that my Elaine Whitney theory was completely bogus. If there was any consolation, it was that Alice was still alive. I asked Gina if she would provide pictures of her aunt, but she wanted to talk to her mother (Alice's sister) first, to get her thoughts on that. It was looking more likely that Gina and Sharon were first cousins, and not aunt and niece.

I called Sharon to tell her what I'd learned from Gina, and how that information fell in line with what she already knew. I told her if what Gina reported was true, then I was very sorry for providing her false information two weeks earlier. I could tell she was excited about these findings, and yet she still seemed reserved. We were very close to solving the mystery now, and I think Sharon was realizing that half of the questions she'd wondered about throughout her entire life were about to be answered.

Reaching out can be the trickiest part of the search process. I was following the recommendations of my DNA Detectives group and taking screenshots of all of Gina's information on both Ancestry and Facebook. I did that for all of Sharon's significant matches as well. That group also recommended that no one other than the adoptee should ever reach out to the birth mother. The reason for that is no one other than the adoptee can accurately express their personal feelings regarding the circumstances. And if something goes wrong in a conversation between someone other than the adoptee and the birth parent, that contacting person will effectively feel responsible for the bad results, and possibly destroying the ability for the adoptee to connect. The responsibility should solely be on the adoptee.

But for many adoptees, the anxiety of reaching out is overwhelming and nearly paralyzing. Some are confident and bold enough to reach out by phone. Others would rather write a letter so they can take their time and think through exactly what they want to say and in a way that offers the best chance of avoiding rejection. The birth mother can't hang up the phone on a heartfelt letter, and many times adoptees include pictures of themselves and their children, reflecting different times of their life. But even a beautiful, heartfelt letter isn't a guarantee they won't face rejection.

I have a good friend and fellow adoptee who reached out with a heartfelt, non-threatening letter to her birth mother. My friend was in her late fifties and included pictures of her family. She was only asking to see if her birth mother would be willing to communicate by email or phone. Ten days after she sent that envelope, my friend found the same envelope returned to her mailbox. Her birth mother had opened the letter before returning it, and included a short note inside that effectively said, "You have your life and a family on the West coast that loves you, and I have mine on the East coast. Why don't we just leave it at that?"

Since Gina had already revealed where Alice lived and her married last name, it was easy to find her address and current phone number with my Truthfinder app. But before Sharon or I could formulate a plan to reach out to Alice, most likely by letter, Gina called me back and told me that she'd already spoken with her aunt Alice. The news wasn't good, and a lot of this was on me because I didn't ask Gina to not contact her aunt before Sharon had a chance to.

Gina told me her aunt was shocked to be "found out" and that she wanted nothing to do with Sharon. In fact, she told Gina to stop communicating with "the guy in Las Vegas" (me) and to stay out of it. Alice was furious at Gina for taking that DNA test and exposing her to something she'd hoped would never be revealed. That was unfortunate because Gina only tested because of her curiosity regarding her ethnicity. Like most people who take the tests, she was unaware she could be exposing other family members carrying secrets. This was the first time Alice had to face this exposure since 1966, and my guess is she felt like a criminal on the lam feels after seeing their picture on a local news broadcast.

This is one interesting thing about how DNA technology has circumvented all anonymity for women who gave children up for adoption, after being legally promised their information would never be publicly available. Since 1966, Alice must have felt a sense of security knowing that her past would remain hidden and probably never thought she'd face a searching daughter after all those years. DNA technology has allowed people to discover unknown biological connections that could never be discovered before. Half siblings are showing up as matches and men who would never consider testing are being exposed for fathering "illegitimate" children either before or during a marriage.

In a similar way, before DNA was available to the public, criminals never considered they risked exposure by their own family members taking those readily available tests many years later. Criminals might never consider testing, but they couldn't do anything to stop their siblings, aunts, uncles, or cousins from innocently doing so. As mentioned, CeCe Moore has used genetic genealogy to identify and incarcerate many violent criminals who never tested before their arrest. Today, law enforcement has crime scene DNA processed in such a way that it can be compared to autosomal testing results on GedMatch.com. Then genetic genealogists like CeCe Moore build family trees from those matches to identify the criminal. The search techniques of genetic genealogy used to identify biological relatives is exactly the same as that used to identify criminals.

I could tell Gina was pretty shook up after her conversation with her aunt. She wasn't that close to Alice, but she'd also never had a cross word with her, nor had she ever witnessed her in such an angered state. Since it seemed Sharon's bridge to Alice had just collapsed, I asked Gina again if she would help Sharon by providing some pictures of Alice. She seemed resistant to my request, and I'm sure it was because of her recent encounter with her aunt. But I had Sharon's permission to give Gina her cell number and they eventually spoke. They talked about meeting one day, but never did. But Gina did provide some insight to Sharon regarding Alice, and I think that was important to her.

About two weeks later, Gina decided to cross the line and flooded Sharon and me with many photos of Alice, Sharon's maternal aunts, and grandparents. In our previous conversations, I had explained to Gina what it was like for an adoptee to never know or see pictures of their birth parents and I think she may have been stewing on that. This time, the resemblance was even more uncanny, and no one could doubt that Alice was Sharon's birth mother. More importantly, this time I had used a close first cousin DNA match and the strong known relational evidence provided by Gina to solidify my findings.

I know Sharon appreciated the pictures Gina provided, but she was also crushed. I was hurting so much for her and felt very guilty. After all, I was the one who had led her to this place. For searching adoptees that find themselves in Sharon's position, it often feels like a second rejection. Many adoptees have always felt they weren't good enough to be kept by their birth mother, and now it appears they don't even qualify to meet as adults. The door had been slammed shut again. Alice's gavel had bounced off its wooden block and any hope Sharon had to ever communicate or meet vanished.

But for a birth mother who's given up a child, there's probably a deep sense of guilt and shame. Having to face the child she'd given up, irrespective of the circumstances that led to her pregnancy, generates a complex array of emotion. If she was raped, all those horrific memories might come flooding back. If she had been promiscuous or sexually active before she was of age, or even married, and raised in a family that looked down at such behavior, she'd have to deal with those feelings. For many women who have given up children, their life circumstances were such that they couldn't take care of themselves financially, and there wasn't a path forward to provide for their child. In many instances, a deep sense of love for their child and a desire to see that their child would be cared for by someone else is a noble motivating factor. But even so, there's no escaping the fact that they made a choice to forever disengage from their own flesh and blood. It must be a horrible position to be in.

I'd really hoped that time would soften Alice's heart, and she'd perhaps try to understand Sharon's reasons for wanting to connect. But as of today, Sharon hasn't heard from Gina or Alice since our last communication with Gina. I did tell Sharon I'd help her if she ever wanted to draft a letter to send to Alice. That letter could be soft in tone, simply Sharon sharing her feelings without asking Alice to change her mind about never wanting to communicate with her. I've encouraged Sharon to leave the door open for Alice, and leave room for her if she ever changes her mind. But I've never pushed Sharon to write a letter, and I never will. She knows the offer is available if or when she decides she wants to do it.

Sharon's Paternal Half

Now that Sharon's maternal side was solved, albeit not the way we'd hoped, it was time to try to solve her paternal side. It was easy to separate the paternal from the maternal side because I could run a report to find all Sharon's matches in common with Gina. Every match that was not in that group would be from her paternal side. Sharon had one very large match on that side, screen name "Califna," real name Nancy. Sharon's match level to Nancy was in the same range as Gina's match at 790 cMs, so that indicated their relationship was most likely a first cousin or half-aunt/niece.

Sharon had two other matches that were about half of that value at 450 cMs, which indicated those matches were either a first cousin once removed, half-first cousin, or a half-great aunt/uncle/niece/nephew. I reached out to all of them, and they seemed receptive and willing to help.

Nancy had an interesting story. She told me her father, Eugene Bauwens, was married multiple times and she was the youngest child from his last marriage. She had a couple of half-siblings, but she'd never had a relationship with them. She had an older half-sister named Marsha who she thought lived in Northern California, but they'd never met face to face. Nancy was about fifteen years older than Sharon, which made me lean more toward their relationship being half-aunt/niece.

I searched for Nancy's older half-sister Marsha in Northern California. She was much older than Nancy, and I explained to her why I was calling. Marsha explained that when she was growing up in Omaha, Nebraska, her father Eugene was always out at night with other women and that destroyed her mother, and her parents' marriage. In fact, Marsha told me, immediately after World War II ended, when she was about six years old, she remembered her mother was approached by a woman claiming to be Eugene's mistress, and that she was carrying his child. That mistress later called Marsha's mother and told her Eugene would be divorcing Marsha's mother and marrying her. I didn't know it at that time, but Marsha telling me that she'd grown up in Omaha would help me confirm that Eugene Bauwens and that unidentified mistress were both in that city at the same time.

Marsha didn't have a single good word to say about her father Eugene. There were times during our conversation that I changed the subject just to calm her down. Marsha told me that months after she had her first child at the age of nineteen, her father Eugene came to her house while her husband was at work. He had brought a bottle of wine, and was making passes at her. She threw him out and never saw or spoke to him again. "Hate" would be the kindest word to use to describe her feelings toward her father. It appeared to me that Eugene Bauwens was a scoundrel of the highest order. In fact, I can't think of one person of the many family members I spoke with that had a kind word to say about him.

I then contacted the other two people who matched Sharon at about 450 cMs. Their names were Collin and Patrick. They were half-brothers sharing the same mother, but neither of them matched Nancy, which meant they must have been from Sharon's paternal grandmother. They told me they had another half-brother named Nathan. All three of these men shared the same mother, but had different last names from their respective fathers. Collin told me their mother's name was Denise Burke, and that she had passed away in 2007. Since the ages of those three men were closer to Sharon's age, it was unlikely we were dealing with any half-great aunt/uncle relationships, which left us with either a first cousin once removed or a half-first cousin possibility.

Collin and Patrick told me that their maternal grandmother's name was Patricia Burke, and she was born in 1925 and died in 1993. They told me that their grandmother Patricia had three children (their mother Denise, their aunt Makala, and their uncle Shawn), but the only one alive was their uncle Shawn. I was lucky enough to have them give me Shawn's phone number.

So, as I always do when trying to solve these mysteries, I built family trees with all the DNA matches to Sharon and all the relationship possibilities depending on their cM match values and the known relationships that Sharon's matches provided for me. And as I was doing that for my sister Sharon's tree, it was becoming obvious that Sharon's paternal grandmother was in fact Patricia Burke. There was only one way to fit Sharon into that tree and that would have been for Collin, Patrick, and Nathan to have been Sharon's half-first cousins. That also required Shawn to be a half-uncle to Sharon. A bigger question loomed, as to who Patricia was impregnated by who had a son that could be Sharon's birth father.

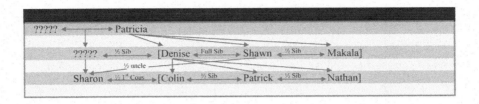

I reached out to Shawn. He was in his sixties and he, like many others, had a very hard time believing that his mother could have had another child without him knowing about it, even before he was born. I tried to explain to him about Sharon's connections as half-first cousins to his nephews, but either he didn't understand it, or he wasn't willing to accept it. But unlike before, when I'd made stupid guesses and wasn't relying on DNA evidence, I felt confident about what I was postulating.

I had a few more phone conversations with Shawn and they seemed to go well. He just kept telling me that he would need to see some hard evidence to convince him that his mother Patricia had a son born before him (a son who would have been Sharon's birth father). But apparently his wife was fed up with my theory and my involvement with her husband. She messaged me through Facebook and told me to never call or have any contact with her husband again, angry with what she perceived as my meddling with their family.

But I knew I was right, and Patricia Burke (Shawn's mother) had to be Sharon's paternal grandmother, so I moved on to try to find another way to identify Sharon's birth father. I contacted Collin again (one of Sharon's three half-first cousins) and asked him about his other half-brother Nathan.

Collin contacted Nathan and asked him to call me. When speaking to Nathan, he told me he had taken a 23andMe DNA test. I'd already planned to have Sharon test there if I wasn't able to identify both of her birth parents through Ancestry and the other three smaller websites that I'd uploaded her results to. So, I sent Sharon a 23andMe test kit and we waited another eight weeks for her results.

I also began sorting out the common matches to Nancy and saw a lot of the Bauwens surnames, which wasn't a surprise because Nancy already told me her father's name was Eugene Bauwens. It was also clear that none of the Burke family ties shared any DNA with Nancy and the Bauwens lineage. So, I contacted many of Sharon's "Bauwens" matches to gain some understanding about their lineage. And that was easy to piece together—it quickly became clear that Eugene Bauwens (Nancy's father) was Sharon's paternal grandfather, and that he was the one who had impregnated Patricia Burke. All the DNA matches and the information those matches provided clearly pointed in that direction. Sharon's tree on her paternal side was coming together, but it was still missing her birth father.

I was sure I had identified Sharon's paternal grandfather (Eugene Bauwens) and her paternal grandmother (Patricia Burke), but who was their son? If no one living in that Burke family knew anything about this mystery son who was born before two of his other three siblings, where did he go? She obviously didn't keep him, or Shawn would have known about him. I searched for marriage records for both Eugene and Patricia, but found nothing. I searched on Ancestry for any child born near 1946 (immediately after World War II) with the mother's maiden name of Burke but came up empty-handed as well. It was looking more and more likely that Sharon's birth father was the product of an affair or a one-night stand, and that Patricia Burke had given him up for adoption.

More results

Sharon's 23andMe results came in and it was time to dig in. Surprisingly, there was another high match with a girl named Chloe. Sharon and Chloe matched at 918 cMs, which indicated that Sharon and Chloe were most likely first cousins or had a half-aunt/ niece relationship. It was also clear that Chloe's match was on Sharon's paternal side because both Chloe and Sharon had the Bauwens match connections. I needed to reach out to Chloe to understand her upline lineage and help me solve this. I messaged her through 23andMe's website, but didn't hear anything back from her. I searched using her full name on Facebook and came up with a lot of Chloes with her last name. I narrowed my search to only those Chloes who lived in California, as it seemed most of Sharon's matches were from there. I messaged all of them through Facebook Messenger, but only few responded, and they clearly weren't the Chloe who had tested on 23andMe. I even searched my Truthfinder app and found phone numbers, but none of those produced a Chloe who tested.

I knew that if Chloe was a half-niece to Sharon, then Chloe's mother or father must share the same birth father as Sharon. But I couldn't get Chloe to reply through 23andMe's website or find the correct Chloe through Facebook. This went on for about five months and it was so frustrating. I messaged her at least ten times through 23andMe, but she never replied. I was close to solving this and there was nothing more I could do. One of Chloe's parents had to be a half-sibling to Sharon and the person who could break this wide open if they knew the identity of their birth father. Here's the speculative tree that I assembled at that time that was still missing Sharon's birth father and her half sibling (one of Chloe's parents):

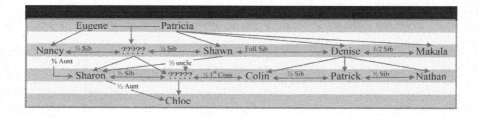

I did a lot of research on Eugene Bauwens and the places that he'd lived during his life. That research indicated that he'd lived in Omaha, Nebraska, in the mid- to late 1940s, just as his eldest daughter Marsha claimed. I could also place Patricia Burke in Omaha in the mid-1940s. When speaking with Nathan, he told me he had a picture of his grandmother Patricia Burke standing in a park with her first daughter Makala as a toddler, and he texted it to me. Near the top, it was written "Omaha, 1946." I didn't need this information to prove my theory, but I did want to show that picture to Shawn once I discovered who his half-brother (Sharon's birth father) was. But I wouldn't be contacting Shawn again until I knew who his mystery half-brother was. I wanted Shawn to know that it wasn't just DNA that proved this, but that I could also place both Eugene and Patricia in the same city at the same time. Patricia Burke and Eugene Bauwens both ended up living in the Bay Area of California in their later years, but they were not in a relationship, as far as I could discover.

And then the unthinkable happened, about seven months after Sharon tested on 23andMe. Every day I had checked all five DNA sites multiple times, both for my results and for Sharon's. Sharon had a huge new match and shared 2,208 cMs of DNA with a woman, so it seemed likely she was a half-sister match to Sharon. Her name was Francine, and she shared the same last name as Chloe. When I compared Sharon's DNA to both Francine and Chloe, it was clear that Francine was Chloe's mother. I took screenshots of her information and stalked (in a nice way) her on Facebook. I noticed one of Francine's Facebook friends was her daughter

Chloe, so I knew I had the right Francine. I messaged her, and within two hours she called me.

That phone call was a dream come true because what she told me would complete my research. Francine said that her daughter Chloe had received my messages, but thought I might be a scammer and that's why she never responded. I told Francine about Sharon's connection to her, and that I knew Francine's father had to also be Sharon's birth father. Within the first five minutes, she revealed his name, James Rexford III, and that she knew that her father was adopted, which made complete sense to me. It confirmed my theory that Patricia Burke had hooked up with Eugene Bauwens in Omaha in the mid-1940s and that encounter had produced an unwanted pregnancy. And it was likely in sync with what Eugene Bauwens' oldest daughter Marsha told me about her father's mistress, claiming she was pregnant with her father's baby in 1946—that mistress must have been Patricia Burke. So, Francine provided all I needed to know, and I could place Sharon's paternal biological family in a completed tree.

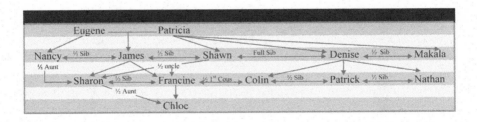

Francine continued that her birth father James Rexford III was killed in 1980. He'd had a troubled past with the law, and had been shot to death working as an informant for the police when he was only thirty-three years old. But Francine wasn't privy to that information until many years later, as she wasn't living with her birth family.

Francine's story was even more horrific. Francine told me that her birth father and birth mother had three children, two girls and a boy, and she was the middle child. After her father and mother divorced when they were all very young, their mother sent Francine and her brother to foster care, but she decided to keep Francine's older sister. Francine and her brother lived with the same foster family, until their mother decided to take her brother back. Francine continued to live in foster care for a long time before being adopted. But her adoptive parents divorced after the first six months she was living with them, and she was sent right back into foster care. It wasn't until she was about seven years old that she was permanently adopted by her forever family, into a home where she received the love she needed. Unfortunately, her adoptive mother died of cancer when Francine was twelve.

Francine had been estranged from her birth mother for many years. They had found each other when Francine was almost thirty, but they just couldn't get along. That's when she found out that her father had been killed, and also discovered that her older sister had been shot and killed accidentally in her home. She told me her mother was unstable and they just couldn't further their relationship. By the time I reached Francine, she was in her early fifties, and she hadn't seen or spoken to her mother in over seven years. She was also estranged from the brother her mother raised.

I felt so much of Francine's pain as I listened to her story. No child deserves to have that much rejection and tragedy in their lives. It still amazes me that Francine was able to overcome all those experiences and grow up to be a respectable, kind person.

I asked her if she would send me pictures of James Rexford III, so I could forward them to Sharon as soon as possible. Francine only had a few, but they were great to have. There was also a picture of their whole family, which included Francine (at about four years of age), her birth parents, and her two siblings. But it was hard to call Sharon and report the news that there wouldn't be an opportunity to meet her birth father.

I then had the bright idea that Francine's birth mother must have a lot of pictures of Sharon's birth father. I searched for her and found her phone number and called her. Francine had already warned me that I shouldn't try to communicate with her because she wasn't good person, but I thought I could overcome any of that with my charm. As I began telling her why I was contacting her, it was the same old story. She knew my DNA evidence couldn't be incorrect, but she didn't want to have a lengthy conversation about something that had been painful for her when she was younger. And it almost seemed she wanted to tease me a bit when it came to providing pictures of Sharon's birth father. She told me she had albums filled of pictures of James, but now she was so hurt to find out that James had a child with another woman when he was in high school, that she didn't want to provide a single picture to me and Sharon. I pleaded with her to find some compassion for my sister, who was looking for as much closure as she could find, but this woman had no interest in helping us.

About a week later, her son, Francine's estranged brother, called me and began threatening me. He told me he planned to see that I would never be able to contact his mother again. He actually told me he would be coming to Las Vegas to blow my brains out. Although Francine had warned me that her mother and her brother were "off their rockers," I certainly wasn't expecting that. Sharon was a half-sister to this guy, and yet he never mentioned Sharon in our conversation because he obviously had no interest in her.

I asked her brother how serious he was about coming to Las Vegas— if he was, I'd pay for a limo to pick him up. I told him that I had a chronic form of cancer and that his threats didn't have me concerned in any way. I never heard from him or Francine's mother again. They weren't caring or compassionate people, and they couldn't have cared less whether Sharon found closure through the additional photos they refused to share with us.

Sharon and Francine met for lunch on two occasions, as they only lived about fifty miles from each other. I gathered from them that they both enjoyed meeting. But as in my case with my half-brother Luke, Sharon and Francine seemed disinterested in furthering a relationship. Blood doesn't make you family. Loyalty, love, and trust makes you family. Sharon and Francine are now Facebook friends, but I don't think they've ever directly communicated with each other since they last met for lunch.

I had one final item on my to-do list in this case, and as much as I hate to admit it, I was doing it out of spite. I was so angry at Shawn's wife for not trusting my research and telling me to cease all lines of communication with her family. Shawn's nephew Nathan had given me a picture of Shawn when he was in high school. And I'd already found a senior high school photo of James Rexford III from Ancestry.com, who I had now confirmed was Shawn's half-brother. I was astonished at their resemblance in those two pictures: they nearly looked like twins. I placed the pictures next to each other, snapped a photo, and texted it to Shawn. I wrote: "I know you didn't seem to believe the DNA evidence I provided, so I thought you might find this comparison picture between you and who I am convinced was your half-brother, James Rexford III, interesting." I also sent the picture of his mother Patricia from Omaha dated 1946 that his nephew Nathan sent me. Shawn called me about an hour later. Ironically, the pictures did the trick. He told me that if he had two half-nieces (Sharon and Francine) out there, he'd want to speak with them. I told him I'd give them his phone number and if they wanted to call him, that would be up to them. Neither my sister nor Francine called him, and I never spoke with him again.

My mission was complete, and I'd solved Sharon's mystery. And although Sharon was crushed by her birth mother Alice's rejection, I know how important to her it was to finally see pictures and identify the origins of her physical features. We are forever indebted to Sharon's cousin Gina and her half-sister Francine for providing pertinent information and all those pictures.

[15]

I'M YOUR FATHER, LUKE

WHILE HELPING OTHERS SOLVE THEIR MYSTERIES, I WAS RELIGIOUSLY checking all my DNA sites at least five times a day, waiting for a closer Jewish DNA match. But as time went on, my hope of getting a close Jewish match was fading. I'd also never figured out why my birth mother Betty wrote that letter giving her last name as Roberts. I'd been going over different scenarios that could make sense of it. But a year and a half into my paternal search, I hadn't figured out that mystery nor did I have any closer Jewish DNA matches.

But I enjoyed helping solve these mysteries so much that I thought about seeing if my half-brother Luke had an interest in identifying his birth father. Plus, it would be a good way to find out what was happening in his life and maybe that could jumpstart our relationship. I didn't feel good about how I didn't engage with him more after we first met. By this time, seventeen years later, Luke and I were Facebook friends and communicated only by messages there about every two to three years. Luke has a unique sense of humor and some of the stuff he posted on Facebook had me laughing out loud.

When I called him, he didn't seem over-the-top enthused about my offer, but he was intrigued enough to agree to do it. I sent him an Ancestry kit and we were on our way. I also had my wife Debbie and my son take an Ancestry test. As we waited for my son's results, I kept teasing Debbie that she'd better start formulating a real good explanation in case it turned out that my son was not biologically related to me. But she simply rolled her eyes at my banter as she always does.

Before Luke's results came back, I decided to contact Tom Brent (who was married to Chiquita in 1962, had a child with her, and divorced her in 1963) again. I hadn't contacted Tom after I first discovered Luke. Since Luke was born in 1964, I wondered if Tom might know who our birth mother Betty was with in early 1964, when she would have been impregnated. If you recall, Tom had told me seventeen years earlier that my birth mother had numerous boyfriends in 1962 and 1963.

I hadn't spoken with Tom in eighteen years. It was a great conversation and I told him about all the other discoveries I'd made since I'd last spoken with him. I told him about Luke, and he wasn't surprised my birth mother gave up another child after me. I revealed to him my Jewish paternal lineage and that I still hadn't identified my birth father. When I asked Tom if he remembered who my birth mother may have been dating just as he was leaving my maternal family, he seemed to be struggling to go back so far in time. After all, it had been over fifty-six years since he'd divorced Chiquita. But it started to come back to him—he told me that my birth mother was with a man named Ray, but he could not remember his last name. Ray had a crew cut hairstyle and he worked for a moving company. Of course, that didn't guarantee that my birth mother was with this "Ray" a few months later in early 1964 when Luke was conceived. And knowing my birth mother's promiscuity, even if she was with Ray, that didn't guarantee he was Luke's birth father.

When Luke's results came in, I was shocked. I wasn't shocked that our match was almost 1,800 cMs which was in the correct range for half-siblings. What floored me was that he had a match to a woman named Linda at nearly the same cM value that he and I shared. That high match level could mean that Linda and Luke could be half-siblings or an aunt/nephew or uncle/niece. Double first cousins or a grandparent relationship were also in play, but both of those possibilities were unlikely scenarios, especially after I learned Linda was born in 1962, only two years before Luke. That eliminated the grandparent relationship possibility.

I reached out to Linda through Ancestry.com's website, but to my surprise, it wasn't Linda who replied, but rather a seventy-two-year-old man named Butch who lived in Pennsylvania. In a phone conversation, he explained that he bought that test for Linda a year earlier because he was certain that her father was his father. He came to that conclusion after reading love letters he had found in his mother's belongings after she died. He said that he had grown up without a father and his mother never disclosed his father's identity to him. The letters he discovered were from a man named Bert Sigler who was in the Navy at the time he was with Butch's mother. Butch searched for Linda and her three brothers (surname of Sigler) and when he found Linda, he asked her if she would test. But after she tested, Butch found out that Linda was not a match in any way to him. So, Butch moved on, but he was still the manager of Linda's Ancestry profile. After I explained to Butch why I was looking for Linda, Butch provided Linda's phone number, and I called her right away.

Linda was an extremely kind-spirited person and wanted to help in any way she could. She told me that she had two older brothers and one younger brother and that they had all grown up in Azusa, California. Azusa was only about ten minutes from where I grew up and about twenty minutes from where Luke grew up. She confirmed what Butch told me and said that her father's name was Bert Sigler.

I was theorizing that if Luke and Linda were half siblings, and Bert Sigler was her father, then Bert Sigler was also Luke's father. That would mean that Bert stepped out on his wife Glenna (Linda's mother) with my birth mother Betty in early 1964. And if Linda was correct that all of her siblings were full siblings to her, then Luke would be a half sibling to all of them. Another possibility was that Linda's mother Glenna had stepped out on Bert in 1961(Linda was born in 1962), and had an affair with a man who was also Luke's birth father, and then never told Bert that Linda was not his child. And that would mean that Linda would only be a half sibling to her brothers. But at the time, I couldn't prove that Linda and her siblings were actually full siblings, or that Luke was also a half sibling to her brothers, because none of the brothers had tested. It was clear that Luke and I shared the same birth mother, Betty Jo Heady, and Linda and I didn't match each other. So, I was leaning toward Luke's match to Linda being from her birth father's DNA. I couldn't rule out the aunt/nephew or uncle/niece relationship based on their age difference. If you recall, I'm two years younger than my half-nephew Tommy, and yet I'm his half-uncle.

I did research on her father Bert Sigler and discovered he'd committed suicide in 1978, about eight years after he and his wife Glenna (Linda's mother) divorced in 1970. Linda told me that they divorced when she was about eight years old and that her mom remarried another man a year later in 1971, Linda's first stepfather. I say "first" stepfather because her mother Glenna was married five times. But her mother and first stepfather's marriage also ended in divorce about four years later.

I asked Linda if she'd be willing to ask one of her brothers to take an Ancestry test to confirm my theory that her father Bert was also Luke's father. She contacted her oldest brother Eddie and he agreed to test. I'd been reporting to Luke about my findings, and he seemed a lot more interested now that I seemed to be getting closer. Since Linda was so sure that she and her brothers were all fathered by Bert Sigler, it seemed as if this was going to be solved quickly and effortlessly.

On Ancestry, I found Bert Sigler in a few incomplete family trees. As expected, one of the trees showed that he had married Linda's mother Glenna and then divorced in 1970. Linda's mother was also in that tree, and when I clicked on her profile, it showed her maiden name and the five last names she'd taken from the five men she'd been married to during her lifetime: Sigler, Roberts, Sheets, Cook, and Shepard. Seeing "Roberts" in that profile had my mind running all over the place.

I started to consider the crazy possibility that Linda didn't share the same birth father, Bert Sigler, with her three brothers, but that maybe this guy Ray that Tom Brent claimed was with my birth mother Betty in late 1963, was Luke and Linda's father. So, I messaged Linda and asked her if anyone in her family had the first name Ray. Her answer sent shock waves through my soul. She replied: "My stepfather's name was Ray. He's the one who married my mom Glenna in 1971 when I was eight years old, just after my parents divorced. He taught me to drive when I was sixteen and he took my brothers on camping trips in the summertime."

I asked her what Ray's last name was, and her answer: "Roberts"!

I thought, "Roberts??!!!" Stop the train! My birth mother called herself Betty Roberts in the letter she wrote to my grandparents from Las Vegas in 1965, a year after she gave up Luke for adoption. Tom Brent told me my birth mother was with a man named Ray in 1963 before Luke was conceived. And now Linda is telling me her stepfather's name was Ray Roberts. And most importantly, Luke and Linda shared enough DNA to be half-siblings. I asked Linda if her stepfather Ray had a crew cut and she confirmed he did. All exactly as Tom had reported.

This wasn't looking good for Linda, and I was doing everything I could to not insinuate that her "stepfather," Ray Roberts, may have been her birth father. If Ray Roberts was Linda's birth father, that meant that her mother Glenna was having an affair in 1961 while she was married to Bert Sigler. Linda wrote back to me and said, "Jeff, you mentioned Ray Roberts, but he was not related to me. He was my stepfather." It appeared she wasn't considering the possibility that Bert Sigler, the man she loved and believed was her father, was not her birth father. I wanted to wait until we had her brothers' results back before making her face that reality. If Linda's brother Eddie's match came back as a half and not a full sibling to her, and Eddie didn't match Luke, it would prove that Bert Sigler was not Linda's birth father.

More Players

While I waited for Eddie's test results, a new match to both Luke and Linda showed up on Ancestry.com, a girl named Hillary who lived in Texas and shared 400 cMs with Luke, and about the same with Linda. Hillary was not a match to me, so it was clear she matched Luke and Linda from their paternal side. That 400 cM shared DNA match had the following relationship possibilities:

First cousin once removed

Half-first cousin

Half great-uncle/aunt/niece/nephew

Second cousin

There were two other possible relationships, but their probabilities were very low.

I messaged Hillary to see where she could fit into the Luke and Linda's puzzle. I wanted to know if she had any relatives that were living in Southern California around the time that Luke was conceived. I also asked Hillary if she knew of any family connections to the Roberts surname. She replied with the following by email:

"Hi Jeff,

Thanks for getting in contact with me. It's funny that you should wonder if I had a connection to anyone in the early 60s in LA...

My mother Denise was born in 1962 in La Jolla, Southern California. Her birth mother was Beverly Swank, and father unknown. She was adopted by her aunt, her birth mother's sister Barbara Swank. We are trying to find out who her bio father is, that's kind of why we started researching on Ancestry.com. My mom asked me to test first to see what kind of matches I have before testing herself.

My mom's birth father was a sore subject among the family, and the few people who knew the truth are dead. We have heard rumors that the man died young of diabetes. Also, that he had other children. There were two names my mom had narrowed from high school love letters and yearbook photos.

I'm waiting to hear back from her if the name you gave me resonates. I'm fairly certain Roberts was the last name of the man in the yearbook.

I will let you know as soon as she contacts me. Thanks again!"

To read Hillary's comment regarding the surname "Roberts" was promising. And then Hillary emailed me again about an hour later: She wrote:

"I remembered his name. Here's the high school photo album picture. This is the one my mother Denise's aunt Barbara Swank showed my mom and me only days before she died, saying this was my mom's bio dad. We didn't know if she was telling the truth or not, or if she even knew."

"He was born in 1944 and went to Warren High school in Downey California with my mother's birth mother Beverly. If this name means anything to Luke and/or Linda please let me know. Thanks!"

Hillary attached a black and white high school yearbook picture of a man named Jerry Roberts. After I reviewed Hillary's email, I began to sketch out a possible family tree based on DNA and birth years that would have Ray Roberts as the father of Luke, Linda, and this newly discovered Jerry Roberts. All three of those people would be half-siblings to each other, fathered by Ray Roberts with three different women. I placed Hillary's mother Denise (who hadn't tested yet) as Jerry Robert's daughter. And I already knew that Hillary was Denise's daughter.

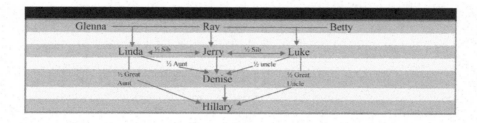

If this proposed family tree was correct, it would mean Hillary was a half great-niece to both Luke and Linda. The DNA was clearly lining up with my theorized family tree, but I wasn't going to make any final calls on this until we received Linda's brother Eddie's DNA results.

It was about a week later that Hillary's mother Denise and I spoke on the phone. She was very reserved about the subject, and I could tell she suffered because of this mystery. She was about my age, and her early life story seemed so unfair. She was angry that her birth mother Beverly never revealed the identity her birth father. But even more damaging to Denise, her birth mother sent her to live with her aunt (Beverly's older sister Barbara), prearranging that even before Denise was born. Denise was told when she was about five that she was adopted. But it wasn't until she was twenty-four years old that she found out the adopted mother she was raised by was actually her biological aunt, and that her "aunt through adoption," was actually her biological mother. It was nothing less than pure deception.

It wasn't until Barbara was on her deathbed that she asked Denise to retrieve her high school yearbook so that she could reveal to Denise who she believed to be her birth father. That's when Barbara showed Denise a high school yearbook picture of Jerry Roberts. One of Denise's half-siblings from her birth mother Beverly had found high school love letters after Beverly died, and those were from a boy named Pete Lewis. So Denise thought there were two contenders for her birth father, Pete Lewis and Jerry Roberts.

Devastating Results

About three weeks later, Eddie's results were in, and just as I suspected, Eddie and Linda only matched at half-sibling levels and Luke was not a match to Eddie. It was clear now that Linda and Luke shared the same father, but it was not Bert Sigler as Linda had always believed. Now I had to make the dreaded call to Linda. As much as I was glad to have identified Luke's birth father Ray Roberts, I didn't want to tell a sweet fifty-seven-year-old woman that the man she always believed was her father (Bert Sigler) was not her biological father. To make matters worse, I would need to tell her that her mother Glenna had an affair in 1961 with Ray Roberts while she was married to Bert Sigler, before marrying Ray Roberts in 1971.

I'd been keeping my wife Debbie in the loop about my searches. She was privy to all the details and at times, she seemed interested. But there were certain times along the way where she seemed to become frustrated with what I was doing. We had had some "intense forms of fellowship" (arguments) about why I circumvented my sister Sharon's birth mother's anonymity and exposed her to something she probably had feared coming for the past fifty years.

With Luke's search and discovering that Linda's stepfather Ray Roberts was actually her birth father, Debbie's frustration seemed to be boiling over. Before I called Linda, Debbie said to me, "Who do you do you think you are to create all of this chaos and reveal things you know will hurt others? If you hadn't meddled in other people's lives with your searching, Linda would never know the difference, and she'd never get hurt. What right do you have to inform people about matters they may never have wanted to know about?" Debbie's points were well taken, and I knew I needed to really consider those ethical questions.

It appears callous to simply say that sometimes the truth hurts. But I have learned over time that it's best to operate on the principle that honesty is the best policy. I can understand the argument that just because Linda's mother Glenna may not have been honest about the identity of Linda's father, people like me aren't required to disclose that truth to someone like Linda. Staying out of it would have been the easy thing to do.

But I will argue that there were others who were searching for their truth. Even though it was horrible for Linda to become collateral damage along the way, should that have quelled the desires of the others seeking their truth? Should Linda's mother's indiscretion nullify the deep desires or rights of others to find their answers? And perhaps in a greater sense, many adoptees have felt deceived and frustrated by different entities (local governments, parents, other family members) that hold or hide the information they desire. What about those people? My sister Sharon took risks to find out the truth, and at the end of her journey, it wasn't the information that hurt her. It was her birth mother who hurt her. Similarly, if Linda's mother deceived her, Linda shouldn't be angry at the truthful information, her hurt and anger should be directed at her then deceased mother (assuming her mother knew that Ray Roberts, not Bert Sigler, was Linda's father).

I finally mustered up the courage to call Linda and give her the results, but she didn't answer. She knew her brother Eddie's results were due any day and she had asked me about them through Facebook Messenger on more than one occasion as we got closer to the six-week mark. She messaged me and told me that she was leaving work and felt like she was coming down

182

with the flu, so she didn't feel like communicating by phone. But she did tell me to go ahead and give her the results through Messenger. To me, that wasn't the correct forum to announce results like that, and I didn't want to do it. I wanted to be able to show my compassion if I was hurting her by sharing this news. She added, "You can tell me here on Facebook and as soon as I'm feeling better, I will call you." I'm pretty sure she'd been preparing herself for it and maybe she wanted to have a private emotional reaction, rather than an emotional reaction on the phone with me. If that was true, I could certainly understand. So, I just came out and told her through Facebook Messenger that she was only a half-sibling to her brother Eddie. I also reiterated the circumstantial evidence I'd learned about Ray Roberts' son Jerry and his connection to Denise and Hillary. I added Tom Brent's information regarding my birth mother dating a man named Ray at least a year before Luke was born. Linda simply wrote that she'd call me when she was feeling better. I hated not being able to share my concern in the way I could have if I was having a phone conversation with her.

When we spoke a few days later, it didn't take long for her to express her hurt and anger. She said she wished her mother Glenna was still alive so she could ask her why she had an affair with Ray Roberts and why her birth mother never told her that Ray Roberts was her birth father.

I pushed back on that just a bit. I said, "If I was you, I'd be angry about the affair, but what if your mother was being intimate with both Bert Sigler and Ray Roberts during the approximate time you were conceived? If that was the case, how could she tell you it was Ray Roberts when she may not have known which man impregnated her?

I stay in contact with Linda through Facebook, and I try to remember to call or message her every Father's Day. I want her to know that I sympathize for her hurt. I sent Linda some pictures of Luke for her to have as well. There's definitely a resemblance, especially when they both were younger. Neither Luke nor Linda expressed any interest in meeting the other, which for me reaffirmed my belief that "blood isn't always thicker than water." Later, Linda embraced that she had family that loved and cared for her, and that seemed to overshadow her hurt feelings.

Now it was time to reveal to Denise exactly how I saw this family tree coming together, which is what she really wanted to confirm. She wanted to know if her aunt Barbara (the woman who raised her) knew or told her the truth about her who her birth father was, and if it could be confirmed through DNA. I called her and texted her a simple family tree that provided the DNA relationships to everyone who'd tested and their positions in that tree. Denise finally tested and she fit perfectly in that tree as Jerry Roberts' daughter, the granddaughter of Ray Roberts, and a half niece to both Linda and Luke. And with that, the short letter from my birth mother that I'd held in my files for eighteen years finally made sense to me. I can't explain why she considered herself a Roberts. But I know she was with Ray Roberts, had a child initially named Baby Boy Heady, and later named Luke, who she gave up for adoption in 1964.

I did more research and helped figure out the names of Jerry Roberts' two other children. Jerry married his high school sweetheart, but they later divorced. I asked one of Jerry's daughters (a half-sister to Denise) for pictures, and she provided many of both Ray Roberts and his son Jerry. A year or so later, Denise flew to Washington state to meet her two half siblings who were also fathered by Jerry Roberts. My understanding is that they had a wonderful time. Ray Roberts passed away in 1975 at the age of fifty-six from complications of diabetes. His son Jerry died from those same complications at the age of only forty-three. My half-brother Luke has suffered with that disease as well. Luckily, Linda and Denise didn't inherit the disease.

This was one of my most rewarding cases to solve because I had to find and verify or reject so many pieces of evidence until it all fit together. I would sit and think late into the night, writing and rewriting family trees, until they all fit perfectly, with no other way to interpret the DNA evidence. Although Linda was hurt from the revelation, simultaneously helping Luke and Denise solve their mysteries was worth the effort.

[16]

BROTHER FROM ANOTHER MOTHER

BY NOW, IT HAD BEEN OVER TWO YEARS SINCE I'D INITIALLY TESTED on Ancestry.com and I still didn't have the answers I desired. I became more and more frustrated, especially as I continued to read other people's success stories on my DNA Facebook group pages. At the same time, I was happy for those people, and seeing their family reunion pictures had me fantasizing that perhaps it could happen for me. And I was certainly happy for those I'd helped find meaningful relationships with biological family they'd never known existed. And yet the emotional toll of checking my results on five DNA sites multiple times a day was becoming tiresome. It was the same old story day after day, month after month, and now year after year.

I decided to devote my time to finishing my first book, which I'd set aside while I was helping others search. As I focused most of my attention on that book, I stopped paying as much attention to my DNA results as I had before. In fact, there were weekly stretches when I didn't check for new matches.

And then my beautiful daughter called to tell Debbie and me that she was pregnant and that we were going to have our first grandchild. Debbie and I were over the top about the news, and the baby was due in March 2020. Little did we know just how much coronavirus would turn everyone's lives upside down and limit our opportunities to spend time with our little granddaughter.

Debbie started to plan our daughter's baby shower, and although our daughter and most of my son-in-law's family lived in Southern California, we decided to have the baby shower in Las Vegas. We thought, who's not looking for an excuse to come to Las Vegas? We scheduled it for December 14, 2019. Debbie is a talented and an incredibly creative person, and she began planning and making special decorations for the shower.

Shock and Awe

It was December 13, 2019, the day before the baby shower, and now two-and-a-half years since I took my first DNA test. All of Debbie's extended family from Colorado had already arrived, and we were waiting for our daughter and son-in-law to arrive from LA later that day. My two nieces, my sister-in-law, Debbie's parents, Debbie, and I were all sitting in our family room drinking coffee. And for the billionth time, I decided to check the five DNA apps on my phone for new matches. I always checked Ancestry first, before checking 23andMe, and then the other three smaller DNA sites. Ancestry had no new close matches that morning. I logged into 23andMe.com, and I must have looked like one of those cartoon characters when they get electrocuted: you know, eyeballs detached and springing about three feet away before returning to their sockets.

At the very top of my matches, it listed the following:

Douglas Behr - Half brother

Shared DNA 28.1% - 2089 cMs

I sat there quietly in front of all our family. I must have been in shock and my heart felt like it was beating out of my chest. My first thought was to compare Douglas' DNA to others I knew were very distant paternal Jewish matches to see if he was Jewish. I was hoping this wasn't another half-brother my birth mother gave up for adoption. My hands were shaking and my heart was racing while I ran that quick comparison report. As soon as I ran the report it was clear he was Jewish and none of our common matches were with anyone from my birth mother's side. I got so excited I forgot I could have simply run a report to compare our ethnicities which I did next—Douglas was 100 per cent Ashkenazi Jewish.

I stood up from our couch and quickly walked straight over to Debbie who was standing in the kitchen. And all I could say as I approached her was, "Oh my God! Oh my God! Oh my God!" Debbie and everyone else wanted to know why I was so worked up, but I could hardly speak. I held my phone up to Debbie's face and said, "I have a new half-brother DNA match! It says his name is Douglas Behr, he's 100 per cent Jewish!" She was a little shocked, and so was everyone else. They all knew that I'd been waiting for news like this for years.

I had many things to do that day to get our house ready for all the people coming over for the shower the following day and a flood of emotions came over me. This is it. This is what I've been dreaming of. My birth father had at least one other child, and I didn't have to worry any more that all of my birth father's family may have been exterminated in concentration camps.

But there was another relationship possibility. That 2089 cM match to Douglas could also mean that one of us was a full uncle to the other. And that would have been fine by me. If Douglas was my uncle, it was likely he would know who my birth father was because my birth father would have been Douglas' full brother. If I was Douglas' uncle, it would mean that his birth father was my full brother. That would mean my birth mother Betty had had two children with my Jewish birth father. But that wasn't a possibility because Douglas was 100 per cent Jewish and therefore couldn't be carrying any of my birthmother's DNA. I wouldn't discover until later that there was no way for Douglas to be my uncle.

I began to recount all I'd learned about preparation before contacting from my DNA Detectives Facebook group. I knew I needed to take screenshots of Douglas' 23andMe page and then check for all the common matches we shared and take screen shots of those results. I needed to see if I could find him on Facebook. If so, I would need to take screenshots of all his friends and try to identify which of those friends might be part of his immediate family. All of this needed to be completed before I attempted to contact him. That way, if Douglas didn't want to connect with me and he decided to block my access to either his 23andMe or Facebook account, I'd still have the information. But collecting that amount of information would take hours, and I was in a time crunch, so I was contemplating contacting Douglas before screenshotting the information.

I was also concerned that Douglas might be adopted and also searching for our birth father. What if his reason for testing was to identify his birth parents because he didn't know their identity? I've seen that happen before, where two adoptees share a biological parent and yet neither one of them have closer matches that could help them solve their mysteries. Instead of one searching adoptee alone on an island with no close matches to go on, it becomes two half-siblings standing on the same remote deserted island. If you want to take that to the "nth" degree, sometimes fifteen or twenty half siblings match on a DNA test site because their birth father was a sperm donor. If those siblings don't have close matches to other relatives of their birth father, it's nearly impossible to identify him. It would be nice to have a newfound half-brother, but if Douglas didn't know his paternal lineage, I'd be no closer to identifying my birth father.

I started to panic. Some of these DNA websites emailed their clients not long after a very close match entered their database. I wasn't sure about 23andMe, but I knew Ancestry emailed close match notifications within twenty-four hours. I couldn't have Douglas be notified of our half-brother match and block me before I had a chance to introduce myself in an undemanding way. That would be unthinkable. But with all of that was going on at our house in preparation for the baby shower, I just didn't have the time to do the all the required research. I was going rogue and hoped to get to Douglas before he discovered our match.

In the past two years, I'd given so much advice to others, and yet now I was uncertain about what to do. Connecting with Douglas was deeply important to me and it all depended on how I handled it and how I would present myself. It was certainly easier when I was doing it on behalf of others. I was swinging between excitement about the possibility of finding out who my birth father was, and fear of communicating in a way that would be unappealing to Douglas. It was the same feeling I had twenty years earlier when I first called Luke from Hawaii. This was the culmination of efforts starting twenty years earlier. If I screwed this up, the closure I'd dreamed of could be gone forever.

Reaching out

While everyone was still sitting in our family room, I began to compose a message to send to Douglas on 23andMe's message portal. I was so focused on what I was writing, all my family members could have left the room and I wouldn't have known the difference. I must have reread the message twenty times before clicking the "Send" button. Here is what I sent to Douglas:

"Hi Douglas, my name is Jeff Eddins, and I was adopted at birth in Los Angeles in 1961. I was able to identify my deceased non-Jewish birth mother 20 years ago without the aid of DNA. It wasn't until two-and-a-half years ago that I was shocked to discover that I was 50 per cent Ashkenazi Jewish. Since my birth mother had no Jewish roots, it must mean that my birth father was nearly 100 per cent Jewish."

"I have spent the last few years waiting for a close Jewish DNA match that would enable me to ID my birth father. My goal has always been to find pictures of him. I may have wrongly been assuming he's already passed away because my birth mother told the adoption agency that my birth father was her age. She was born in 1926. Over these past few years, I have helped many people identify their birth families using DNA, but I've personally never had a match that was closer than a third cousin. I would love the opportunity to speak with you by phone, but I want to make it clear that I will not be stalking or pestering you to reply. As I am for most of the people I've helped ID their birth family's, I'm worried that our match as half-brothers or uncle/nephew may be a huge surprise to you. You may be concerned that this newfound discovery could cause a disruption in your family. Please understand I have no desire to barge into anyone's family. At this point, I'm hoping you'll at least be willing to confirm you've received my message and that you'll be receptive to it. Above all, I will respect your privacy."

"My hope has always been that I could receive some pictures of my birth father and if you are willing to help me, that you too are not searching for his identity. If you're willing to communicate with me I can be reached at (my phone number) or by email (my email address) at any time of the day. I live in Las Vegas, NV, and I am on Pacific Standard Time. Kind regards, Jeff."

It should be noted that adoptees should never disclose they are adopted when making initial contact with a close match. The reason, of course, is because with a close match like that, disclosing I was adopted increased the probability that Douglas would be completely taken off guard. When people are surprised, they can become startled to the point of shutting down lines of communication. This especially occurs when a searching half-sibling was conceived while their match's father was still married to the match's mother. Clearly, I didn't remember that piece of advice from my Facebook DNA groups before reaching out. If Douglas' father was married to Douglas' mother when I was conceived, it might create a flood of negative emotions; he might become angry not only at his father, but with me for exposing his father's indiscretions.

Pins and Needles

And now the waiting began. The message I sent to him through 23andMe's website would be sent directly to the email address he provided when he signed up for their service. I hoped he didn't have multiple email addresses and the one that he used for 23andMe was one he didn't check very often. I had a huge pit in my stomach, but was also feeling pressure to help Debbie and everyone else prepare our house for the baby shower. My daughter called me from their car when they were about halfway between LA and our house, and I told her the exciting news about my match to Douglas. She seemed as excited as I was. She knew just how much I wanted to identify my birth father.

I decided to search on Facebook and my Truthfinder app to see if I could identify him. I counted fifteen Douglas or Doug Behrs on Facebook. Most of them didn't have profile pictures, but there were about five that did. One was way too young to be my half-brother, unless our birth father fathered a child in his late seventies. The others seemed more in the correct age range. The first one I looked at resembled me, but he was a little heavier than I was. I showed his profile picture to my visiting family, and they could see similarities as well. The other three Douglas Behrs didn't look anything like me, but they were close to my age. I wasn't drawing any conclusions about who the correct Douglas Behr was; I was just curious.

When I searched my Truthfinder app, there were many more Douglas Behrs. That app doesn't provide pictures of anyone, but it does link to people's social media accounts. When I clicked on the first one in the list, ironically, it took me to the Facebook page of the Douglas Behr that most resembled me. He had an address in the northern part of LA, in the city of Sylmar. I recognized the 818-area code of his phone number because it was the one from where I grew up.

Debbie could see how enthralled I was trying to identify the right Douglas Behr, and I appreciated her not pushing me to do more around the house. The rest of our family was helping with the preparations, and I really appreciated that too. I spent the next hour taking screenshots of Douglas' 23andMe's DNA page, and then did the same for the Douglas Behrs I'd found on Facebook. I didn't have time to try to identify the family members on any of those Facebook profiles before the party.

So, I spent the next few hours hoping for a phone call, email, or message back on 23andMe. I tried to distract myself from the discovery by preparing the house, but it didn't seem to do the trick. I never let more than ten minutes go by without checking my email, and made sure my cell was set to ring at the loudest volume. We have a few dead spots for cell service around our house and I made sure to avoid them at all costs.

Debbie asked me to go to a store to pick up some large strings of pink colored popcorn that she'd ordered for the shower. My daughter and son-in-law had already thrown a gender reveal party in LA months earlier, and we knew we were having a granddaughter. My thirty-five-year-old niece Eryn (Debbie's sister's daughter) asked if she could tag along. Eryn had loved finding out about my Jewish ethnicity, and not long after the discovery, Debbie and I were visiting Debbie's sister's house for Christmas. Eryn's children had bought a little paper menorah and placed on the kitchen table for me to see when we first arrived. I loved it!

This is it, Maverick!

We picked up the popcorn and headed back to my house. On our way, the phone rang through my truck's Bluetooth system and when I looked down at the screen, I could see an 818-area code. I looked over at my niece Eryn and used a line from the movie *Top Gun*: "This is it, Maverick!" I took a deep breath and then pressed the green answer button on the screen of my dashboard.

When I answered with, "This is Jeff," the man on the other end immediately identified himself as Douglas Behr. I started shaking, thinking about all the things I wanted to say and how much I wanted this phone conversation to go well. This wasn't the environment I wanted to be in for an important conversation like this, but I also felt like I couldn't miss the opportunity to answer. Douglas had a deep voice and he seemed to have a foreign accent that I didn't immediately recognize. The other problem was that my hearing had been diminishing as I'd aged, and any deep, lower-toned frequencies were especially difficult for me to pick up.

I remember looking over at Eryn and shaking my head with a huge smile on my face. I was trying to silently convey to Eryn, "Can you believe this is finally happening for me?"

Doug (as he prefers to be called) began to tell me the story of "his" birth father and I was nothing but ears. He told me that his father died at the age of seventy-nine in 2004 from multiple myeloma (a cancer of the blood plasma cells) in La Jolla, California. Doug didn't use the term "our" father, I think because he wasn't completely convinced that the DNA connection listed on 23andMe was accurate. Although 23andMe's algorithm suggested our relationship as half-brothers, it was possible he could have been a full uncle to me. Doug was only five years older than me, but I couldn't rule out he was my uncle. Later in the conversation he said, "If we're really brothers" and before he could continue, I interrupted him and explained my complete understanding of DNA, and how I was certain that the DNA indicated we were either half-brothers or he was my uncle. Later that night, it would become clear to us that we could only be half-brothers. After that, and even today, Doug has always referred to his father as "our" father, or even "your" father when addressing me. I've always appreciated that, even though to Doug, our birth father was his father, and for me, my birth father was my birth father, and my father was the father who raised me.

His Name!

He told me that our father's name was Selig Stanley Behr, but he went by his middle name, Stanley. By this point I needed to understand what his accent was, and he told me it was South African. It wasn't a strong accent, but coupled with his deep voice I was struggling to make out everything he was saying. He added that his whole family was from South Africa, and they all moved from South Africa to the US in 1979, just as I was graduating from high school. They wanted to escape the civil unrest occurring there because of apartheid.

He informed me that I had another half-brother named Barry and a half-sister named Carol who lived in the Bay area of Northern California. I thought, "How crazy is this? I started this journey twenty years ago because I saw two brothers reuniting and now, I seemed to be flooded with siblings." He also told me that Stanley divorced his birth mother in South Africa in late 1958 and gained full custody of him when he was two-and-a-half years old. He then remarried, to a woman named Margo fourteen years his junior. She was still alive, and lived in the San Diego suburb of La Jolla. He was clear that he didn't consider Margo his stepmother, but the mother who raised him, and his only mother. My two other half-siblings, Barry and Carol, were the children of our father and Margo. So, like me, Doug would genetically be a half-brother to both Barry and Carol.

By this time, we'd arrived at my house, and to my surprise, the cell service wasn't spotty. There was no way I was getting out of my truck and risking having our call drop. As I sat there in the driveway with my niece, Doug told me something about our father that he seemed very proud of. He told me our father voluntarily left South Africa with 800 other men to fight in the infamous Arab-Israeli War of 1948. He was highly decorated and was even presented a metal twenty years later and then again forty years later by the prime minister of Israel. Doug was so proud of his father's service that he had a memorial website made showcasing many of his pictures, newspaper articles indicating where he fought, and the many medals he was awarded. He told me to check out the website, www.stanleybehr.com, when we finished our conversation.

There came a point in our conversation where I found myself tearing up a bit because all of this was so overwhelming to me. As we sat in my truck listening to Doug, I remember I had my elbows resting on my thighs, and I was holding my head in both hands. I would glance over at my niece from time to time. I'm sure she could see how overcome with emotions I was. As much as I didn't want to get off the phone, eventually I did tell him about my daughter's baby shower, and how much I needed to get done before the next day. Before we hung up, I asked him if he would text me some pictures of our father.

When we walked into the house, I told everyone about that phone call, and they seemed excited for me. But I didn't waste time providing too many details because I wanted to go to the memorial website to see my birth father for the first time.

I was amazed by what that simple website provided. The first picture I saw of Stanley in his later years didn't really resonate with me. That picture was taken at the second medal ceremony that Israel held that honored him. He must have been in his mid-to-late seventies by then and I didn't see a lot of resemblance to me.

The next thing I saw was a collage of grainy, black and white pictures of soldiers, but I couldn't be sure which soldier was Stanley. It wouldn't be until later that Doug would identify him for me. But there were two more photos where I could clearly see my resemblance to Stanley.

In the first one, Stanley stood in the foreground of what appeared to be a group of British soldiers who were also there defending Israel. He was wearing military fatigues and a long coat. He was in his early twenties and had a cigarette hanging from the left side of his mouth. That picture really resonated with me (except the cigarette).

In the other, he was in his forties. It showed him having a medal pinned to his white dress shirt. That picture was from the first time Israel invited him and other volunteers back for a tribute ceremony. And for some reason, I found myself feeling proud that my birth father, who I'd never met, was a war hero of some sort. According to Doug, our father was a Zionist who believed in the development and protection of the Jewish Nation (Israel), and willing to die defending it.

By this time, my daughter and son-in-law had arrived, and they seemed excited for me as well. I showed all of Stanley's pictures to my family, and they seemed to see the same things I did. We finished up the prep work for our house and everyone except me seemed exhausted. I was walking on cloud nine, but also disappointed because I knew I wouldn't be able to speak more with Doug until sometime after the shower the next day. I decided to message Doug through 23andMe's website. The message read as follows:

"Doug, the baby shower is tomorrow and we've all just slowed down to relax after a long day of preparation. I've been reflecting on our conversation today and it is finally sinking in exactly what has come to fruition for me after waiting all these years. For adoptees like me, it's extremely important to see where we come from even in the absence of ever meeting our birth parents. I've been staring at the pictures of Stanley from the memorial website you referred me to. I've waited over fifty-eight years to see photos of him and I feel extremely elated and lucky to have done so today. I would really appreciate any other photos you'd be willing to provide, including ones when he was younger. Please feel free to text or email them to me at your convenience. I'd even love to have any photos of his parents (your grandparents) if you have any."

"I'm not a big Facebook user, but I'm sending you a friend request now so you can at least see who I am. I have plans to come to Southern California this Christmas, but now I'm not exactly sure what dates I will be there. I would love to take you up on your offer of maybe getting together when I come down there. Maybe we could meet up for lunch or dinner. I'm thankful that you were receptive to calling me back and speaking with me today. I've helped others locate their biological family members before and it hasn't always gone as well for some of them. I forgot to mention to you in my first message that I'm not looking for anything of material value from you or your siblings. I'm interested in photos and things you can tell me about Stanley. In saying that, I'm open to getting to know you and having a relationship with any one of you that has that same desire. Looking forward to hearing back from you. Regards, Jeff."

Within ten minutes, he'd read that message and called me. I had so many questions and I was sure Doug knew the answers to many of them. Some of the details he would reveal to me in our conversation that night would add more pieces to my genetic puzzle.

[17]

SORTING IT ALL OUT

IN OUR DISCUSSION, I TOLD DOUG WHAT I KNEW FROM THE background document and what I'd discovered through my paper trail research eighteen years earlier. At some point, I disclosed to him that my birth mother moved to California in August of 1960. I told Doug that I had to have been conceived sometime in August of 1960, but wasn't sure if it was here in Las Vegas or right after she moved to LA. And that's when Doug rocked my world with a crazy story he'd remembered since he was a young boy living in South Africa.

He told me that when he was four or five years old, our father left him with his uncle Andrew, who was our father's oldest brother. It was a year or two after his divorce, and Stanley had made plans to travel alone. He took a ship to England to visit with some aunts and uncles from his mother's side who he hadn't seen in years. He planned to visit with them before going to the US and taking a cross county road trip from New York to California. But Stanley had decided to surprise his aunts and uncles by not telling them he was coming. After he arrived in England, he called one of his long-lost uncles, but his uncle told him that too much time had passed, and he had no interest in continuing any kind of relationship. Stanley did visit with another aunt (his mother's sister) while there, but after that, he left for the US, earlier than he'd originally planned.

After landing in NY and spending some time there, he either rented a car or took a bus (Doug wasn't sure) and made his way west across the country. But before he arrived in California, he stopped, in all places, Las Vegas, Nevada. I asked Doug how he knew that our father stopped there, and he told me that he still had a souvenir from Las Vegas that our father had given him after he returned to South Africa. It was a small notepad from one of the local Las Vegas hotels, the now defunct Wilbur Clark's Desert Inn. He was digging around his house for it as we were on the phone that night. I heard him say, "I found it."

I was flabbergasted that Doug could remember the story, but even more so, that he still had that notepad in his possession after nearly fifty-nine years! Later, when we first met, he gave that notepad to me. It has about ten pages and it's still intact.

Now it seemed more likely that Stanley and my birth mother met in Las Vegas, and not in LA. If you recall, my birth mother worked in the culinary union as a server in local hotels here in Las Vegas. Now I wanted to know exactly when Stanley was here in Las Vegas. Doug wasn't sure about exact dates, but he was sure our father left him with his uncle Andrew sometime early in the summer of 1960 and returned to South Africa sometime late November of that same year.

Not Another Twin!

Doug told me that our Grandfather David Behr was born and raised in Plunge, Lithuania, and our grandmother Dora (maiden name Figdor) was born in Glasgow, Scotland. They were both Jewish and both migrated to South Africa in the early 1920s, where they met and married. Stanley and his two brothers were born in Bredasdorp, which is about a hundred miles southeast of Cape Town, South Africa.

Then Doug dropped the "twin" bomb on me. He told me that our father's oldest brother was Andrew, and he was a pilot during World War II for the South African Airforce. But my heart sank when he informed me that our father had a twin brother named Frank. Although Doug didn't have any scientific evidence that Stanley and Frank were identical rather than fraternal twins, he was convinced they were, and said nearly every family member had a difficult time differentiating between the two of them.

Why did that revelation make my heart sink? With the standard autosomal DNA testing that companies offer to the public, there is no way to determine which children of identical twins belong to which twin parent. Those children who are known by birth observation to be first cousins would appear through those testing sites as half siblings. If Frank and Stanley were identical twins, it was possible that Stanley's twin brother Frank could have been my birth father based on my shared DNA results to Doug. I was hoping Doug could assure me that his uncle Frank was nowhere near Las Vegas or Los Angeles in August of 1960.

Initially, Doug wasn't sure exactly where his uncle Frank was in August of 1960 because he was being cared for by his other uncle Andrew. Although Doug said Frank spent most of his life in South Africa, he knew that Frank had visited the US many times. But I had Doug's recollection of Stanley's trip across the US, and knowing he'd stayed in Las Vegas (the notepad) where my birth mother lived.

Doug also told me that after we first spoke, he called his mother Margo to tell her about our DNA results. He also called our half-brother Barry and half-sister Carol. He didn't tell me their reactions to the news, but that was something I was very concerned about. I hoped the timing of my conception had no overlap with our father's courtship and marriage to Margo. Luckily, it didn't take us long to figure out Stanley hadn't cheated on Margo.

I asked Doug exactly when our father had married Margo and he knew the exact date after searching for only two minutes through one of his photo albums. In one of those albums, he had a paper napkin preserved from their wedding in South Africa on June 25, 1961, about a month after I was born.

That was good news, but that didn't mean that our father wasn't already courting Margo when he left South Africa in the summer of 1960 and encountered my birth mother. Doug didn't have the answer to that question, but he knew where to find it. He called Margo again, and she told him that a month after my birth father returned from the US, he met and began dating Margo. It was such a relief for me to hear. The family may have been surprised that Stanley was "sowing his oats" as a single divorcee, but it was clear he hadn't stepped out on Margo. Doug also mentioned that he remembered Margo talking about Stanley having a "traveling companion" during some portion of his trip. I didn't know what to make of that. Could that traveling companion have been my birth mother? Most importantly, Margo knew that Stanley's twin brother Frank did not accompany him to the US in 1960. So unless my birth mother flew to South Africa and randomly hooked up with Stanley's brother Frank in August of 1960, Frank could not have been my birth father.

What puzzled Doug was that he was sure our half-brother Barry had tested on either Ancestry or 23andMe over a year earlier, and he wondered why I hadn't noticed his match to me. When Doug said that my heart began to sink again. If Barry had tested on either of those sites, he would have surely been a match to me if we shared the same birth father. I was worried that Barry might not actually be our half-brother, which would have meant that Margo had stepped out on Stanley. I wasn't going to suggest that idea to Doug, and knowing what I know about Margo today, that idea was completely preposterous. He told me he would ask Barry when and where he tested the next time he spoke with him.

Later in our conversation, Doug asked me what I did for a living. I told him I was in the communications business, specifically pagers. He told me he had a close friend and mentor who was in that business over twenty years earlier in LA, but had recently passed away. When I asked him what his friend's name was, his answer almost made me fall out of my chair. He told me his friend and mentor's name was Hal Lindon (not the former actor) and his company was called Page Prompt USA. I thought, what a small world. It was hard to believe that in a city as large as LA, both Doug and I would personally know the same person.

When I started my business in 1992, I did a great deal of business with Hal's company. In fact, I sold a portion of a separate pager business I'd created to Hal. I'd traveled to his LA office multiple times to negotiate and finalize that deal. Doug told me he used to visit Hal at his office from time to time. Who knew, we could have been in Hal's office at the same time, never realizing we were related. What a crazy coincidence.

By now, we'd been talking for over two hours and it was past midnight. I could have sat there for another ten hours if my daughter's shower wasn't the next day. We ended our call and he promised he'd text more pictures to me the next day. It was extremely difficult for me to fall asleep with all the excitement of the day. All I could do was try to process that information and formulate more questions for the next time we talked. Despite all the information that was spinning through my head, I also felt a deep sense of peace. I'd been living in the paternal familial desert for over fifty-eight years, and on December 13, 2019, I'd finally arrived at the most amazing oasis.

Identification and Introductions

The next day, my daughter's baby shower went off without a hitch, and everyone seemed to have a great time. My daughter was glowing in her pregnancy, and I was so proud and happy for her and my son-in-law. And throughout that day, I couldn't stop thinking about the day before. In the afternoon, Doug sent more pictures of his younger self, and more of our birth father and grandparents. The pictures of my birth father's earlier years weren't quite resonating with me as much as the ones on the memorial website had. Debbie saw it in every picture right away. But over the next few weeks, I couldn't help but see just how much resemblance we shared. I constantly went into our guest bathroom and stared at myself in the mirror as I intermittently glanced down at my iPad, comparing my facial features to Stanley's pictures. Although it's been over two years since I first received those pictures, I still find myself reveling in my resemblance to my birth father Stanley. I came from somewhere else now, and that somewhere was Stanley Behr.

Even more striking is how much Doug and I looked like each other in our younger years. He sent a picture of himself when he was about two years old, and I actually thought it was a picture of me.

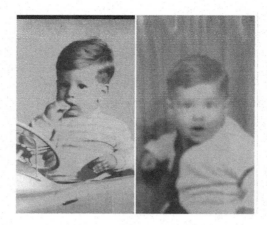

Doug / Jeff

Then he sent some pictures of himself in his twenties and thirties, and the resemblance was even more uncanny.

Jeff / Doug

As I mentioned, he was a little heavier than I was, but our facial features almost made us appear to be twins. I'm surprised that when I first met Hal, he never mentioned he knew someone who could be my twin. Doug and I even wore the same style of glasses.

Apparently, news in the Behr family travels fast. Later that night after the shower, I received a Facebook friend request from my new half-brother Barry's wife Victoria. I'd already searched her Facebook profile and the profiles of her and Barry's two daughters to gain a better understanding of their family. Barry didn't seem to have a Facebook page. So, after accepting her request, I decided to message her through Messenger with the following:

"Hi Victoria and thanks for sending your friend request. Obviously, you've been speaking with Doug about our DNA match as half siblings. To be clear, I'm not trying to barge into anyone's family so please do not think that's the reason I reached out to Doug yesterday. Finding this kind of closure through the identification process is very important for adoptees. I'm hoping to have the opportunity to speak with you and your husband Barry at some point, but only if either of you have an interest in doing so. I do plan to be in LA for Christmas and visiting with my mother and meeting Doug for the first time. If either you or Barry have an interest in speaking by phone, I can always be reached on my cellphone. All my best, Jeff."

The next morning, I received the following reply from Victoria:

"Hi Jeff. Thanks for your note. I completely understand your need for identity as an adoptee. I personally think that the opportunity DNA and Ancestry websites give to people like you are such a gift. I'm looking forward to speaking with you and/or meeting you. At this point, Barry is, as you can imagine, struggling a little with his feelings. He is a very stoic kind of person that keeps his emotions close. He would like to talk to you eventually. He's not ready. We haven't told our two daughters yet. Family is so important to us we are all very close. Our kids will be open for sure! I think it's quite amazing. I'll give you a heads up before Barry calls."

That was the first mention from anyone about some form of resistance to the news of my existence. I was expecting it. I had tried to put myself in their shoes, and I can understand being taken aback while trying to process it. It's likely Barry and Carol asked Doug for my birthdate, subtracted nine months, and compared that to when their father began courting their mother Margo. Even knowing there wasn't any infidelity, maybe the image they had of their father was tarnished in some way. I'd hoped they'd be able to get past that. In some ways, rejection of adoptees by biological family feels as though the birth family wished the adoptee had never existed. What's an adoptee supposed to do with that?

The next day I received another message from Victoria. She wrote:

"Hi Jeff, we've been talking about you all day. It was a shock as you can imagine. Barry is settling with the information now. I think it's a gift, but that is me."

And about two hours later she wrote another message: "It seems Barry will reach out today!"

I wrote back: "That's great news, Victoria. As I mentioned to Doug, I'm open to where any of this goes with no expectations and certainly no demands. I do care about people, and I don't want to hurt or disrupt anyone's life."

About two hours later, I received a call from an area code that I recognized as being from the Bay Area of California. I had just arrived at a local park to walk our two dogs. It was Barry, and it was yet another awkward place to have an important conversation with my other newfound half-brother. We seemed to hit it off and discussed things in our life that were similar. He also had two adult children. He didn't drink alcohol, and neither did I. He liked to drink Dr. Pepper or Coke and so did I. He was a dog person, and like me, he was getting closer to retirement.

At some point, the discussion turned to Stanley, and he admitted he'd been struggling with the reality of my existence. I'd already been prepared by his wife, so that wasn't a surprise to me. And as much as I didn't want him to be in that position, I was glad he was willing to share that with me. I told him that I wasn't looking to force any long-term relationship with him and I gave him my "blood is not always thicker than water" theory. I was trying to let him know that I had no expectations that he should like me or want to spend any time with me in the future. And I added that I'd be open to developing any kind of relationship he was comfortable with, and seeing where it went.

That's when he came straight out and laid it down. He said he told his wife Victoria, "If this guy is a good person, then I'll be interested in getting to know him better. If he's not, then it will be easy to just leave it as it stands." I thought that was great because Barry was essentially confirming my theory that blood is not always thicker than water. Blood brought us together, but that certainly didn't guarantee we would have any kind of good long-term relationship.

Barry mentioned that his wife asked him the day they first heard the news from Doug why he wasn't already making plane reservations to Las Vegas to meet with me. I thought that was hilarious, but I know women can have different emotions of greater intensity than men about these kinds of birth family discoveries.

Whew!

Barry was certainly a bit more reserved than Doug—once Doug and I start chatting it was almost like two close sisters yapping and blabbing for hours. Doug never made me feel he was disappointed that his father impregnated my birth mother during a one-night stand. Barry didn't try to make me feel that way, but I knew he struggled with all of this more than Doug did.

Even so, I had a pit in my stomach the entire time I was on the phone with Barry, and it wasn't because I was worried about how well it would go, or that he despised my existence. I wanted to know if Doug was correct when he said that Barry had tested on one of the DNA sites. Finally, I just came out and asked him, and he told me he'd tested at 23andMe about two years earlier. That just didn't make sense to me, and as I mentioned previously, could indicate that Barry's birth father was not Stanley. Luckily, before I mentioned my concern, I remembered something about those DNA sites and their privacy options: both Ancestry and 23andMe allowed the DNA tester to make their results and profile private. As much as adoptees dislike the existence of that option, I'm sure many people who are either wanting to only know their ethnicity, or are concerned about being "found out," simply set their DNA results to private. Searching adoptees would never consider setting their results to private. If we could afford it, we'd hire one of those single engine planes to tow a giant banner displaying all of our DNA results and pertinent information for all the world to see.

I asked Barry about it, and he told me he wasn't sure, but that he'd check it out later that night. Two hours later, I checked my 23andMe results and Barry's results were there. He had changed his privacy settings to "public" and matched Doug and me at 1,800 cMs, which is in the range for half-siblings. I was glad that I hadn't mentioned the possibility that Stanley may not have been his birth father.

I had waited over two-and-a-half years for Doug to show up on 23andMe. If Barry hadn't set his results to private, I would have found him only six months after I first tested, and two years of waiting and anticipation could have been avoided. The next time I spoke with him, I jokingly told him I planned to sue him for emotional damages.

Five days after my daughter's baby shower, I'd still heard nothing from my newfound half-sister Carol, and I wanted to reach out via Facebook Messenger, introduce myself, and make sure she knew I was sensitive to how she may be struggling to reconcile all of it. I'd already seen pictures of her that Doug had texted me, but there were pictures on her Facebook page I hadn't seen. She also had a few pictures of her cute little daughter Sara, who would be my half-niece. But it turned out that Carol wasn't much of a social media person, and I didn't receive a response from her. I was certainly worried she was hurting over this news and may want nothing to do with me.

As these events were unfolding, I was texting pictures of my birth father and some comparison pictures of Doug and me to my son and daughter. My son called me, and we talked about all of it. He hadn't been here for my daughter's baby shower, and wasn't privy to the events as they unfolded.

About a week after discovering my birth father's identity, I felt the desire to post my success story on the DNA Detectives Facebook group. That group had been an essential part of my success, not just with the scientific knowledge and techniques they shared, but also as a support group. When a group member had to deal with painful biological family experiences, group members provided emotional support. When a member had a successful search and the familial outcomes were good, group members were all there to chime in and celebrate.

After posting my story, including pictures of Doug, me, and our birth father, I had over a thousand reactions and hundreds of comments. Some people said my story provided inspiration to them to never give up, no matter how long they needed to wait for closer matches. I knew there were other group members who were still waiting, often many years longer than the two-and-a-half years I waited for a close match. Others commented on the pictures, astounded at how much Doug and I resembled each other. I can't tell you how good that made me feel. Writing that post was another

JEFF EDDINS

line of demarcation for me. After fifty-eight-and-a-half years, I had crossed
over from knowing nothing about my paternal side, to nearly complete
understanding.

Doug and I talked almost every day for the next two weeks. We
planned to meet when I would visit my mom in LA over the Christmas
holiday. I had so many questions about other family members, and he was
able to provide every piece of information I asked for. I could tell how
much he enjoyed talking about his family history, and I loved listening to
him. He was effectively helping me fill in the other side of my family tree
that had been completely blank for my entire life. As of today, I've been
able to go back to the mid 1700s with the paternal side of my family tree.
To make it even more interesting, as I built the paternal side of my family
tree, I discovered that my three half siblings and I are all distant cousins to
Anne Frank through our paternal grandmother Dora Figdor's family. My
newfound family wasn't aware of that either, and it was fun sharing that
with them.

Doug also told me that after our father divorced his birth mother
in South Africa when he was two-and-a-half years old, he never saw her
again. He took that DNA test to try to identify others on his maternal side
of his biological family. He knew that his estranged mother moved to the
US from South Africa, and that she'd passed away many years ago in New
Mexico. He'd met his maternal grandmother years before, when he was
visiting Switzerland, and she provided Doug with many pictures of his
birth mother. So, in some ways, Doug was like me. He never really had
a relationship with his birth mother, and never communicated with her
after she left his family. I've tried to sort through his maternal matches, but
Doug is in a similar position I was. He's Jewish, and endogamy is in play.
Unfortunately, right now he doesn't have any closer maternal matches than
third cousins, so we just have to hope that someone closer from his birth
mother's side tests.

Now We're Talking

Within a week or so, Doug told me that his mother Margo wanted to have a telephone conversation with me and gave me her phone number. I was excited about that because they'd been married for nearly forty-four years, and I doubted there was anyone else on the planet who knew more about Stanley. I looked at this as an opportunity to learn more, but I wanted to be very respectful to her. After all, I was the illegitimate bastard child who had just showed up and possibly disrupted her and her adult children's lives. And I was afraid that the news of my existence may have tarnished Stanley's reputation for her.

Margo was eighty years old, and I could tell early in our phone conversation she was sharp as a tack. Her South African accent was a little stronger than Doug's or Barry's, but it wasn't a problem. I loved hearing that accent. Sometime after Stanley died in 2004, she married a man named Walter who had also spent his early years in South Africa.

At the beginning of our conversation, she seemed a bit leery of the DNA results and had questions for me about them. I wasn't sure if Doug had already shown her pictures of me, but I would have guessed he did. And if he did, I would have been surprised if she didn't see enough resemblance between Stanley and me to quell any doubts. But I didn't ask her what made her question the results. Perhaps it was because she may have hoped Stanley's twin brother Frank was my birth father, which could also explain my match to Doug and my resemblance to Stanley. I told her I was relying on what Doug knew about Stanley being in Las Vegas sometime in the summer of 1960 when I was conceived, and that there was no evidence that Frank was anywhere else but in South Africa during that time.

She seemed to be okay with that, and then proceeded to tell me something about the "traveling companion" that Doug had mentioned who was with Stanley through some portion of on his trip across the US. I asked her if that companion was male or female, and Margo said that

Stanley had told her that his traveling companion was a woman. So perhaps it was possible that my birth mother and Stanley met in Las Vegas in August of 1960, and after following him to Los Angeles, I was conceived there. I didn't have a way of knowing that, and the location of my conception wasn't that important to me.

But there was something I remembered about my background documents, which implied that my birth mother didn't know my birth father very well. If they were traveling companions during Stanley's time in Las Vegas and Los Angeles, wouldn't she have known that Stanley was from South Africa? Remember, my birth mother had told the social worker my birth father was of "English" descent. Now it seemed likely that my birth mother mistook Stanley's South African accent for an English accent, which meant that it was likely they didn't spend very much time together, at least not enough for Stanley to tell her where he was from. Maybe he simply told her he'd traveled from England to the US, which was true, and she had just assumed that meant he was from the UK.

As Margo and I were finishing up our conversation, she wanted to tell me something about Stanley's character. She said it for the first time then, and she has repeated it many times in our later discussions. She said, "Stanley was a very highly principled man, and very well respected by anyone who knew him. If Stanley would have known about you, he would have done something about it." I'm not sure exactly why, but it always makes me feel good to hear her say that. Perhaps it's confirmation that my birth father had such a passion for his family, that if he had known I was out there, connected to him in that way, he would have searched the entire Earth to recover one of his "lost sheep" and return it to his home.

Margo also wanted me to know how her other children felt about their father. I'm guessing, but I assume she wanted me to know that whatever led to my existence would never tarnish Stanley's image or reputation in their family. She sent me an article written by the staff at Stanford

University, where Barry worked. Barry has a PhD, and is the director of the IVF laboratory at that prestigious university. In the article, they asked Barry who his hero was. He answered, "My dad, although he probably didn't know that unfortunately. He taught me 'HIP': "Honor, Integrity, Principles." After what I'd already heard from Margo and Doug about Stanley, it made me even more disappointed that I would never have the chance to meet him. I couldn't help wondering what my life would have been like if my birth mother had contacted Stanley after he returned to South Africa and told him she was carrying his baby and that she'd planned to give it up for adoption. Would he have returned to Los Angeles and taken me back to South Africa?

Many adoptees try to play out possible scenarios and alternative life paths that may have existed if they had not been given up for adoption. From my experience, that's a risky game to play. For some adoptees who've had a bad experience growing up with their adoptive parents, fantasizing can lead to them feeling robbed of a better life, even when there's no way to be certain of that. For others who have had a good experience with their adoptive parents, it can diminish their memories of the good life they had growing up with parents who loved them.

In my case, I believed my life was likely to have been miserable if my birth mother had kept me because it was clear just how much generational suffering was present in that family. And I just couldn't know with any certainty what it could have been like growing up in South Africa in a Jewish family with two brothers and a sister.

I've learned over time to push away those fantasies when they begin to creep in. I know with certainty just how much I was loved by my adoptive parents, so how can I allow myself to consider the "what ifs" that can never be validated? I wouldn't ever trade my life experiences with my parents, and I'm not just saying that because it's all I've ever known. But in some way, it is nice to know that Stanley was a good man and likely would have rescued me if given the opportunity.

Irrefutable Evidence

In mid-February of 2020, Doug texted me a picture of Stanley, with the Statue of Liberty in the background. It was a custom tourist post card he had mailed to South Africa when he was visiting NY. He was dressed in nice slacks and an informal, short sleeved shirt, and was leaning against a waist high chain link fence that held a sign shaped like a life saver. Along the circumference of the preserver it read, "Statue of Liberty, N.Y., with the year, 1960, in its center. Stanley dated that postcard July 25, 1960.

So, Doug was correct about the year that Stanley was in the US and that Stanley was in Las Vegas (the hotel notepad). I just wanted to get Stanley from NY to Las Vegas by August of 1960.

A few days after our phone call, Margo emailed me ten pictures of Stanley through different stages in his life. Two days later, she texted me a black and white photo of Stanley and an unidentified man facing each other and smiling. In the background of that picture, I could see a pool and a large sign on the hotel roof that clearly displayed the same outline of the Wilbur Clark Desert Inn logo that was on the notepad that Doug had texted a picture of. On the upper right corner of that photo, there was handwriting that said, "Las Vegas 1960." It didn't list the month, but there seemed to be plenty of time (July 25 to sometime in August) for Stanley to drive cross-country from NY to Las Vegas.

Stanley on the left

There was simply too much evidence that not only was Stanley's twin brother Frank not my birth father but also that Stanley was in Las Vegas where my birth mother was living and working up until August of 1960. It was clear that when my birth mother claimed she'd moved to California in August of 1960, she'd moved from Las Vegas.

I received a text from my half-sister Carol the day after I spoke with Margo. I assumed Margo had given Carol the "all clear" signal—that Margo had enjoyed our conversation and told Carol I was non-threatening and respectful. Later that day, I called Carol and we had a very nice conversation. Like her brother Barry, she was struggling with the news of my existence. I'm pretty sure she'd never considered that her father may have been with another women between Doug's birth mother and her mother Margo. In our discussion that day, she told me my discovery had her wondering just how many more women he'd been with, and if their family would be facing more "Jeffs" showing up on the DNA websites in the future. I sympathized with her feelings. She had only good things to say about her father, and I also learned more from her about what her life was like living first in South Africa, then moving to the US when she was in high school. It was clear she loved her dad, and my discovery wasn't going to impact who he was to her.

[18]

A DAY TO REMEMBER FOREVER

DEBBIE AND I SPENT CHRISTMAS DAY TOGETHER IN LAS VEGAS, and then I planned to stay at my mom's house for a few days, then drive to Doug's house in Sylmar on the 30th. His house was only twenty-five minutes from my mom's house, which made it very convenient. It was quite a lucky coincidence that when their whole family moved to the US, they all settled and stayed on the West Coast. Doug and Margo were a four-hour drive from Las Vegas, and Barry and Carol were only an hour away by plane.

I headed to my mom's house on the 27th, and during the drive I was getting the same pit in my stomach I'd had so many years ago when I was preparing to meet my half-brother Luke at his restaurant. I wasn't feeling fear or anxious that things might go bad. Doug and I had already established a comfortable relationship over the phone, and I felt good about that. It was more about this being the culmination of everything that had begun over twenty years earlier. All my hopes were coming to fruition. I'm not sure any adoptee can clearly express what it feels like when they know they are on the doorstep of their "meeting day."

December 30 finally arrived, and as I left my mom's house, every emotion seemed ratcheted up to its highest level. It was going to be another, "This is it, Maverick!" moment. I arrived in his neighborhood about fifteen minutes early. I knew I was close to his house, but my GPS had me sitting in a parking lot that seemed to be connected to a condo, and I knew that wasn't correct. So, I waited until 8:55 a.m. before calling him, and he told me his house was just around the corner. When I pulled in front of his house, he had an American flag covering his numerical address plaque, and I couldn't see it. So, I drove right past his house and turned around and started looking again. As I got closer to his house, he walked out into his driveway and motioned for me to park in a vacant lot across the street.

When I got out of the car, I could see how much taller he was than me, about four inches more at a good six-foot four. As I started to walk across the street, he began to approach me from the top of his driveway toward the middle of the street. I wanted to be more reserved, and had already thought about how we would greet each other. I remembered when Luke and I first met, it was just simple handshake—hugging didn't seem to be an option for either of us. But I tend to be a hugger, especially with people I'm close to.

I didn't want to make it awkward and reach out to hug Doug if he wasn't open to that. So, I extended my hand to shake his, and he reciprocated in like manner. But then I felt him pull me toward him, and we hugged awkwardly with our right hands forced into our abdomens as we reached around with our left hands to embrace. I remember thinking, "I can't believe this guy is welcoming me like this." That one hug took the edge off so much of my anxiety.

He invited me into his house, asked me if I wanted something to drink, and it was on. He already had family albums stacked on his kitchen table, and I was so excited to start going through them. We spent three hours going through his pictures, and he'd also already set some aside for me to take home. Doug is a great storyteller, and he knew so much about his family's history. He was providing me so much information that it was hard to keep up with—I was learning about my paternal grandparents from South Africa, and even a little bit about our great grandparents who spent their lives in Lithuania and Scotland. He also gave me a lot of family information about Margo's side of the family, including that some of them currently lived in Las Vegas. I also saw pictures of Doug's Bar Mitzvah and many of him in his early years. I just couldn't get over how much we looked alike, from our toddler years up to our late forties. And unlike when I met Luke for the first time, I hadn't thought to bring my pictures of different stages of my life to show Doug to compare with his pictures. I had some on my phone, but mostly recent ones.

At some point, he removed some items from a gallon-sized Ziploc bag he'd also prepared to give me. He gave me an old black comb that Stanley used regularly, and a pocketknife that Doug said "our" father always carried with him. He also gave me Stanley's original identification card from South Africa as well as his most recent California Driver's License. But the two most prized physical possessions I received that day were that little note-pad from the Las Vegas hotel and a money clip that had a small retractable knife on its side. Engraved on the side of the clip was: "S. Behr." I've carried it with me since that day, and show it to anyone who shows any signs of life.

This was quickly becoming one of the most rewarding days of my life, and there would be so much more to come, more than I could have ever dreamed of. We decided to go have lunch at a local Italian restaurant. This was late December 2019, and there was no public knowledge of the COVID-19 pandemic in the US, so we just strolled into the restaurant without wearing masks.

I could tell that Doug was a joker and a prankster of some sort, which is exactly how I've operated my entire life. We just seemed to hit it off so well, I was buzzing inside. Our waiter approached and asked us what we'd like to drink, and before Doug could give him an answer, I blurted out, "I'm just meeting this guy for the first time, and we used DNA to discover that we're half-brothers." The waiter seemed astonished by the remark, and I could tell he was interested. As he stepped away from our booth, Doug reached across our table and forcefully grabbed my left forearm, saying in a stern tone, "Hey! Knock off the 'half' $hit!" At first, I didn't know how to respond. I was only trying to be "genealogically" correct and I certainly didn't want him to feel forced into considering us having some sort of brotherly relationship if he didn't want that.

But Doug wasn't having any of that. I recalled in our first conversation what he'd said about his "stepmother," Margo, and that not only does he consider and refer to her as his mother, but he also expected others to do the same. He was only a biological half-sibling to Barry and Carol, as was I, but he only referred to them as his brother and sister. In a similar way, I never refer to my sister Sharon as my "adopted sister." I simply refer to her as my sister. For Doug, his family relationship terms were based on his love for them, no matter if or how they were genetically related to him, and placing fractions in front of relational terms of endearment was out of bounds. It was at that point that I understood how he perceived family, and I never made a "correct" genealogical reference regarding our relationship in front of him again. I gained a lot of respect for Doug for his take on family, and it felt great he apparently already considered me his brother.

We had a great time at lunch as we learned more about each other and as I learned more about my birth family. As soon as we returned to his house, he took me on a tour. He had many other family pictures on his walls that were not included in the albums he'd already shown me. I couldn't help but take pictures of those pictures with my phone. I'd been doing that with nearly every photo in his albums. When we entered one of his spare bedrooms, he pulled out a very large picture frame that I immediately recognized. The frame contained all the information that Doug had put on our father's memorial website. He also removed a pistol from that closet—it was the pistol that our father carried during the Arab-Israeli War of 1948. It was an old pistol, and the chamber for loading it opened on a hinge at the base of its barrel. I'd never seen gun like that before, and it intrigued me.

The Next Best Thing

But what happened next was something I'd never considered as a possibility, especially after knowing Stanley had died before I had a chance to meet him. And Doug had never mentioned it during our previous two weeks of phone calls. Doug had a plethora of videos, many on older VHS tapes and some on DVDs, of our father and his family. He seated me on a couch in his family room, close to a large wall-mounted TV.

He handed me a remote control and told me to press play. He wanted me to have the control so I could stop or rewind and replay it at my choosing. My heart was racing with excitement because I realized this wasn't going to just be still pictures: it was going to be the next best thing to seeing him alive. I'd never considered the possibility of seeing him talking and hearing his voice. Perhaps that's because that wasn't my experience after identifying my birth mother because many of her close family members didn't even have a single picture of her.

I just couldn't believe what I was seeing. There were videos of Stanley and his two brothers in England from sometime in the 1980s. All three brothers were playing musical instruments: Stanley was playing the guitar and singing; his twin, Frank, was playing a banjo-like instrument and had a harmonica holder around his neck as he played both instruments simultaneously; Andrew was playing a small accordion from the couch he was sitting on. I had loved playing acoustic guitar when I was younger, and I could see that Stanley was a very talented musician. They were playing songs I didn't know, but they seemed to really be enjoying themselves. I was getting my first glimpse of what was not only a live performance of them singing and playing but also how they interacted with each other. Between songs they were laughing and making jokes to and about each other.

I can't tell you how many times I rewound different segments of those videos so I could replay and capture them on my cellphone. And at some point, it became so overwhelming to me that I just pressed the pause button on the remote and placed it on the couch. I found myself in that same position I had been in weeks earlier when I had sat in my truck with my niece and listened to Doug telling me about my birth father. I held my head in my hands as I leaned forward, trying to fully grasp what I was experiencing at that moment. Soon after, tears began streaming down my cheeks as I glanced over at Doug. There was no way he could completely understand what he was doing for me, but I could tell he was enjoying me watch different video segments and listening to his commentary about each family member. I remember trying to speak without my voice cracking as I explained to him just how amazing this was making me feel.

There was another video of Stanley sitting around a kitchen table with his two brothers. Andrew's son Steven was filming, and asking Stanley what the best part of his trip to England had been. He answered, "Buying antiques." His nephew asked him, "What kind of antiques?" and he answered, "Silver antiques." His nephew then asked, "What kind of silver antiques more specifically?" and Stanley replied, "I can't fancy such a range. It's too big." This video was a closeup, and I could see my birth father's facial features and his expressions that matched mine. When the camera got closer, I recognized myself in his jawline, the shape of his hands, even his fingernails. I'm sure a video like this might seem trivial to most, but it wasn't to me. I've re-watched many of the videos I captured that day, and continue to enjoy listening to his South African accent and some of the different British words that are rarely, if ever, used in the US. Those videos haven't become old to me, and I doubt they ever will.

Unforgettable Words

Doug and I spent nearly eight hours together, and then it was time for me to return to Las Vegas. It was the day before New Year's Eve, and although Doug offered to let me stay at his house that night, I didn't want to be on the road with all the people headed toward Vegas for the celebration. Doug walked me out to my car, and I put all the pictures and memorabilia he'd given me on the backseat, then stood in front of the driver's side door, facing him. I knew we were going to hug, as all the fears and potential awkwardness had evaporated after our first greeting, and certainly after the experience we just shared. I will *never* forget what he said directly into my ear as we hugged:

"You're one of us now."

I can't even write that sentence now without tearing up. With every bit of courage I could muster, trying not to break down like a little child, I tried to say, "Thank you." But the words wouldn't come out of my mouth. I was so choked up I wasn't sure I could speak. I had to look away for a few seconds to collect myself before looking directly at him with tears in my eyes and saying, "You'll never be able to fully understand what you have done for me today and I will never forget one moment of it." I added, "I've waited fifty-eight-and-a-half years for a magical day like this, and you were so gracious to welcome me into your family as a brother."

After I left his neighborhood, I pulled into the parking lot of a nearby park. I was so overwhelmed, it probably wouldn't have been safe for me to drive until I could pull myself together. I called Debbie to tell her about my experience and she was incredibly happy for me. I could hardly tell her about it because I was still crying through our entire conversation. I told her about the "Knock off the half $hit," and "You're one of us now," comments, and even she started crying. I was emotionally spent during the drive, and I just wanted to be home. I needed to sit and reflect on my experience and sort through all the important items that Doug had given me.

[19]

EXPERIENTIAL OVERLOAD

WEEKS AND MONTHS WENT BY AS I CONTINUED TO COMMUNICATE with Doug, Barry, Carol, and Margo. Our granddaughter was due at the end of February 2020, and Debbie and I were eagerly anticipating her arrival. By this time, the coronavirus was gaining attention, but no one was wearing masks or under stay-at-home orders. That allowed us to travel to LA and sit in the waiting room of the maternity ward as our daughter and our son-in-law began their journey as parents. We were allowed to go into the delivery room after she was born, and what an amazing experience that was. Two weeks later, everything started to shut down. Loved ones weren't allowed to accompany their family members into doctors' offices or hospitals.

We spent the night of the birth in a local hotel and returned to the hospital the next day to see them for a few more hours before they were on their way home. Debbie and I didn't want to crowd them, and I'd already told Doug I'd like to drop by and introduce him to Debbie. So, we left the hospital without trying to abduct our own granddaughter, and then went to Doug's house. We visited with him for two hours, and then headed home. I couldn't know then how the pandemic was going restrict my ability to see Doug again or meet the other members of his family.

Barry and Victoria's two adult daughters reached out and friended me on Facebook. I messaged with both, and they, too, were graciously welcoming to me. I wanted them to know that I wasn't expecting either of them to consider me an uncle, and that I hadn't earned that term of endearment, at least not yet. I spoke with their younger daughter over the phone, and I really enjoyed getting to know more about her. She told me how much she loved her grandfather and how important he was to her. I see her posts on Facebook from time to time, and she's a very wise young woman.

Their elder daughter replied to my initial message with the following:

"Hi Jeff! Thank you so much for your kindhearted and thoughtful message. Quite honestly, I haven't known what to say, and your picture really took my breath away as I think you look a lot like my grandpa. I have heard nothing but wonderful things about you from my family and can't even imagine what you must feel in all of this. I had a VERY special relationship with my grandpa (I was the first grandchild) and he had a very significant impact on my life. I carry a lot of the lessons I learned from him with me in my life. I think about him often and am absolutely open to welcoming you into our lives and our family. It feels so special to have another piece of him still with us."

Wow! I cannot completely express what a message like that feels like for an adoptee. Her message was a far cry from some of the horrific family "reception" messages I'd read about in my DNA groups.

As months went on, it was becoming extremely frustrating that I couldn't just catch a plane to Northern California and meet Barry and Carol. It was June 2020 by this time, and the pandemic seemed out of control, but it wasn't as bad as it would become later that year. Barry was taking a trip in his motorhome back to Ohio to visit one of his daughters, and he was planning to take the southern route home and stay at his mother's house in San Diego for a few days. Carol was also planning to go to San Diego with her husband and daughter, and they were planning to stay at a hotel near the beach. Doug would be driving there from LA, but I wasn't privy to any of this.

Sometime in late June, Margo called and invited me to come to her house in July when everyone would be there. She told me that everyone would need to wear masks and we would be social distancing on her outdoor patio. I immediately accepted her offer because there was no way I was going to miss an opportunity like that.

When I arrived at her house, I could see Barry and his wife's motorhome in the driveway and as I approached it, I saw Barry come out of the front door of his bus. We said "hello" and greeted each other with an elbow bump. No handshaking or hugs this time. We went into his motorhome where I met Victoria as well. Then they led me through the back gate into the patio area of Margo's backyard. Barry went to the screen door and announced, "Mom, we have a visitor!" Within seconds, Margo and Carol opened the screened sliding door and stepped out onto the patio where I was standing. I wanted to reach out and hug them, but I knew not to consider that during the pandemic. Both of them, like Barry and Victoria, were wearing masks, and Doug hadn't showed up yet. We greeted each other and the next thing I heard from Margo was, "Jeff, can you step back to the rear of the patio?" When she said that, I immediately felt uncomfortable, and I assumed that I was standing too close to them. So, I took a few steps backward and then Carol said, "Can you step all the way back to the edge of the concrete?" I knew I was already way past the six-foot distance recommended for safe social distancing, and I just couldn't understand why they wanted me to move so far away, and I half-shrugged, insinuating I didn't understand.

Then Carol said, "We've seen pictures of you, but we want to see your facial expressions when you're speaking without your mask on." Whew! I had been worried they decided they didn't care for me already, and wanted me to be as far away from them as possible. So, I stepped back to the edge of the concrete and removed my mask. It didn't take long before I could see Carol tearing up and she simply said, "Oh wow!" Margo immediately followed with, "I cannot believe how much you look like Stanley."

Again, I'm not completely sure why hearing that seemed so important me. Perhaps in some way it connected me to them, and that made me feel so good. Stanley wasn't there, but the people who were there must have felt a connection. As we ate lunch on the patio after Doug arrived, I noticed Carol was staring at me. At one point, she announced, "I feel like our dad is here with us right now." I don't believe she said that in reference to my appearance, but rather in a more spiritual sense.

While we were all sitting around the patio table, and only Doug was still eating, I approached him from behind and put him in a loose, pseudo chokehold, then joked, "You may have been the big dog all your life, but there's a new sheriff in town. You've got two younger brothers to contend with now and we'll be running the show going forward." I had everybody laughing at that. It's what I imagined our family dynamic might have been like if I had been part of their family growing up in South Africa.

Near the end of my time there, Margo asked us to line up so she could take a picture of all four siblings. That was an incredible moment for me. I recalled all the disappointments and incremental triumphs I experienced throughout my twenty-two-year journey and how incredible it was that all of my puzzle pieces had finally come together.

Doug, Jeff, Barry, and Carol

Before I left, I wanted to let all of them know just how grateful I was for the way they welcomed me into their family. I needed them to know just what that meant to me, and how I would forever be indebted to them. I knew I was the bastard child, and it could have been very easy for any or all of them to reject me and carry on with their lives.

That is how many searching adoptees believe the "legitimate" family members will perceive them, or even consider themselves. Adoptees are often the product of lust and, therefore, unwanted pregnancies. "Legitimate" family members are usually the product of loving relationships, not solely lustful desires. We speculate we may be looked at by our newfound biological families as defiled, the product of one of their family members at their worst, the real-life version of the Charlie Brown character

Pig Pen, covered in the dirt stains of sin. And if an adoptee is rejected by their newfound family, it solidifies their presupposition they are unworthy of inclusion. We're the outsiders and may never be taken seriously or accepted. Mercifully, that's not what happened to me.

When I was about to leave, I just couldn't take it anymore. I shook both Doug and Barry's hand (against COVID protocols) and simply thanked and said goodbye to Margo and her husband Walter. I really wanted to hug Margo because she had been so gracious to me, but held back because she was eighty years old, and I simply did not want to take any COVID risks. But I asked Carol, while we both were wearing our masks, "If I promise to hold my breath, how much will you charge me to let me hug you?" Even through her mask I could see she was smiling. And then we embraced. Such a strange, yet wonderful feeling. Someone I'd just met, closely biologically related, who'd I'd been physically separated from by oceans for most of my life, and here I was now, hugging her. That hug was another unforgettable moment in my life.

When I returned to Las Vegas, I was on a high like never before. All the initial concerns about rejection and potential awkwardness were behind me now, and I had such a great time meeting my other siblings, Margo, and her husband. I couldn't be sure where things would go from there, but I was very optimistic.

However, all of this was complicated by the COVID pandemic, which made travel and in-person meetings risky. Margo called me sometime during the fall of 2020 to tell me that she and her husband Walter were coming to Las Vegas to visit her brother Geoff and his wife Charlene. She wanted me to meet Geoff because he had been very close to Stanley when they all lived in South Africa. Geoff was retired, but had been a renowned IVF doctor. Doug had already mentioned that his aunt and uncle lived very close to me in our first conversation. And, like the good little Facebook stalking researcher I was, I'd already found pictures of Geoff, Charlene, and their four adult children.

About a week before Margo and Walter were coming for their visit, I was on a walk in my neighborhood. As I was walking I saw a woman, probably in her mid- to late forties, approaching me from the opposite direction of the sidewalk. And since we were in a pandemic, I moved off the sidewalk and onto the grass that was adjacent to it, allowing her at least six feet of clearance to walk by. As we passed, we both said "Hi." I took another ten steps, stopped, turned around, and blurted out, "Excuse me, is your name Rosanne?" The woman spun around, obviously a bit surprised that I recognized her. I started to walk toward her, and she seemed a bit hesitant, but met me about halfway. She looked at me and asked, "Do I know you?" As I removed my baseball hat, I said to her, "I don't want to freak you out, but in some weird way, we could have been related to each other through law. I'm another biological son of your uncle, Stanley Behr." Her eyes lit up like a Christmas tree and she started rubbing her arms, indicating she had the chills. She hadn't heard about me yet, but I could tell she saw my resemblance to Stanley. I told her that I knew of her parents, and that I would be introduced to them by her aunt Margo that very weekend. I provided a few details about my adoption, and that seemed to convince her. She asked me how I had recognized her, and I had to fess up that I was a stalking Facebook researching adoptee.

As I completed the walking loop about twenty minutes later, I saw that she was on the phone, and as I approached her, she stopped me and told me she was talking with her father Geoff, and how she just couldn't believe what had just happened. Her father later told me how much

Rosanne thought I looked, and even walked like her uncle Stanley. Just another crazy, improbable life experience.

In the summer of 2021, while texting with Margo, I asked her if she'd be willing to read a rough draft of this manuscript. I told her how important it was for me to have her input, and she wrote to me, "I would be honored to read it. I think about you a lot and wish you well."

I replied, "This has been very cathartic and emotional to review my life through this book over the past few months I've been writing it. One of the top days in my life was the day I came to your house. I will never forget, nor will I ever be more thankful to anyone for the gracious kindness you extended toward me."

She wrote back, "I must admit I don't think it had sunk in at the time we heard the news, but as time has gone by, I realize that I am grateful that you are who you are. Anyone of a lesser person could have turned our family upside down. I am sure after the first shock of it all, we all agree that we could all be proud to have you as part of our family."

I replied, "I wish you could fully understand what those words mean to me."

To which she replied, "I meant every word of it."

In early June of 2021, as around half of US adults were fully vaccinated, and the pandemic began to temporarily subside, Carol and her husband invited Debbie and me to attend her daughter Sara's Bat Mitzvah. I'd never attended a Bat Mitzvah before, and I very much wanted to go to Northern California to witness that ceremony, get to know my birth family a little more, and introduce them to Debbie. But Debbie and I just couldn't fit it in to that weekend. We did, however, get to watch it live online. It was a two-hour ceremony, and we enjoyed every part of it. Sara looked and sounded so cute as she spoke Hebrew and my brothers and sister also spoke in the synagogue. As we finished watching, I remember asking Debbie, "What would you have thought if someone told you four years ago, before I took that DNA test, that we'd someday be sitting on a couch, watching my niece's Bat Mitzvah?" It was mind-boggling.

CONCLUSION

MY MAIN PURPOSE FOR WRITING THIS BOOK WAS TO HELP FELLOW adoptees identify with some of my feelings and experiences as I sought closure. If you're an adoptee and either considering your own search or in the middle of doing so, perhaps I've helped you understand some of the required techniques to aid you along the way. I also hope I've presented my journey in a way that helps non-adoptees understand the deep yearning many adoptees feel to identify with their genetic origins.

For so many years after identifying my birth mother, I was sure I would go to my grave never knowing the identity of my birth father. No, I never had the opportunity to meet him, and that is disappointing. He most likely never knew I existed, and never saw what became of the person he created—he never got a chance to watch me play football, get married, or meet my children. And as painful as that realization has been at times, I'm grateful that he did leave behind three other children and a wife that have provided glimpses of who he was. They're here to tell me what they know of him. I'm not as close to them yet as I'd like to be, and I know it's unlikely I'll ever be as close to them as they are to each other. But the time that I have spent with them has provided a sense of joy that is deeper and more meaningful than I could have possibly imagined.

If I die after completing the last sentence of this book, I know I'll have died feeling like the luckiest person on the planet. I am certain my life would have been much more difficult had my birth mother chose to keep me. I never considered myself her trash, and so my self-esteem was not affected knowing she surrendered me. Whether it was because she considered children an inconvenience, or because she really wanted to keep me but couldn't, I am forever grateful that she gave me a chance to live and experience a more abundant, love-filled life with my parents. I had two parents who deeply loved and supported me. Words will never be able to adequately describe my heartfelt gratitude to them. And it seems extremely clear that my birth mother could never have provided that.

I'll never know what it would have been like to live with my paternal biological family, and none of that really matters anyway. I've been lucky enough to find them, and I will be forever grateful that they have accepted me and welcomed me into their family. I've had an amazing fulfilling life, and now I have found closure because all the important pieces of my genetic puzzle have been completely assembled.

The End